STUDIES ON
VERTEBRATE NEUROGENESIS

Santiago Ramón Cajal

Studies On Vertebrate Neurogenesis

By

PROFESSOR SANTIAGO RAMÓN Y CAJAL
Faculty of Medicine, University of Madrid

Translated by

LLOYD GUTH, M.D.
National Institute of Neurological Diseases and Blindness
National Institutes of Health
Public Health Service
Department of Health, Education and Welfare
Bethesda, Maryland

CHARLES C THOMAS · PUBLISHER
Springfield · Illinois · U.S.A.

CHARLES C THOMAS • PUBLISHER
BANNERSTONE HOUSE
301-327 East Lawrence Avenue, Springfield, Illinois, U.S.A.

Published simultaneously in the British Commonwealth of Nations by
BLACKWELL SCIENTIFIC PUBLICATIONS, LTD., OXFORD, ENGLAND

Published simultaneously in Canada by
THE RYERSON PRESS, TORONTO

© *1960 by* CHARLES C THOMAS • PUBLISHER
Library of Congress Catalog Card Number: 59-8505

With THOMAS BOOKS careful attention is given to all details of
manufacturing and design. It is the Publisher's desire to present books
that are satisfactory as to their physical qualities and artistic possibilities
and appropriate for their particular use. THOMAS BOOKS will be
true to those laws of quality that assure a good name and good will.

Printed in the United States of America
Cape Girardeau, Mo.

TRANSLATOR'S FOREWORD

IT IS UNFORTUNATE that no comprehensive and systematic treatise on vertebrate neurogenesis exists today. Publication of the present volume partially fills this gap by making available to the English-speaking scientist the studies of Ramón y Cajal dealing with neuronal histogenesis in the spinal cord, cerebellum, cerebral cortex, retina, and peripheral nervous system.

In addition to its obvious value to neurologists and embryologists, this book should serve the biology student well, for these studies reveal how the static techniques of histology can be employed in solving the important dynamic problems of development.

I have attempted to render Cajal's text into current scientific English. The style of the French text is often awkward; therefore any attempt to retain the tone of the original would do disservice to the reader. However, in the purely polemical sections of the book (portions which are more valuable for their historical and psychological aspects than for their scientific merit) I have attempted to maintain the atmosphere of the original text.

I have rearranged some chapters and some chapter parts, hoping to improve the continuity of the book and more clearly outline the subject matter. For the sake of consistency some illustrations have been inverted. No portion of the text or figures has been eliminated. I have also added an author and a subject index as they were not included in the French edition.

I wish to thank Dr. J. G. Frontera for the photograph of Cajal that serves as frontispiece. This photograph was made in 1914 and appeared shortly thereafter in *La Esfera.* I am grateful to Professor F. DeCastro for having given me the copy of this little-known book from which I prepared the translation, and I sincerely acknowledge the encouragement and assistance of Dr. W. F. Windle in the preparation of the manuscript.

Bethesda, 1959   LLOYD GUTH

ÉTUDES
SUR LA NEUROGENÈSE
DE QUELQUES VERTÉBRÉS

RECUEIL DE MES PRINCIPALES RECHERCHES
CONCERNANT LA GENÈSE DES NERFS, LA
MORPHOLOGIE ET LA STRUCTURE NEURONALE,
L'ORIGINE DE LA NÉVROGLIE, LES TERMI-
NAISONS NERVEUSES SENSORIELLES, ETC.

PAR

S. RAMÓN Y CAJAL
Professeur à la Faculté de Médecine de Madrid.

MADRID
1929

AUTHOR'S ACKNOWLEDGMENT

THIS COLLECTION of my neurogenetic studies, of which some are quite old, has been compiled by a group of scientists from Montevideo. Inspired by love of science, they have nobly and generously desired to pay a magnificent tribute of affection and veneration to an old investigator. Would that all those who have contributed to this spiritual endeavor will accept this statement of my most profound and cordial gratitude; I shall be eternally grateful. At the risk of offending their modesty, I wish to cite the most renowned of the editors and offer special thanks to Dr. Alfredo Navarro, Dean of the Faculty of Medicine and to his worthy colleagues, Dr. Pou y Orfila, Manuel Quintela, Lasmier, Isola, Scaltritti, and Poney. My sincere thanks also to Dr. Vincent Arcelus, President of the *Institución Cultural Española,* to the sympathetic students of the *Instituto de Estudios Científicos* who have brought the zest and warmth of youthful enthusiasm to this undertaking, and finally to my dear and learned friend Dr. Estable, President of the *Comité d'Hommage.*

Madrid, May 20, 1929   S. R. CAJAL

PREFACE

In this volume we have collected some monographs which are barely or not at all known because they were published a long time ago in Spanish. These results have been especially neglected following the death of the master neurologists such as His, Kölliker, Waldeyer, Golgi, van Gehuchten, Retzius, Edinger, and others who had the kindness to confirm our findings. For the convenience of those who are interested in the question of neuronal development, we have added some other works which were published a long time ago in journals that are either infrequently consulted today or that have ceased publication and are consequently difficult to obtain.

All the studies are faithfully reproduced here, insofar as the text and illustrations are concerned. We have only permitted two modifications, for the benefit of the reader. We have omitted certain polemical arguments which no longer are of interest and which would have excessively lengthened this book. We have added several footnotes describing our current views when, by virtue of subsequent investigation by ourselves or others, our present opinions differ from our old interpretations. These footnotes terminate with the statement: (*Note for the French edition.*).

We hope that this compilation of more or less old, but scrupulously objective, neurogenetic facts will be useful to modern neurologists. Understanding of these facts will allow the neurologist to trace the history of each discovery and to impartially evaluate the contributions of all those who, like ourselves, have devoted themselves to the study of the difficult but enticing problem of the ontogeny of the central nervous system.

Madrid, May, 1929

CONTENTS

Part I

Histogenesis

Part V

Cerebral Cortex

Part VI

Retina

STUDIES ON
VERTEBRATE NEUROGENESIS

Part I

HISTOGENESIS

DEVELOPMENT OF EMBRYONIC NERVE FIBERS AND OBSERVATIONS CONTRARY TO THE CATENARY THEORY [179]

INTRODUCTION

IN RECENT YEARS there has been propagated a concept of nerve development which is in frank opposition to His's and Kupffer's classical monogenetic view. This erroneous *catenary theory,* revived by Beard, Dohrn, Balfour and their enthusiastic disciples, has been refuted a thousand times by scientific observation. But it springs up again ceaselessly, cultivated by scholars in whom the spirit of paradox and the thirst for novelty leads them to the denial of the best-demonstrated facts, and to the sterile and naive endeavor of attempting to rediscover that which has already been discovered.

This conception consists of the hypothesis that the axon is not the result of the growth of the principal process of the neuroblast or primordial nerve cell, but that it represents the common product of the activity of a great many embryonic cells of ectodermal origin. The primitive cellular series, whose supposed fusion gives rise to the axis-cylinder, are said to be in the form of a chain. A conductive portion, in secondary continuity with nerve cells, and an adventitial part, formed by the Schwann cells, supposedly differentiate subsequently within this communal protoplasmic mass. Several nerve fibers could arise within the protoplasm of each chain.

Such is the simplest form of the rash *catenary hypothesis.* It has now been supported for a long time by Beard,[6,7] Dohrn,[30] and Balfour[5] for peripheral nerves and by Paladino[136] for central nerves.

It is in vain that this opinion, based on the questionable disclosures of unselective methods, was refuted by His, Lenhossék, Retzius, Kölliker, Harrison, ourselves and all those completely impartial and objective scholars who have scrupulously studied the development of nerve cells and fibers in the embryonic vertebrate spinal cord. The error is repeated daily and one can even say that it has been gradually transformed in recent times, while countenancing the most bizarre fantasies. And, as it is with all concepts that lack objective reality, each of the supporters of this theory professes a particular belief which is at least partially irreconcilable with the view of his fellow-believers. It is really very distressing to see how these research romanticists, instead of occupying their talents by expanding and consolidating the biological edifice, have no other care than to bring it down under the pretext of rebuilding its foundation!

Proof that our judgment does not err by intemperance is found in the opinions recently expressed by the partisans of the catenary theory, among whom Sedgwick, Bethe, Capobianco and Fragnito, Joris, Besta, and Pighione merit especial mention.

According to Sedgwick,[214] the nerve elements lack individuality at the outset; the gray matter is merely represented by a group of nuclei disseminated throughout a common protoplasmic mass. The nervous and protoplasmic processes later differentiate within this intercellular matrix. The neuroblast of His and the formation of cellular processes by growth and ramification would therefore be purely illusory. Such a neuroblastema would form the primitive nervous framework, and the axons would be created in the midst of this amorphous matter.

There is no positive proof for such a supposition. The hypothesis in question results from the application of methods that are incapable of revealing cell contours and from an excessively literal interpretation of the appearance of badly-stained fine funiculi. Is it not true that by failing to utilize all the advances of histological technique and critique we have retraced our steps towards the unsophisticated age of the blastema of Schleiden and Robin?

Nevertheless, this fantasy of Sedgwick is warmly welcomed by Bethe,[14] an eminent investigator whose scientific labor, although remarkable in many respects, tends excessively towards negative criticism. The Strasbourg physiologist begins by reporting that although the works of Kupffer, His, Lenhossék, Harrison, Grunsberg, and ourselves do show that the neuroblastic expansions emerge from the spinal cord during the first phases of embryonic development, these studies do not prove that the extramedullary portion is the result of the stretching of these neuroblastic prolongations. On the contrary, it seems more probable to him that axis-cylinders result from the fusion and differentiation of a chain of peripheral neuroblasts, in accord with the opinion of Balfour, Götte, Beard, Dohrn and others.

In support of such a supposition he makes use of 2 to 3 day chick embryos fixed in alcohol and stained with hematin or aniline acids. He finds that in their first phases, the ventral roots are composed only of cellular chains which are united at their poles and have apparently emigrated from the spinal cord. He mentions some elements of this class which show half of the soma within the spinal cord and half outside. But strangely enough, and contradictory to the catenary doctrine, among the constituents of the root he also detects some processes arising from spinal nerve cells (cells not neuroblastic, although of ectodermal origin).

Thus, the peripheral nerves would supposedly be engendered at a distance from the central nervous system by the differentiation of cellular, neuroblastic chains. He regards the origin of these chains as uncertain, in spite of his agreement that those chains which compose the ventral root originate from the cord. From the second to the fourth day of incubation in the chick the nerves change in appearance, and in the depths of the cellular chains appear some brilliant axons which are perfectly detached from the common protoplasm. Their independent appearance, in his opinion, is the cause of the error of the monogenesists.

Finally, the nerve cells of the spinal cord supposedly form very prematurely. Contrary to Lenhossék's and our assertions, the dendrons appear after the second day of incubation. These processes do not arise by growth of neuroblastic protoplasm but by apposition and condensation of an intercalary plasma (the plasma of Sedgwick) in the midst of which the embryonic nerve cells reside. Both the growth of nerves and the multiplication of their axons takes place by successive solidification and apposition of this blastema. The Schwann nuclei multiply by mitosis.

Although Bethe's praiseworthy aim was to reconcile the catenary theory with the positive facts of neurogenesis, we see that the vague assertions and complexities of his doctrine present every appearance of a scientific preconception. In his great desire to solidify the theory of discontinuity, this author zealously gathers every indication that seems favorable in this regard, and he omits citing (and consequently refuting) the contrary facts which are provided by the clear and conclusive disclosures of the Golgi method. Nevertheless, in spite of himself, the truth frequently slips from his pen, appearing in the objectivity of his descriptions and in the realistic accuracy of his figures. His valuable confession that the ventral roots represent processes from cells of the gray matter; his declaration that many axons lie intercatenarily or intercellularly (although they were previously intracatenary); the recognition that nuclei are plentiful in nerves and that the number of nuclei increases as the nerves are more advanced in development; the figures in which he draws fascicles of fine, independent and continuous axons, located between a series of cells, just as the partisans of the monogenetic doctrine have described them, are all further proof that the Strasbourg physiologist has come very near to the truth. He only lacked the necessary independence and serenity of spirit to recognize and proclaim it.

Other observers imbued with the same prejudice as Bethe, including Capobianco, Fragnito, Besta, Pugnat, Joris, Olmer, Pighini and Schültze* have studied the subject of nerve development.

To attack the neurogenetic problem, Schültze [211,212] has chosen to study a very specific subject: the peripheral sensory nerve terminations of newt and salamander larvae. He fixed the larvae in an osmium bichromate bath, and stained the skin *en masse* afterwards in an alcoholic solution of hematoxylin. In preparations of this kind he recognizes numerous fusiform or stellate neuroblasts in the depths of the subcutaneous connective tissue. These neuroblasts are joined to each other by their ends and are laid out in a complex network having narrow polygonal meshes. The ensemble forms a true multinucleated reticular syncytium of protoplasm, in the midst of

*In this French translation we exclude discussion of these scholars' opinions because they have lost all interest since the modern investigations by Lenhossék, Kölliker, Held, Tello and us. We only retain the criticism of Schültze's opinion with a view to demonstrating the difficulties faced by those who attempt to resolve the problem of neurogenesis by means of routine histological procedures which are incapable of clearly revealing axons and their ramifications. (*Note for the French edition.*)

which the future axons will be differentiated. As several other authors have recognized, these nuclei multiply by mitosis.

Simple inspection of the prints attached to Schültze's monograph is sufficient to demonstrate that his error is the result of the method employed. Hematoxylin or basic aniline dyes do not differentiate the protoplasm of the embryonic Schwann cells from that of the axon; this method uniformly stains them equally, and demonstrates them as continuous and fused. Because of so grave a technical defect, the nuclei of the connective or adventitial elements seem enclosed within the substance of the primordial axis-cylinder while in reality they lie outside the latter. In some figures Schültze himself pictured arrangements which suggest this interpretation, e.g., alleged fusiform neuroblasts with tangential nucleus and, still more significantly, angulated vacuoles instead of interfibrillary spaces where the processes of diverse elements converge. In reality, what this author takes for interneuroblastic anastomoses are nothing more than loci of growth and ramification of fine independent nerve fibers. These fibers are surrounded by a common sheath formed by the protoplasm of connective satellite cells.

Proof that such is the case can be found by examining reduced silver nitrate preparations of the subcutaneous nerve plexus and the fine intermuscular plexus of frog larvae. Figure 1 is a composite illustration of the plexus as observed by several techniques (hematoxylin, methylene blue and silver nitrate.) The hematoxylin method alone (Schültze's technique) only visualizes the continuous protoplasmic branches without revealing appreciable axonal differentiation. Nevertheless, one notes how each trabecula, although massive in appearance with routine methods, actually surrounds several very fine nerve branches which disperse, ramify or come together at the level of the anastomotic bridges. These packets of extremely delicate filaments are surrounded by the Schwann cell protoplasm. At their thin ends, the Schwann cells appear anastomosed or in intimate contact. The isolated (probably terminal) nerve filaments lack nuclei and marginal protoplasm (Fig. 1, d) and dichotomize. Finally one occasionally notes some connective tissue expansions abutting against Schwann cell protoplasm and perhaps fused with it.

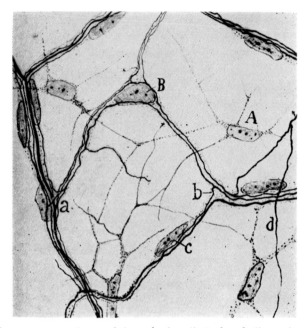

Fig. 1. Sensory nerve plexus of the tadpole tail. Reduced silver nitrate method.
A) Connective tissue cell; B) Schwann cell; a, b) region of bifurcation of
fine, unmyelinated nerve fibers.

From what we have just described it is seen that we no longer accept Kölliker's interpretation [84] of Schültze's nets. According to the Würzburg scholar, these nets are not an early phenomenon and are not composed of neuroblasts, but are the result of fusions or secondary anastomoses occurring in nerve fibers which have developed and grown from the central nervous system.

Such are the theories defended by the principal adversaries of the doctrine of His. It is unnecessary to add that to support them it was first necessary to omit all the precise observations of the esteemed Leipzig embryologist and, furthermore, by a retreat of more than thirty years, to systematically set aside the marvelous, precise and definitive disclosures of silver chromate.

But the refutation of the catenary theory is not based only on the results of staining techniques which are selective for nerve protoplasm. Do not forget that the renowned His, founder of the neurogenetic doctrine or doctrine of continuity, made use of routine procedures exclusively.[70] It is very true that, in compensation for the poor quality of the analytical resources employed, the Leipzig embryologist was gifted with a rare critical faculty and talent for observation. Observations and facts absolutely irreconcilable with the polygenetic error abound in his vast and fruitful work on the development of the spinal cord, medulla and brain. Let us add moreover that, following in the footsteps of the master and employing analogous techniques, Harrison, Gurwitsch, Neal, Kerr, Lugaro and Kölliker arrived at the same results.

Harrison[52] has confirmed almost all the discoveries of His in embryos of salmon and other vertebrates. He describes the neuroblast as absolutely independent and provided with a cell process which is devoid of nuclei. After having crossed the basal exterior region of the spinal cord, the neuroblastic prolongation travels freely through mesodermal tissue, from which tissue it ultimately receives the adventitial cells which form the Schwann sheath. This author also illustrates the tip of the growing axon, representing it as enlarged and rounded like the tip of a probe, just as Stroebe had already represented it in regenerating adult fibers. According to Harrison, this enlargement corresponds to our growth cone, the only difference being that instead of presenting diverging appendages it is smooth. As for the origin of neuroglia, the formation of the Schwann and myelin sheaths, and the development of the ganglia, Harrison's conclusions do not essentially differ from those of His, Lenhossék and ourselves.

Gurwitsch[49] published a curious observation which is singularly compromising for the catenary theory. On examining the sciatic nerve of the cow embryo, he noted that in the earliest stages this nerve consists only of a single fascicle of denuded axis-cylinders, absolutely free of nuclei and Schwann cells. Only later, by a sort of migration, do adventitial cells penetrate among the axons. These adventitial cells are destined to form the protective apparatus of the myelinated fibers. A long time ago, moreover, His, Kölliker and others made similar observations.

Neal[129] applied the same questionable techniques, which are so dear to the polygenesists, to embryos of *Squalus Acanthus*. He observed the formation of monocellular neuroblasts which migrated ventrad, adopted the typical pyriform shape, and extruded the primordial axon of the ventral root. This axonal process arose independently of any cellular chain. The nuclei only appear later and take no part whatever in the formation of axis-cylinders. As Kupffer, His, and Kölliker demonstrated a long time ago, the axis-cylinder is only a simple prolongation of the neuroblast.

Graham Kerr [75] also proposes an identical doctrine as the result of his observations in *Lepidosiren paradoxa*. In this animal it is easy to trace the ventral roots from the spinal cord to the myotome during the first developmental phases. During their long course these roots are composed of denuded axons without any relationship of continuity with Schwann cells. The latter are mesodermal derivatives and invade the nerve trunks later.

Lugaro [109] also proclaims the validity of His's conception, opposing the theory of discontinuity which he attributes to errors of interpretation. Since the formation of pathways in the embryonic central nervous system has been proved to be independent of chains or nuclei, he believes it reasonable that peripheral nerves should be produced by an identical mechanism.

Finally, a posthumous article by the worthy Kölliker [84] appeared this very year (1905), in which he once more takes up the defense of the unitary conception of nerve fibers, supporting it with conclusive new observations. In this work, Kölliker begins by recalling all the positive irrefutable facts stated by himself, His, Lenhossék, Retzius, Harrison and ourselves concerning the unicellular development of embryonic axons. He emphasizes the thousand-times-confirmed observation that all central nerve pathways (funiculi of white matter of the spinal cord, central bundles of sensory nerves, thalamocerebral radiations, etc.) are devoid of nuclei and Schwann cells and are produced by simple elongation of axis-cylinders. Finally, he completes his work by recounting some observations relating to the formation of sensory and motor terminations in larval amphibia. From these observations he deduces that the supposed primitive peripheral network of Schültze is an accidental secondary phenomenon due to the fusion of originally free nerve branches. Moreover, Kölliker displays doubts about the origin of the Schwann

cells and the capsule cells of sensory neurons. He is inclined to believe that they are of ectodermal origin.*

From the preceding historical statement, the reader can well
imagine our stand in the lively debate about neurogenesis. We have
never had the least doubt about this subject. Our investigations [170,
172] undertaken long years ago, employing a method giving definitive results (Golgi method) have permitted us to confirm His's
discoveries. His's findings had aroused considerable doubt because
they were based upon the use of routine methods which did not give
absolutely convincing results.

Later, the precise and confirmatory investigations of Lenhossék,
[97] Retzius,[208] Harrison,[51] Neal, Kerr and others strengthened our
convictions even further. Finally, any shadow of doubt was dissipated when, in our recent studies on nerve regeneration, we observed
the phenomena of continuous growth from the central end of
interrupted axons and the terminal club or button of the wandering young fibers.[178]

In our opinion, the process of neurogenesis was judged without
appeal many long years ago, and all attempts at revision are unnecessary. But our conviction, which is also that of worthy neurologists, is not shared today by all scholars, nor perhaps even by the
majority of them. In the present intellectual environment, the
polygenetic error is so general and so infectious that it threatens to
stifle the truth for a long time and perhaps to retard the advance
of scientific progress for half a score of years. We therefore deem

---

*A work by von Lenhossék [100] appeared at the time this memoir was in press
in which he reaffirms the validity of His's doctrine and discusses the origin of
Schwann cells, which he names lemmoblasts. Just as two different kinds of
cells (neurons and neuroglia) develop in the central nervous system from the
ectoderm, Lenhossék belives that the two principal factors of the peripheral
trunks, axon and Schwann cell or sheath, derive from the same line. After
having remarked that, contrary to Kohn's assertions, the ectodermal origin of
lemmoblasts has nothing to do with the mechanism of axon formation, he
describes some observations concerning a 7 millimeter human embryo which
are absolutely irreconcilable with the catenary theory. He observes for example,
that the glossopharyngeal nerve totally lacks nuclei during the first phases of
its formation and that the same is true of many motor and sensory nerves. The
infiltration of nerve fascicles by emigrant lemmoblasts only occurs considerably
later.

it an inescapable duty for all those who have calmly and independently studied the question to bring to the controversy all possible
information, and to minutely itemize, even to the point of verbosity,
the observed facts and the conclusions to which these facts lead. In
short, this is the justification for this work.

MATERIALS AND METHODS

We have preferred to use chick and pigeon embryos for the present investigations. In the part dealing with mammals we have not
been able to obtain all the necessary material. In general, the rabbit
and cat embryos used for this purpose were too far advanced and
consequently more appropriate to the study of the fundamental anatomy of nerve nuclei and pathways of the spinal cord and medulla
than for histogenetic analysis.

Along with the routine methods and that of Golgi, we have preferentially employed the reduced silver nitrate technique, previously used by us in this kind of research and recently employed by Besta
and others scholars as well.

As Besta has noted, the first formula (direct fixation in silver
nitrate) stains the embryonic spinal cord very early. From the third
day of incubation, and perhaps even earlier, the motor nuclei and
sensory pathways stain almost constantly. The metallic deposit is
selectively fixed to the neurofibrils of the soma and axons of centrifugal neurons. This fortunate circumstance permits relatively easy
access to the problem of the appearance and metamorphosis of the
neuroblasts, as well as to that of the advancement and growth of the
sensory and motor axons.

The studies which we have recently performed with this procedure have convinced us that not only the first formula, but also the
second (prior fixation in alcohol for 24 hours) give excellent impregnations. Today we prefer the latter because it gives greater contrast to the stained elements, and also because it furnishes perfect
impregnation of cell nuclei, comparable to that obtained with Bis-
marck brown or any basic aniline dye. Let us add that the reaction
penetrates very deeply into the material, even to the point of rou-
tinely obtaining a complete series of strongly-stained sections of
the medulla and cephalic region in 5 to 7 day embryos. Also at

times, although it is not indispensable, we turn to nuclear counterstaining by thionin (Cajal) or safranin (Veratti). Gold-toning is superfluous.

In order to accurately interpret the preparations made by this method, it is necessary to recall what it colors. We assert that the metallic deposit precipitates exclusively on nerve cells and fibers, entirely sparing the neuroglial and epithelial elements as well as the non-neural cells.

The principal object of this work is the examination of the origin and mode of formation of the axons of sensory, special sense and motor nerves. However, we will also devote some attention to the study of the morphologic development of their cells of origin and to the development of the association neurons.

We will therefore distinguish the five following parts: 1. origin and formation of motor nerves; 2. origin and formation of sensory nerves; 3. origin and formation of nerves of special sense; 4. development of association cells and pathways; 5. origin of neuroblasts and sympathetic nerves.

ORIGIN AND FORMATION OF MOTOR NERVES

Spinal Cord. As His demonstrated and von Lenhossék, Retzius and we have confirmed, the indifferent or germinal cells of the chick embryo are transformed into neuroblasts as early as the second day of incubation. In Golgi preparations these elements are stainable at the third day. At this time they are pyriform with their large end directed towards the ependyma. Their bulky nucleus is surrounded by a small amount of protoplasm, and their sturdy conical appendage is externally directed and of variable length. As we have discovered, the free end of this appendage possesses a terminal enlargement or excrescence garnished with spines (*the growth cone*). During this stage (third day of incubation) dendrons are lacking in nearly all the neurons. Only considerably later, in an occasional funicular or commissural neuroblast, is an internal appendage observed which gives a bipolar form to the cell. Perhaps this appendage is only accidental and transitory, as Lenhossék and Retzius thought.

Let us now see if such facts are confirmed in silver nitrate pre-

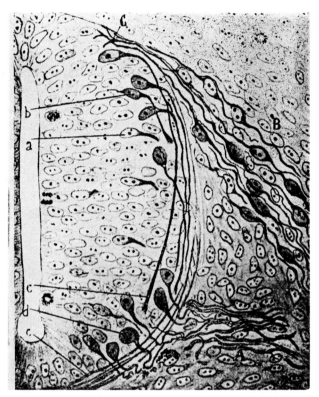

Fig. 2. Section of the lumbar cord of the 76 hour chick embryo. Reduced silver nitrate method with alcohol fixation. A) Ventral root; B) spinal ganglion; C) bifurcation of the dorsal root; a) rudimentary association neuroblasts; b) bipolar commissural neuroblast possessing a growth cone; c) commissural growth cones; d) motor neurons.

parations. In Figure 2 we reproduce a section of spinal cord of a 3 day chick embryo. As the reader can imagine, the great majority of nerve cells and all the epithelial cells are unstained, save their nucleus, which exhibits one, two, or more strongly impregnated nucleoli. At maturity, i.e., when they are able to attract the metallic deposit, the motor neuroblasts are ventrally-placed and the commissural elements dorsally and laterally-placed.

Motor neuroblasts have a pale protoplasm, accumulated exclusively at the peripheral pole which is the site of origin of the axon. The protoplasmic bed of the internal side of the motor neuroblast is so fine and so transparent that it is impossible to delineate any trace of structure in it. In its external side, one can just about make out a compact neurofibrillar network in which longitudinal filaments condense to form the axon. The nucleus is more voluminous than in other elements. It contains a large nucleolus (rarely two or more) composed of an aggregation of spherules which, because of their close proximity, are not always easily separable (Fig. 2, d).

The process travels directly externally, becoming progressively finer; it then passes through a fine layer of commissural axons and after having pierced the basal perimedullary layer, it moves on freely across the mesodermal tissue to give rise to the ventral root. Only very rarely can one succeed in identifying the tip or the growth cone of one of these radicular fibers. This fact undoubtedly results from the early formation of these fibers and their rapid migration toward the periphery. Certainly, most of the axons have left the spinal cord before the third day of incubation, when the motor neuroblasts are not yet stainable (Fig. 3, A). However, we have occasionally noted some retarded axons in the middle of a root which are terminated by a slight intumescence, comparable to a growth club. Less frequently one or more axons are left behind in the basal layer of the spinal cord.

First let us record an important fact, one singularly compromising for the catenary theory. Throughout their journey toward the periphery, the motor axons lack nuclei and are absolutely continuous. In no way do they show any remains of a segmental organization. This fact presents itself so clearly that it is free from all possible objection. The axons appear well impregnated in a transparent coffee-colored tone that is admirably distinguishable from the general yellowish background and perfectly distinct from the mesodermal cells (Fig. 2, A).

Perhaps the polygenesists will object that the cellular chains correspond to a prior phase, e.g., at the second day of incubation in the chick. They might say that the appearance of continuity and independence results from the fact that the undifferentiated protoplasm of these chains is not stained. The small fascicles of axiscylinders or free axons would actually be lodged within this protoplasm.

To answer these possible objections, we have made several attempts at impregnation of the two day chick embryo and have occasionally obtained a fairly energetic staining of the ventral roots,
as well as the connective tissue cells which surround them. Figure
3 reproduces a transverse section of these roots in a 58 hour chick
embryo. The constituent fascicles of the root are fine, small in
number, and appear surrounded by cavities or vacuoles which separate the connective tissue cells. As is seen in Figure 3, c, there is no
protoplasmic crust or cellular chain around each axon. The latter
seems to travel freely through the intercellular fluid. Note, furthermore, that the neighboring mesodermal elements have not undergone any transformation, being polygonal, fusiform or stellate, and
without the least tendency to form sheaths or coverings for the fine
nerve fascicles. Finally, the above-mentioned sections reveal one
very positive fact which is capable of clarifying the mechanism of
growth of the roots. Simultaneously with the differentiation of the
motor neuroblasts, the mesodermal region between the notochord
and the sensory ganglia shows a tremendous number of spaces or
intercellular vacuoles filled with transparent liquid. The axons
easily migrate across these vacuoles by means of a continuous growth
process (Fig. 3, b).

Despite what the polygenesists say, transverse and longitudinal
sections of the 56 to 60 hour chick embryo stained by routine

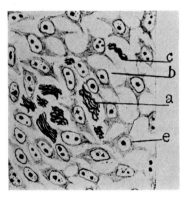

Fig. 3.   Transverse section of the ventral root of a 58 hour chick embryo. Reduced silver nitrate method. a) Fascicles of naked axons; b) intercellular spaces;
c) axons travelling through an intercellular space; e) connective tissue cell.

methods (hematoxylin and eosin, etc.) do not show the famous cellular chains. They merely have the same appearance as silver impregnation preparations, although they are vaguer and less distinct. As can be seen in Figure 4, a, there emerge from the cord certain pale, longitudinal striated tracts in whose interior no nuclei are perceived. Any aspect of cellular series or chains, if manifest at times, corresponds to the interstices between nerve fascicles and has nothing to do with the process of nerve formation. We have not succeeded in observing the emigration of neuroblasts that Bethe suggested.

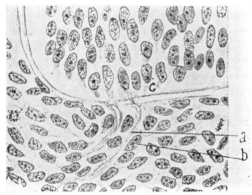

Fig. 4. Ventral root of the 60 hour chick embryo. Alcohol fixation, hematoxylin and eosin stain. a) Pale tracts composed of naked axons which are leaving the spinal cord; b) free connective tissue nuclei; c) periphery of the spinal cord showing several motor neuroblasts.

Longitudinal sections of the roots at the third day of incubation (silver impregnation) are equally demonstrative (Fig. 2, a). In addition to the above facts, one also notes that the axons cross the basal layer, describe a long detour and then form compact plexiform fascicles which frequently wind in and out adapting themselves to the contours of the connective tissue cells. During this journey the axons do not drag any cellular retinue with them. The very small number of intercalated elements in the roots are lodged, as we have said, between the bundles. Their presence is explained simply by the growth and migration of the roots, the latter having been obliged to forge a path among the mesodermal cells.

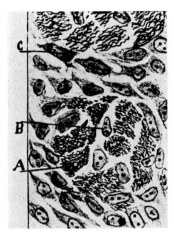

Fig. 5. Transverse section of the ventral root of a 4 day chick embryo. A) Fascicles of axons; B) disoriented intercalary cell; C) undifferentiated connective tissue cells about the periphery of the roots.

Figure 5 is a transverse section of the ventral root of the 4 day embryo. The radicular fascicles now contain a multitude of axons, separated from each other by plasmatic spaces which represent the remains of the previous tunnels of the mesodermal region that had been invaded by the roots. A small number of connective tissue nuclei have penetrated among the nerve bundles but have not established any intimate relation with them. Only around each root does one note a certain concentration of the connective tissue cells and a tendency toward a concentric orientation of those nearest the nerve; but there is no indication as yet of formation of a neurilemma or of Schwann nuclei.

Not before the fifth day of incubation does one perceive indications that the indifferent relationship between mesodermal cells and nerve roots will be converted into a process of active collaboration (Fig. 6, B). The intercalated nuclei then multiply and intimately embrace the fascicles and the periradicular elements become flattened, forming a rudimentary protective membrane.

During the following days the number of intraradicular nuclei increases still further, at least in the vicinity of the cord, but none of them penetrate the fascicles yet. Thus, while the number of ad-

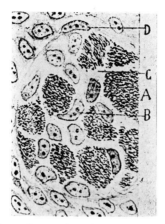

Fig. 6 Ventral root of a 5 day chick embryo. A) Fascicles of naked axons; B) intercalary cell arranged about a nerve fascicle; D) Marginal connective tissue cell.

ventitial elements increases, the contingent of axons newly arrived from the cord increases as well. It is curious to note that the number of intercalated nuclei ordinarily is considerably less at a distance from the pia mater. A similar condition has been observed in the cranial nerves.

Finally, examination of the progress of the roots across the mesoderm during the second, third and fourth days of incubation suggests the idea that the connective lattice is passively penetrated by the nerve axons. The connective tissue cells have no relation with the axons other than the fortuitous ones of proximity and contact deriving from the mechanical stress of the invasive act.

During this entire development the nerve fibers are exceedingly fine and form bundles in which no remnants of undifferentiated elements or matter can be detected. This exceptional tenuousness of the embryonic axons which compose the small compact fascicles, has contributed in good part to the error of the polygenesists. Having worked with unselective methods, they could easily err by considering the vague striation of the compact fascicles (the only thing visible in such routine preparations) as proof of a differentiation in the midst of massive protoplasmic cords.

The same independence of adventitial elements is observed in

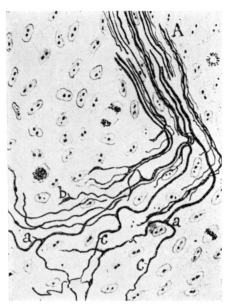

Fig. 7.   Course and divisions of a spinal root of a 3.5 day embryo. A) Root near
the cord; a) axonal division; b) fusiform growth mass; c) terminal branches
lacking marginal nuclei.

the most peripheral portions of the root near its termination. In following the root forwards it is readily noted that the root divides
into two large fascicles, ventral and dorsal, from which emerge
small bundles destined for the muscles or the sympathetic system.
Bifurcated fibers are often found not far from the origin of these
large fascicles. The branches of bifurcation describe an initial curve,
undoubtedly by adaptation to one or another mesodermal cell.

Figure 7 illustrates several of these bifurcations. The same axon
may bifurcate several times. Observe that neither in the trunks nor
in the branches are there any discontinuities or traces of cellular
chains.

During the fourth day of incubation, the number of motor cells
which attract silver nitrate increases considerably, the first dendrons
already being very conspicuous. The neurofibrillar framework,
which previously was concentrated in the cone of origin of the axon,
spreads distally and proximally, thereby forming a reticular clump

or center from which the axonal and dendritic fascicles emanate. As is shown in Figure 8, c, most of the protoplasmic processes are directed obliquely dorsomedially; some pale fine ones reach the vicinity of the ependyma. At this time many neuroblastic cells which are devoid of internal radial process (Fig. 8, b) still abound, especially in the region of the dorsal horn and in the neighborhood of the root. The bipolar elements which were so well described and drawn by Besta from silver nitrate preparations of the embryonic cord undoubtedly correspond to this phase. The error incurred by

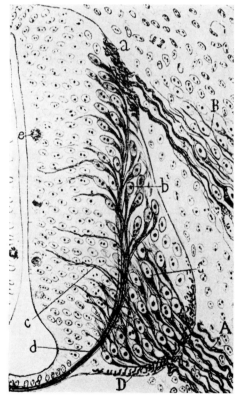

Fig. 8. Section of the spinal cord of a 4 day chick embryo. A) Ventral root; B) spinal ganglion; C) motor neurons; D) rudiment of the ventral funiculus; a) rudiment of the dorsal funiculus; b) commissural neuroblasts; c) internal dendrites of the motor neurons; d) ventral commissure; e) cells undergoing mitotic division.

this author consists only in that he considers as primitive some morphological types which are relatively well developed and far from the neuroblastic phase. By this we do not claim to deny that in some particular cases neuroblasts exist which are provided very precociously with radial processes; in fact we called attention to this a long time ago in preparations made with the Golgi method.

At the fifth day the motor neurons approach the definitive multipolar type still further, as we show in Figures 9 and 10. The perinuclear protoplasm has increased and dendrons emerge in all directions, although those oriented dorsoventrally are still the most numerous. Among them the dorsolateral ones stand out especially clearly and, gathered into fascicles, spread across the thickness of

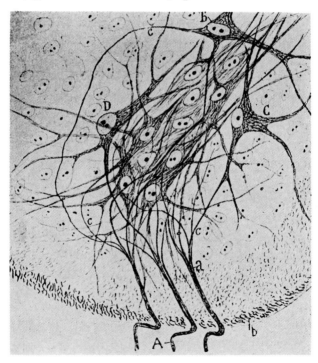

Fig. 9. Section of the ventral horn of the cervical spinal cord of the 5 day chick embryo. A) Ventral root; B, D) motor neurons whose axon has been successfully traced to the ventral root; a) fascicles of axons without nuclei which are crossing the ventral funiculus; b) superficial portion of the ventral funiculus which is composed of large axons.

the ventrolateral funiculus. They terminate there, the longest reaching very near to the external basal region. The ventral dendrons, destined for the ventral funiculus and ventral commissure, and the dorsomedial ones of the central gray substance are less numerous and shorter. As for the axons, they may emerge from any side of the motor cell. However, they often spring from the ventral or lateral side of the cell body or from a large dendron. After having traveled forwards and described an arc with lateral concavity, the axons are gathered into fascicles which cross the substance of the ventral funiculus (Fig. 9, a). These intramedullary fascicles are absolutely devoid of nuclei, as many authors have recognized, and they are continuous with the motor roots which are now very numerous and arranged in large bundles.

A most interesting fact, which we intend to deal with at length in another work, is that illustrated in Figure 10, B. Besides the superficial motor nucleus common to the mammals, there is another deep one, formed of elements having a very advanced neurofibrillar framework and strongly stainable by silver. Most of these cells are fusiform and possess large dendrons of which one, the posterodorsomedial one, penetrates among the bodies of the epithelial cells. Their axon travels ventrad at first and then curves laterally to cross the principal or superficial motor nucleus and mix with the roots.* The most external elements of the above-mentioned deep nucleus are singularly amenable to study. They are completely isolated and provided with dendrons which are very easy to trace. It is unnecessary to say that one never observes the slightest trace of nuclei in Fragnito's colonies.

The motor elements do not all differentiate simultaneously. Within the superficial nucleus one always notes a region, usually located dorsolaterally, in which the cells do not acquire the ability to attract silver nitrate until very late. It is sufficient to compare the number of motor roots in transverse sections of the cord at the third day of incubation with those evident in succeeding days to realize that the process of maturation of motor cells occurs in successive waves.

---

*This nucleus has been confirmed by Terni,[225] who considers it as the nucleus of origin of the sympathetic nervous system. (*Note for the French edition.*)

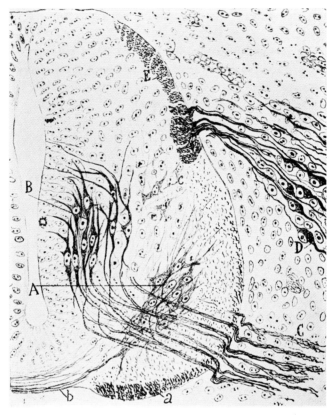

Fig. 10. Section of the thoracic spinal cord of a 5.5 day chick embryo. A) Ordinary or superficial motor nucleus; B) deep motor nucleus; C) ventral root; D) spinal ganglion; E) sensory path of the dorsal funiculus; a) pathway composed of large axons; b) ventral commissure.

In the historical section of this work, we alluded to the results obtained by Besta, Fragnito and Pighini in the chick spinal cord using the silver nitrate method. We stated that the anastomoses and nets described by these authors have no real existence and result from faulty interpretation. To avoid similar errors it is certainly necessary to bear in mind what this method stains and what may cause it to lose its ability to simultaneously impregnate all the mature neurons of a single nucleus. It seems to us that these Italian scholars have not given enough thought to the error which may be committed by taking for granted the very complicated factors which surround this property. Besta's cellular chains and anastomotic network and Fragnito's multinuclear colonial neurons are easily explained by the three following peculiarities of neuroblastic development and location. The reduced silver nitrate procedure singularly demonstrates these peculiarities.

1. In the majority of young neurons, the nucleus is eccentric, almost external to the cell body, and seems supplementary to the neurofibrillar cluster or system which is coextensive with the axon and dendrons. Because of the lack of stainability of the thin perinuclear shell of protoplasm, it follows that, without scrupulous examination with an oil immersion objective, it is not always easy to determine the neuron to which the nucleus in question belongs (Fig. 9, C, D).

2. In their growth and migratory movements neighboring neurons, as well as their dendrons, avail themselves of the same interepithelial spaces and approach each other in such a way that it becomes difficult at times to determine the boundaries of separation. The formation of series or groups of cells in the same interstice, for example, is very common, as is the gathering of neurons into compact colonies, lodged in the large interspaces which belong to the radial processes of the ventrolateral epithelium (Fig. 9). Furthermore, this proximity of young neurons, easily explainable by the absence of intercalary dendritic plexuses and terminal nerve nests, militates against His's hypothesis that the epithelium or neurospongium is reticularly arranged and that the neuronal protoplasm passively runs through the hollows of the reticulum. In reality, on encountering the least resistance the neuroblasts are displaced and regrouped; but the growth and progress of their processes could not be explained without invoking other influences.

This successive accumulation of neurons in the same interepithelial spaces leads to a paradoxical phenomenon which is seriously upheld by Besta: that the neuroblasts are cellular units initially, i.e., when small and hardly differentiated, but later take on a *syncytial* appearance. From the point of view of the colonial doctrine it is not suprising that, in every nucleus, the peripheral or marginal cells which have more space to extend their processes comfortably, appear perfectly independent. Thus, for example, the motor neurons illustrated in Figure 9 would give rise to a nervous network or syncytium, while those situated in the lateral or medial margins of the cluster (Fig. 9, C, D) would enjoy a complete autonomy. Is it necessary to insist that such differences are illusory and subject to the purely mechanical conditions which produce such anastomotic appearances?

In Golgi preparations the afore-mentioned appearances are never present, thanks to silver chromate's fortunate property of impregnating only some of the cells of a nucleus. The impregnated cells are ordinarily separated by neurons lacking affinity for the metallic deposit. But the reduced silver nitrate procedure—we repeat—impregnates all the mature neurons of a given nucleus simultaneously. It follows that if the neuroglial cells are not yet developed, as in the 4 to 7 day embryo, the cellular cluster forms a very complicated plexus in which somas and dendrons often pursue the same direction and enter into intimate contact.

3. Finally, employing the first impregnation formula (fixation in 1.0-1.5 per cent silver nitrate) as did Besta and Fragnito, we have observed some fairly well-developed dendrites exhibiting varicosities and vacuoles at which level the neurofibrillar plexus is lacking or considerably rarified. In preparations fixed in 40 per cent alcohol the alternations that Fragnito and Pegna have erroneously taken for nuclei undergoing resorption never appear. Furthermore, the fact that such swellings are not in the nucleus, but are rather protoplasmic alterations, is easy to verify by examination of the figures presented by these two scholars. One searches in vain in these figures for the nuclear membrane and the nucleolar spherules that are characteristic of all true nuclei.

Medulla Oblongata. As His demonstrated, the neuroblasts of the medulla develop at the same time as those of the spinal cord and exhibit the same properties as the latter. By means of the silver nitrate procedure the motor nuclei of the hypoglossal, trigeminal, oculomotor, abducens and trochlear nerves of the chick may be impregnated at the third day of incubation. Only later do the facial and vagal motor nuclei attract the metallic deposit. As proof we present a section of the oculomotor nucleus (Fig. 11, B). Not far

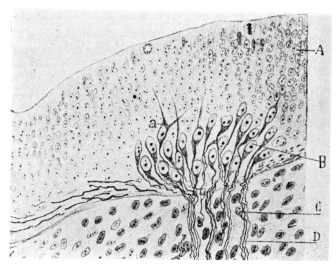

Fig. 11. Transverse section of the basal portion of the midbrain of a 3 day chick embryo. A) Epithelial zone with germinal cells; B) common oculomotor nucleus; C) nuclei of adventitial cells; D) naked axons a) multipolar cell.

from the midline and ventral to the great epithelial mass, the broad thin basal portion of the midbrain exhibits a cluster of pyriform neuroblasts which lack intercalated nuclei for the most part. Like similar spinal cells, the protoplasm is accumulated almost exclusively at the pole from which the axon emerges, and where a very evident neurofibrillar network is found. One notes, by way of exception, a small number of cells at the medial boundary of the nucleus in which the neurofibrillar network extends higher than the nucleus and gives rise to one or more ascending dendrons. The axons are directed basally. They cross the basal portion (Fig. 11, D) and, reunited in undulating fascicles, they cross the underlying mesodermal tissue. Between these bundles of slender filaments lie small connective tissue cells which have no predominant orientation and are completely independent of the axis-cylinders. Needless to say, no trace is seen of the supposed cellular chains, either inside or outside of the nucleus. The same is true of other cranial motor nuclei, as may be seen in Figure 16, A, which shows the nuclei of the trigeminal nerve, during the third day of incubation.

It is curious that the cranial nerve nuclei are always more advanced than the spinal ones. Thus, although dendrons are usually lacking in the spinal neurons of the 3 day chick, the corresponding cells of the medulla and midbrain exhibit two protoplasmic processes (Fig. 11, a). At any rate, it is certainly the neuroblastic cells (Fig. 11, B) that predominate in the cranial nuclei.

Motor Roots in Mammals. We possess serial sections of the medulla of both the 2 and 2.5 centimeter rabbit embryo, in which the mechanism of formation of nerves can be profitably studied, even though the development of the motor and association neurons is well advanced. We agree with Lenhossék that mammals are more suitable than birds for the study of this question, because of the relative slowness, in mammals, of infiltration of nerve bundles by lemmoblasts or Schwann elements.

In general it may be stated that motor nerves, such as the hypoglossal, facial, motor portion of the vagus, etc., are completely devoid of nuclei during their entire intracentral course. They only possess them in the periphery during their journey across cartilage and connective tissue. Finally, they show a more or less advanced degree of nuclear infiltration while crossing the subdural and

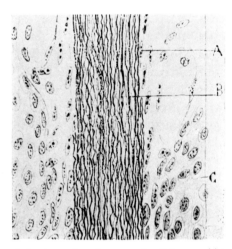

Fig. 12.   Portion of the hypoglossal nerve of a 2.5 cm rabbit embryo. A) Connective tissue cells of the neurilemma; B) axons lacking nuclei C) cartilage of the base of the cranium.

arachnoid spaces of the cranial cavity. In proof of this statement, observe (Fig. 12, B) a segment of hypoglossal nerve in its passage through the occipital foramen. In spite of the numerous fascicles of which this bundle is composed, and despite the very long path comprising this section, one cannot find a single adventitial cell. All the connective tissue cells lie at the periphery where they form 2 or 3 flattened layers of elements on the suface of the nerve trunk. On the other hand, during their intracranial path many lemmo-blasts are infiltrated between the nerve fascicles. Moreover, this ac-cumulation of adventitial cells within the intrameningeal segment of the nerves is also found in chick embryos at the end of the fourth day of incubation and thereafter.

Terminal Motor Plexuses. In the above-mentioned 2.5 centi-meter mammalian embryos as well as in the chick following the sixth day of incubation, some nerve plexuses appear in the depths of the rudimentary muscles. When examined under low power these plexuses show a remarkable resemblance to the network of supposed neuroblasts described by Schültze in the sensory nerves of the tail of the larval urodele. In fact, just like Schültze's network, the muscular tissue (in ordinary preparations) shows protoplasmic ribbons studded with nuclei. These ribbons form a network in the interior of which is an accumulation of primitive muscular fibers cut in cross section. But examination of the knots and trabeculae of this neuroblastic reticulum in silver nitrate preparations clearly reveals that, far from being massive and homogeneous, they are composed of bundles of extremely fine unmyelinated filaments, surrounded by the prolongations of Schwann cells. At the level of the points of union, the nerve fibers divide in a complicated manner. Free fibers emerge from certain parts of the plexus. These fibers are devoid of nuclei; they become lost in the depths of the muscular mass. We again state that the lemmoblasts are ordinarily absent in the nerve trunks as well as in the final independent branches. Lemmoblasts are more abundant in the fine free preterminal nerves where they represent, not the rudiment of the Schwann cell but rather the rudiment of the perineural sheath.

NEUROBLASTS AND SENSORY NERVES

Spinal Sensory Neurons. As we have shown in another work, the reduced silver nitrate method distinctly demonstrates the innate bipolarity of the sensory nerves in embryonic dorsal root ganglia. This was discovered many years ago by His and confirmed by Lenhossék, Retzius, Van Gehuchten, Sala, Athias and ourselves.

Silver nitrate stains the sensory elements of the chick from the beginning of the third day of incubation, even though at this time no more than a small number of cells exhibit neurofibrillar impregnation. In general, these cells are situated in the ventral and central region of the spinal ganglia. The other elements may be recognized by their voluminous nucleus and by their lightly stained yellow-brown or completely colorless protoplasm (Fig. 2, B).

At first (from 60 to 70 hours of incubation) the sensory cells appear frankly bipolar with an eccentric vesicular nucleus, a thick peripheral process and a fine central one. The neurofibrillar framework of the perikaryon is accumulated at one side. It gives rise to a kind of bridge which unites the two processes almost in a straight line. It is not rare to find the slightly enlarged growth cone of the central process, and even of the peripheral one, within the ganglion.

Finally, in more advanced cells one notes that the interpolar bridge suddenly greatly enlarges near the origin of the peripheral process, giving rise to a dense reticular mass which we will call *the protoplasmic mass* (Fig. 13).

We have just said that the most slowly developing cells completely lack selectivity for silver nitrate (Fig. 14, A). In others, less numerous, only the processes attract the metallic deposit, while the interpolar bridge and the protoplasmic mass are very weakly impregnated (Fig. 14, B). Finally, in a small number of sensory elements the stain extends throughout the perikaryon, and one clearly sees the reticular arrangement of the neurofibrils and the fasciculated appearance of the processes (Fig. 14, C).

This arrangement is maintained during the following days (from the fourth to the seventh day), during which the thickness of the protoplasmic mass and of the interpolar bridge continues to increase. The nucleus is still marginal and apparently devoid of

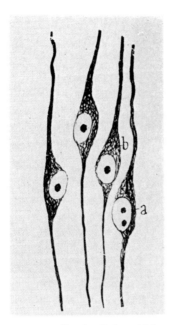

Fig. 13.   Some bipolar sensory cells of a 5 day chick embryo. a) Neurofibrillar
interpolar bridge; b) protoplasmic mass or nucleus.

organized protoplasm (Fig. 14, c). Finally, at the end of the seventh
day and thereafter, the protoplasm seems to double around the
nuclear circumference completely and some cells begin to migrate
towards the periphery of the ganglion. In this way begins the
process of monopolarity which will be completed by 12 to 14 days
of incubation.

It is very easy to follow the sensory roots to the spinal cord and
to observe their bifurcation and continuity with the rudiment of
the dorsal funiculus (round bundle of His). For this purpose,
longitudinal or dorsoventral sections are preferable to transverse ones.
Figure 15 demonstrates that the roots which penetrate the cord
during the fourth day of incubation are quite numerous. They
arrive there in compact bundles which often describe very curious
turns and circumvolutions before crossing the basal portion.

Indeed, some fascicles course backwards from the outset; by
tracing an S they then slide over the basal portion and penetrate

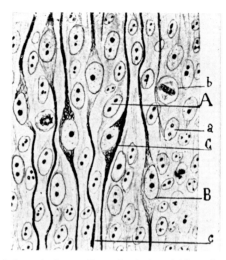

Fig. 14.   Cells of the spinal ganglion of a 3 day chick embryo. A) Bipolar cell which does not attract silver nitrate; B) another cell whose processes only are stained; C) another cell which already demonstrates the neurofibrillar framework of the perikaryon: c) growth mass.

the cord in a more anterior plane. The penetration takes place through a relatively narrow gap through which a great number of stout and fine axons grow. The axons soon bifurcate. The bifurcation occurs very near to the limiting membrane so that it is readily observed in isolated nerve fibers or in those arranged in loose fascicles. On the other hand, in those roots bound in compact bundles (Fig. 15, b) this bifurcation is surmised rather than seen, because of the great number of axons which bifurcate simultaneously. In this way arise two distinct fascicles, ascending and descending, separated by an obtuse angle and often joining with their neighbors to form a longitudinally arranged plexus. Here and there the growth cone of an ascending or descending branch is detected (Fig. 15, e). These growth cones are fine, similar to those of association axons (see below). Finally we repeat once again the assertion that *the intramedullary growth and development of the dorsal roots occurs without the assistance of any adventitial cell.* Lugaro and Kölliker laid stress upon this fact, which is a fatal one for the catenary theory.

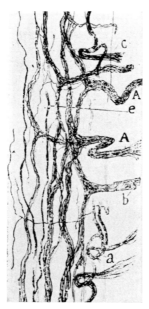

Fig. 15 Longitudinal section of the dorsal funiculus of a 4 day chick embryo.
A) Bundles of root fibers; a, b, c) curves formed by the roots entering the basal
portion; e) growth mass.

Furthermore, the diverse phases of growth of the sensory pathways of the dorsal funiculus may be observed perfectly in transverse
sections of the spinal cord which have been stained by our method.
The examination is all the easier since, as Besta has noted, this
column impregnates intensely and virtually selectively during the
fourth and fifth days of incubation. Even during succeeding days
when the newly differentiated white matter thickens considerably,
the sensory path stands out because of the exceptional compactness
of its fibers and because of its energetic impregnation.

During its course across mesodermal tissues the peripheral branch
of the sensory cell behaves just as the motor fibers do. It maintains
its individuality, is clearly distinct from interstitial cells, and
bifurcates many times. Its final ramifications occasionally terminate in free points, but more often in thickenings or terminal intumescences which serve as growth cones (see below).

Medulla Oblongata. It is unnecessary to say that the sensory neurons of the medulla oblongata behave essentially the same as those of the spinal cord. The cells of the trigeminal ganglion are easily impregnated from the third day of incubation, as are the ganglion cells of the vagus, glossopharyngeal and vestibular nerve. Those of the spiral ganglion seem slower.

As is illustrated in Figure 16, C ($3\frac{1}{2}$ day embryo), the great majority of trigeminal sensory neurons still appear unstained, exhibiting a large marginal nucleus and two barely visible polar processes originating from the lateral protoplasmic bridge.

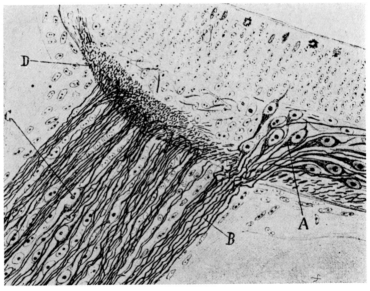

Fig. 16. Transverse section of the basal portion of the hindbrain of a 4 day chick embryo. A) A portion of the trigeminal motor nucleus; B) motor root of trigeminal nerve; C) bipolar cells of the trigeminal ganglion; D) descending sensory root of the trigeminal nerve.

Such prolongations are colorless at their point of origin but become quite intensely colored further away from the cell body, and they can thus be traced very easily. However, in other cells, the neurofibrils of the perikaryon are already impregnated, giving the appearance of a complicated, predominantly longitudinal network located in the intercalary protoplasmic bridge. Just as in spinal ganglia, a considerable portion of the nucleus lacks this neurofibrillar network which gradually becomes concentrated at the point of origin of the peripheral process.

Moreover, the transformation from bipolarity to monopolarity takes place late (from the ninth to the tenth day) by a mechanism described in another work.[175]

As for the central and peripheral course of the sensory paths, it is not worthwhile to repeat here the observations previously described. We repeat that neither the descending portion of the trigeminal, the fasciculus solitarius, nor the horizontal portion of the sensory column of the vagus and glossopharyngeal nerves show any trace of chains or indication of nuclei. Adventitial cells are absent even in 6 and 7 day embryos, in spite of the tremendous length that these centripetal paths have by then attained.

We do not believe it necessary to stress this fact, confirmed by many authors and recently by Lugaro, Kölliker, and Lenhossék. It is so evident, even in routine preparations, that some polygenesists (Bethe, for example) do not dare to deny it but explain it by the absence of Schwann cells within the central nervous system. But, as Lugaro has noted, this very absence of Schwann cells constitutes a strong argument against the catenary hypothesis. It is impossible to understand how the formation of central pathways, of whatever length, can take place by simple axonal growth, whereas formation of peripheral or extracentral pathways requires the assistance of migrated neuroblasts which pass through a stage of cellular chains.

In Figure 16, D, we reproduce a bulbar sensory path: the descending trunk of the fifth nerve. Note that intercalary nuclei are absolutely lacking, and that both the independence of the axons as well as their continuity with the internal process of the sensory cells of the trigeminal ganglion is very clearly shown. The structure of the peripheral process is identical.

Sections made parallel to sensory cranial nerves are very instructive, for they reveal the mode of growth of isolated axons. In Figure 17 we reproduce a portion of mandibular nerve, taken from a 5 day chick embryo. Intraneural nuclei are very rare even at this time. All the fibers are gathered in undulating fascicles and are separated by a transparent liquid substance. Some isolated axons

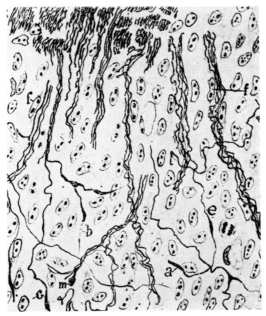

Fig. 17. Sensory peripheral branches of the trigeminal ganglion which, through error, cross the mesodermal tissue. a) Elongated growth mass; c) other fusiform masses; e) isolated fiber which does not show any marginal nuclei; f) marginal nuclei of the fascicles; m) mass in the form of a button.

become separated from the principal course of the nerve and wander at random. They circuitously wind among the connective tissue cords, frequently retracing their path, and ultimately end freely in a small elongated enlargement. Sometimes the terminal end is olive-shaped and quite reminiscent of the terminal button of regenerating adult axis-cylinders (Fig. 17, m). We have become convinced that in their migration these independent fibers are not accompanied by any kind of satellite element. Their path is in the line of least resistance but their orientation may possibly be influenced by very powerful chemotactic forces.

During ensuing days (from the fifth to the seventh day of incubation) there is a slight change, and one now notices one or more oval nuclei in the neighborhood of an occasional isolated axon (Fig. 17, f). These nuclei are so near to the nerve substance that it is necessary to consider them as the first rudiment of Schwann nuclei. Such marginal cells are found exclusively in the oldest portion of the wandering axis-cylinder; they are never in the most recently formed path, i.e., in the part which immediately precedes the growth cone or terminal intumescence (Fig. 17, e).

The arrangement of the peripheral ramifications of the nerves of special sense also mediates against the hypothesis of discontinuous growth. Among the most precociously developing nerves is the vestibular; its developing terminal arborizations in the cristae and maculae are stainable at the fourth day of incubation. At the end of the fifth day the terminal ramification is quite developed, as can be observed in Figure 18. Note the very small number of intercalary nuclei in the depths of the subepithelial path of the nerve and the obvious continuity of the axons with the fine ascending twigs which are insinuated among the epithelial cells. By means of subepithelial and intraepithelial divisions, each axis-cylinder gives rise to a great number of twigs which gradually decrease in diameter until they terminate in a delicate point not far from the free

Fig. 18. Branch of the vestibular nerve and its free terminations in the epithelium of an acoustic crista of a 5 day chick embryo. A) Nerve fascicle; a) fine terminal branch; b) rudimentary hair cell.

surface. Unquestionably such an arborization will in time undergo changes to approximate the type that Retzius described in adult birds and that we described in the 7 day chick embryo. What interests us most here is the simple demonstration of the continuity of axons and their branches, and the total absence of cellular chains or satellite nuclei at all levels.

Ganglia and Sensory Paths in Mammals. Judging by our preparations of the rabbit embryo, ganglia and sensory paths develop later in mammals than in birds. Thus, in a 14 millimeter embryo we have not succeeded in staining bipolar cells in the trigeminal and vagal ganglia, the central and peripheral branches only appearing at a distance from the cell of origin. On the other hand, 25 millimeter embryos show some perfectly impregnated bipolar elements in which may be noted the same peculiarities as were found in avian sensory ganglia. Of especial importance to the question under discussion is the absence of intercalary nuclei in both the central peripheral branches of the afore-mentioned cranial nerves.

Adventitial cells appear only on the surface of the bundles, but along the intracranial path of these fibers the very abundant adventitial cells do infiltrate the interfascicular spaces. In Figure 19, A we show a portion of the path of the vagus nerve roots. Note how the fascicles of the nerve become constricted while crossing the pia mater, as though slinking through a narrow opening. The fascicles dilate later during their interarachnoidal course and become infiltrated by lemmoblasts. These nuclei diminish at the level of the cartilaginous cranium and become arranged in pericolumnar fashion, rudiment of the neurilemma. In the interior of the nerve the axons travel sinuously, touching one another several times which, it may be said in passing, proves that there is no periaxial protoplasmic covering, but only a very fine hyaline sheath that is almost imperceptible under the microscope. A transparent liquid seems to fill the spaces between the axons of each fascicle.

Finally, a similar impression is given by the peripheral branch of the jugular or the superior vagal ganglia (Fig. 20). Note that the bipolar ganglion cells often possess considerable protoplasm and a fine perinuclear network. Note also how the peripheral branches constitute the nerve; all these branches from sturdy fascicles (con-

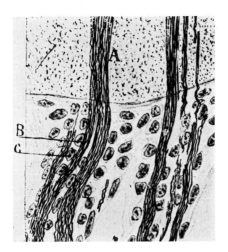

Fig. 19.   Roots of the vagus nerve emerging from the medulla of a 2.5 cm. rabbit embryo.

taining thousands of fibers) in the midst of which, one cannot distinguish any trace of intercalary cells. Only in an occasional interstice can mesodermal elements (completely foreign to the axons) and an occasional blood capillary be perceived (Fig. 20, D, 21).

In addition to the neurons small nuclei are seen within the ganglia. These may correspond to those elements which Harrison, Lenhossék, and Kohn described in the spinal ganglia and believed to represent primordial lemmoblasts. Although we have recorded evidence of migration of such cells towards the peripheral nerve trunk in the chick embryo, we have not been able to verify it in the mammal.

Aberrant Sensory Neurons. Ever since the investigations of His and Lenhossék it is known that sensory ganglion cells are of ectodermal origin and arise by cellular migration from the marginal or pedicular region of the primitive groove. When the medullary canal closes these cells are dislocated ventrolaterally, spreading across adjacent mesodermal regions.

We wish to record an unusual fact which we have noted several times in silver nitrate preparations. Some sensory cells, accidentally misplaced, wander from the main ganglion and develop in an aberrant fashion. Such cells need not be confused with mesodermal elements since they possess a perfectly stained neurofibrillar network, more or less extensive polar processes, and a large nucleus with a spherical nucleolus.

We have observed such misplaced elements in chick as well as mammalian embryos. In the 6 day bird embryo we have occasionally found them behind the spinal cord not far from the raphe and in the midst of the connective tissue. Perhaps the sensory ganglion from which they derive terminates considerably further rostrad. In

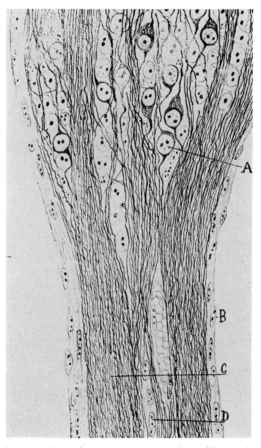

Fig. 20. Jugular ganglion of the vagus nerve of a rabbit embryo. A) Bipolar cell; B) rudiment of the neurilemma; C) large bundles of axons lacking intercalary nuclei; D) some adventitial cells located between 2 large nerve bundles.

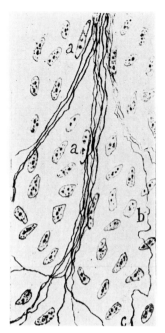

Fig. 21. Portion of the terminal sensory arborization of a cranial nerve of a 2.5 cm rabbit embryo. a) Nuclei beside free fascicles; b) isolated axons which travel freely across the connective tissue framework; c) terminal growth mass (fusiform type.)

shape, size and structure they resemble sensory neurons, except that their relatively short and very undulating polar processes are directed almost dorsad.

Figure 22, A, illustrates a cell of this kind taken from a rabbit embryo (2.5 centimeters). This sturdy fusiform neuron became lost in the internal periosteum of the base of the cranium not far from the path of exit of the hypoglossal nerve. Three processes emerge from the distinct neurofibrillar network. One is directed towards the nerve and appears to terminate freely while the others also terminate nearby. The very sturdy nucleus appears identical to that of large neurons.

There are many opinions concerning the nature and origin of these cells. The one which seems most reasonable to us is that which considers them as aberrant sensory cells.

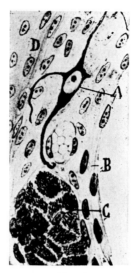

Fig. 22.   Strayed sensory cell of a rabbit fetus. A) Nerve cell; B) internal periosteum of the base of the cranium; C) hypoglossal nerve; D) cartilage.

ASSOCIATION NEUROBLASTS AND
SECONDARY CENTRAL PATHWAYS

Spinal Cord. Differentiation of association or funicular neuroblasts and the pathways they give rise to occurs after the differentiation of the motor cells. Because of this relative slowness of development the funicular cells still appear very embryonic at the end of the third day, whereas the motor neuroblasts have already sent their axons into the mesoderm. In a single section one can often observe the entire extent of a funicular cell axon, including its terminal growth cone. Since these are the youngest elements of all those which have an affinity for reduced silver nitrate, it is important to analyze them conscientiously.

Figure 24 shows that the last funicular neuroblasts to attract the metallic deposit lie immediately outside the zone of the epithelial nuclei. They are pyriform with a very short sturdy process oriented laterad or curved slightly ventrad. This prolongation is really the rudimentary axon, and it terminates in a pale, sometimes slightly thickened point. The nucleus is at the medial side, seemingly lacking in protoplasm, but in reality covered by a thin cytoplasmic zone that is free of stainable neurofibrils. In these rudimentary neuroblasts the central or internal process is generally lacking. The stained portion of the protoplasm seems to possess extremely fine neurofibrils which are apparently packed in a network near the nucleus and condensed into bundles at the level of the cell process.* Naturally this framework is better distinguished in more advanced cells.

In the same figure one observes neuroblasts which are slightly more advanced than the preceding. These cells have migrated towards the periphery of the spinal cord and are characterized by the course and length of their axons. The latter curve to form an obtuse angle and then travel dorsoventrad, not far from the lateral basal region (which acts as a bed to prevent their straying). They terminate in a conical thickening narrowed at the distal end. The most typical terminal swellings are ordinarily found in commissural neuroblasts whose axons, after having traveled towards the surface, stop at the level of the motor cell cluster or near the raphe (Fig. 24, c). *Such intumescences undoubtedly correspond to the growth cones demonstrated by the Golgi method and therefore are not artifacts.* However when one compares sections impregnated by the two methods, one notes important differences in the aforementioned cones. These differences must be appreciated in order to be able to recognize these terminal organs in silver nitrate preparations.

---

*While this work was in press a paper by Fragnito[43] appeared. This author maintained that neurofibrils differentiate tardily, appearing in the chick only after the eleventh day of incubation.

Fragnito should have employed our silver nitrate procedure, instead of using Donaggio's method which is excellent for the study of the adult spinal cord but which is difficult to apply to embryos. He then would certainly have verified, as did Besta, that the neurofibrillar framework is stainable at least at the end of the fourth day and occasionally from the third day of incubation. He would also have been convinced that the neurofibrils, from the time of their appearance, take the form of a network which is especially visible in sensory and association neurons. In reality, the neurofibrillar framework is the result of chemical and morphological differentiation of the fibrillar skeleton that is present in all sorts of protoplasm and which, from this stage on, is not lacking in any embryonic cell.

Let us recall that in silver chromate impregnated sections (Fig. 23, B) these structures appear sturdy, elongated, and terminated by laminar spinous projections. These projections seem to result from the moulding of loose protoplasm on the interstices of the terrain across which the migrating fiber is struggling to find its way. On the other hand, in preparations made with the new method (Fig. 23, A), the cones are finer and completely lack terminal lamellae, or only show them vaguely. The line which gives contour to the base of the terminal excrescence ordinarily has a pale, very finely granular border. It could be said that a transparent cytoplasm begins at the place where the neurofibrillar fascicle ends. The afore-mentioned spines and laminar appendages are formed from this cytoplasm. In some cases the cone is so fine and so short that it can only be recognized by the sudden interruption of the neurofibrillar bundle, or by the presence of a pale border at the point at which the axon disappears. There is no doubt in such examples as Figure 23, A, that the main part of the cone is invisible, because it possesses a protoplasm that is unstainable or without neurofibrillar differentiation.

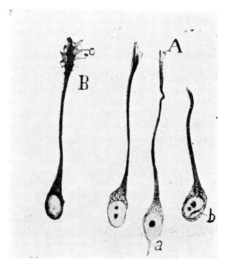

Fig. 23.   Association neuroblasts of the spinal cord of a 3 day chick embryo. A) Neuroblasts impregnated by the neurofibrillar procedure; B) neuroblast impregnated by the Golgi method; a) cell body with an internal process; b) neurofibrillar bundles seen in the framework as a result of cooling.

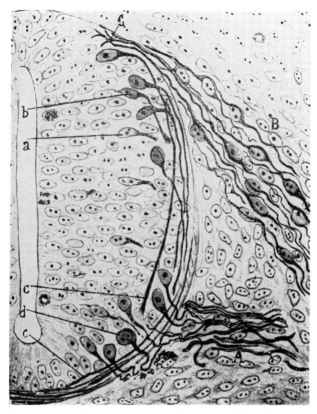

Fig. 24. Section of the lumbar cord of a 67 hour chick embryo. Alcohol fixation, reduced silver nitrate impregnation. A) Ventral root; B) spinal ganglion; C) bifurcation of the dorsal root; a) rudimentary association neuroblast; b) bipolar commissural neuroblast possessing a growth cone; c) commissural growth cones; d) motor neuron.

In summary, growth cones are very probably constituted of two principal substances: the neurofibrillar framework, situated almost exclusively in the initial region of the thickening, and a special cytoplasm, unstainable by silver nitrate but which accepts silver chromate. This cytoplasm, besides surrounding the neurofibrillar portion, is concentrated in the same terminal end, frequently giving rise to appendages and divergent lamellae. Because the relative proportion of these two factors varies slightly in different growth cones, there is great variety in the shape of the terminal axonal structure in preparations made with the new impregnation procedure.

As can be noted in Figure 24, white matter is completely lacking because of the shortness of the association axons. Only in the dorsolateral region, and in the neighborhood of the basal lateral portion do some large longitudinal fibers arise. These are the rudiment of the dorsal funiculus and, as His demonstrated a long time ago, are continuous with the sensory roots.

During the third day of incubation and the beginning of the fourth, the white matter is progressively formed by the arrival of association axons at the medullary periphery. The lateral and ventral funiculi are also formed at almost the same time and are clearly delineated during the fourth day. As Figure 8, C, indicates, the motor cells at this stage already possess well-characterized dendrons. Several funicular elements show a more or less perceptible dendritic or internal radial process. The dorsal funiculus, now thickened by the accumulation of new roots, is of an elongated oval shape. The ventral funiculus is represented by a fine fibrillary cap confined between the motor roots and slightly extended ventrally. It does not approach the raphe. Finally, the lateral funiculus arises from the *round column* of His and is clearly differentiable from the latter because of the delicacy and pallor of the association fibers. In previous stages the commissural fibers seemed to travel indistinctly across zones immediately beneath the lateral basal portion; these fibers now form a fibrillar sheet immediately beneath the motor horn and extend ventrad to the ventromedial epithelium, reaching the ventral funiculus of the opposite side. Among the most advanced association cells it is not rare to find some whose dendritic or internal appendage is so long that it nearly reaches the ependyma (Fig. 8). Terminal dichotomizations are noted in these radial dendrons at times.

By the fifth day of incubation the white matter attains considerable development, and growth masses are rarely found in the gray matter. Thus, as can be seen in Figure 10, E (a transverse section of the thoracic cord of the chick), the sensory pathway of the dorsal funiculus is quite noticeably extended dorsad, having the form of a comma with the head placed ventrally. Several fiber systems, whose origin need not concern us here, may be discerned in the white matter of the ventrolateral column. These include: a marginal fascicle of large axons situated ventral to the ventral funiculus (Fig. 10, a); another composed of finer axons placed in the peripheral margin of the lateral funiculus dorsal to the motor roots; and, finally, an extensive area occupying the greatest portion of the ventrolateral funiculus and composed of an extraordinary number of delicate axis-cylinders. One also notes in this figure that in spite of the development of the motor cells and of many of the association cells, numerous immature neurons still exist, i.e., neurons incapable of being stained by silver nitrate. At the level of the dorsal horn scarcely a cell can be demonstrated. All such immature elements will undergo neurofibrillar differentiation later (at the end of the twelfth day and thereafter). However, even in the adult stage, the small cells of the substance of Rolando never attract the silver precipitate.

Medulla Oblongata and Midbrain. We will not discuss the development of the association cells of the medulla, hindbrain, and midbrain in detail, for it does not differ from that of spinal neuroblasts. It is sufficient to state that in the afore-mentioned centers those association neuroblasts which are differentiated from the third day of incubation are precisely the ones which give rise to the sturdiest pathways of the white matter. Figure 25 serves as an example; we have reproduced part of the basal portion of the midbrain, in which can be seen numerous neuroblasts in the earliest phases and whose axons, still short, demonstrate the characteristic growth cone. The youngest of these neurons send their rudimentary axon towards the basal region where it is sometimes arrested; the terminal cone of other cells curves ventromesad, forming a pathway which we have not been able to homologize with that of the adult. Perhaps such neuroblasts are of diverse nature and give rise to different fiber systems.

Almost all the intrinsic association pathways of the medulla and midbrain are fashioned during the fifth and sixth days of incubation. In general, the large interstitial elements of the gray and white reticular substance and the sturdiest neurons of the sensory and central special sense paths are the most advanced, as measured by

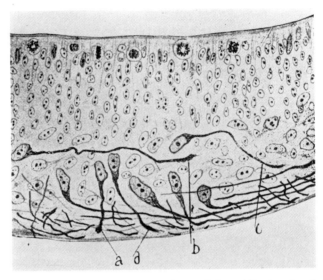

Fig. 25.   Association neuroblasts of the base of the midbrain of a 3 day chick embryo.

abundance of neurofibrils and diverging dendrons. As example of this developmental precocity, we present a section of the medulla of a 6 day chick embryo (Fig. 26). Note the perfectly formed primary descending trigeminal (d) and vestibular (e) pathways. More medially are the medial longitudinal fasciculus, the central sensory path or medial lemniscus, and the *trapezoid body* (a). Because of its developmental precocity the trapezoid body may be very readily traced from its point of origin (the large cells of the cochlear nucleus) to a special region of the white matter that is near the contralateral descending vestibular column. In this preparation, the cochlear nerve fibers have not attained maturity, from which it follows that the trapezoid body, a secondary special sense path, attains maturity before the corresponding primary special sense system. In another work, in which we still study the origin and the course of the cranial nerve roots, we will have the opportunity to cite some equally significant examples of this singular developmental preference of the secondary pathways.

There is no question (it would be superfluous to dwell upon

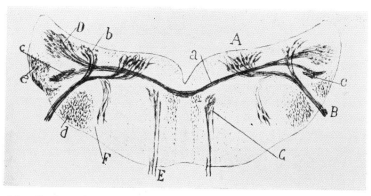

Fig. 26. Section of the medulla of a 6 day chick embryo. Several motor and sensory nuclei and nerve pathways are clearly seen. A) Dorsal vagal nucleus; B) vagus nerve; C) abducens nucleus; D) cochlear nucleus, from which the trapezoid body arises; E) abducens nerve; F) nucleus ambiguus; a) trapezoid body; b) fasciculus solitarius; c) central acoustic pathway; d) descending portion of the trigeminal nerve; e) descending portion of the vestibular nerve.

this after the proof furnished by Kölliker) that all these secondary paths are made up of large bundles of naked axons, without trace of nuclei or cellular chains. The nuclei appear later, after the afore-mentioned systems have completed their development.

Retina. Analysis of retinal neuroblasts is especially interesting because of the relatively simple and organized structure of this membrane. Furthermore, the optic nerve is a pure centripetal association system without admixture of other pathways. Its fibers, like those of other systems, cross a massive intercalary mesodermal substance.

Fortunately, our silver nitrate method impregnates this organ from the third or fourth day of incubation, i.e., many days before the Golgi technique will successfully impregnate the retina. In this way, the revelations of silver nitrate very fortunately supplement those of silver chromate. The latter give relatively consistent results only in postnatal mammals and birds.[163,169]

In the retina of the 3 day chick embryo (Fig. 27), only the nuclei of most of the still-embryonic nerve cells are stained. Near the external border are a great many germinal cells undergoing mitosis (proliferating cells of Koganeï and Chievitz). If we examine the entire retina, we distinguish here and there, disseminated without order, some relatively large cells which are brownish or coffee-colored and possess two polar processes: external and internal. These are the neuroblasts which later produce the ganglion layer of the retina. From the research of Kölliker, Chievitz and ourselves, it is known that the ganglion cells are the most precocious neurons of the visual membrane.

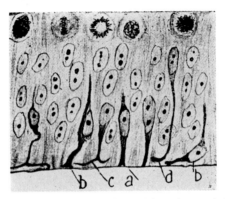

Fig. 27. Section of the retina of a 3 day chick embryo. a) Neuroblasts whose axon terminates near the basal portion; b, d) other neuroblasts with curved axon; c) neuroblast with bifurcated axon.

The appearance and the position of these cells are very variable. For the most part they are bipolar and all located in the deep half of the membrane. However, as we have demonstrated in our study of the mouse retina (15 millimeter embryo), perfectly monopolar cells quite comparable to the neuroblasts of His are not absent. In any case, let us record here that the bipolar form occurs even among the most rudimentary neuroblasts; e.g., in those whose descending process has not yet curved to join the layer of optic nerve fibers. Finally, some of these bipolar neuroblasts lie very near the germinal layer (Fig. 27, d).

Similar to spinal neuroblasts, these also have a large eccentric, or almost eccentric, nucleus and a protoplasm in which a pale neurofibrillar network stands out. This network, like a bridge, is continuous with the filaments of the two prolongations. In every case, the inferior or descending prolongation is quite thick and strongly stainable, while the ascending one is considerably finer, paler, and attracts the silver precipitate but lightly.

We have very carefully studied the shape, course and other properties of the axon or inferior process of these cells, in order to elucidate the mechanism by which the growth cones progress. This is a relatively accessible problem in the visual organ.

When the neuroblast is very rudimentary and its process is very short no growth cone at all exists. The neurofibrillar bundle, a blunted point which terminates rather suddenly, substitutes for the growth cone. That at least is what is noted in our preparations (Figs. 27 and 28). We do not mean to exclude the possible existence of a terminal cytoplasmic excrescence which is not stainable by silver nitrate. In general, the growth cone or terminal axonal intumescence only appears in those relatively long and stout processes which, having arrived at the internal limiting membrane, begin to curve and become parallel to the latter, or in those processes which have traveled in a fairly long horizontal path (Fig. 27, d, and Fig. 28). Frequently, similar to its counterpart in the spinal cord, the cone becomes narrowed towards its extremity. It is always thinner than in Golgi preparations.

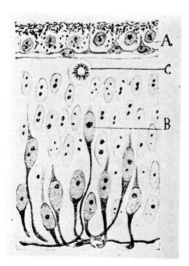

Fig. 28. Section of the retina of the retina of a 4 day chick embryo. A) Pigment layer; B) ganglion cell in the neuroblast phase; C) cell undergoing mitosis.

During their first outgrowth the axons travel perpendicularly to the retina and proceed until they run against the obstacle represented by the basal portion or internal limiting membrane. Only after being stopped before this impassable barrier do the cones curve around and advance in a horizontal direction. They pass between the feet of the epithelial cells which form a sort of vacant bed, a kind of road which facilitates the exodus of the embryonic fibers.

The preceding facts pose an interesting problem. The two principal opinions regarding the mechanism of nerve growth are well known: His's hypothesis of pre-established routes by which the young axons travel in the path of least resistance; and our hypothesis of nerve progression by chemotactic attractions.

The first hypothesis has against it the well-demonstrated fact that the primitive epithelial cells of the retina are only simple, quite smooth radial fibers, stretched between the external and internal limiting membranes. Near these membranes the epithelial cells enlarge (especially near the internal one) to form a conical base. Such an arrangement of the anterior epithelial end with the subsequent adjustment of its terminal plaque gives rise, as we have said, to a bed favorable for the tangential progress of the embryonic axons. But this is not sufficient to establish a dominant orientation towards the optic nerve because the terminal endings enlarge symmetrically and with perfect regularity. Furthermore, if the route across the retina was traced in advance, with the axons gliding there as inevitably as a train on its rails, then the growth cones would follow their path without error or hesitation, arriving *en masse* at the retinal pedicle, or point of union of the retina with the anterior cerebral vesicle. But this is precisely contrary to what takes place.

As can be seen in Figure 27, a, many axons remain for some time leaning against or intermingled within the basal layer which they had entered perpendicularly. They apparently have not succeeded in finding their way. Other growth cones, upon running (perhaps violently) against the internal limiting membrane, divide into two sub-basal branches opposite to one another (c). One of these branches will be resorbed later. Finally, it is not rare to find fibers (and they may be better seen in retinas at the fourth day of incubation) which, by mistake, follow a route contrary to that which they should take and go away from the region of the future optic papilla instead of approaching it. Only by the fourth to the fifth day are these aberrations corrected, at which time the normal axonal orientation towards the nerve predominates.

Even near the vesicular stalk, before the optic bundle is formed (third day of incubation), some growth cones are seen which, without succeeding in entering the stalk, break through the superposed retinal layer and become lost at varying levels in the visual membrane.

All these phenomena, clearly visible in our preparations, seem as irreconcilable with His's hypothesis as they are favorable to the chemotactic theory. In our opinion, the liberation of organizing substances by elements destined to connect with sensory or special sense nerve pathways occurs very weakly at the start, i.e., when the cells are still in the neuroblast phase. This paucity of chemotactic agents results in the useless ramifications and errors of the embryonic nerve fibers.* These fibers do not succeed in becoming oriented, because of the weakness of the chemical attractions and the presence of serious mechanical obstructions. But as the development of the attracted neurons progresses, the quantity of the positive chemotactic material accumulated in the cellular interstices increases, and the axons then are more strongly stimulated. They finally find their route and travel without error until they run against the secretory cell.

This is what must occur in the retina during the third and fourth days of incubation. Because of the lack of morphological and physiological differentiation of the midbrain neuroblasts, the retinal cells travel blindly at first. Only some days later do powerful chemotactic forces (which perhaps enter the retina through the optic stalk) vigorously stimulate the ameboid activity of the axons of the gang-

---

*Among other errors of this kind (with which we will deal elsewhere) let us recall the very long doubling back and initial detours of certain motor axons (trochlear, facial) at the level of their emergence from the nucleus of origin.

lionic layer. These axons travel towards the region of the future papilla* and finally towards the mid- or intermediate brain.

The mechanism of formation of the nerve fiber layer of the retina and of the optic nerve does not lack importance in the debate between the monogenesists and polygenesists. Our preparations are definitive in this regard; they show the optic fibers correctly and strongly impregnated, from their origin in the retinal cells to the optic nerve itself. Preparations of this kind once again prove that the production of association pathways (which includes the optic nerve) takes place without the direct or indirect help of accessory cells; it occurs exclusively by centripetal growth of the axons of the ganglionic layer.

In Figure 29, B, one readily notes that the fascicles of axons travel freely, unescorted by neuroglial or other kinds of cells. The axons pass between the epithelial columns inserted in the basal layer and appear completely continuous. It is certain that axonal fasciculation, a primitive phenomenon of every nerve pathway, is the simple mechanical result of the presence of the epithelium whose columns, like the stanchions of a bridge, force the axons to divide into partial streams. The undulating appearance of such fascicles can also be explained by the fact that the afore-mentioned fibers of Müller are not arranged in straight lines but in irregular series. The axis-cylinders approach the anterior region or border of the retina and change direction to penetrate the optic stalk (Fig. 30, C). The fibers remain within the basal portion, i.e., within the cerebral continuation of the ectoderm. In the region of the optic stalk they constitute a mass of fibers which is totally devoid of any kind of intercallary cell. These fibers represent the rudimentary optic nerve.

Furthermore, the ganglion cells of the retina do not all reach maturity simultaneously. During the third day, the only apparent neurons lie near the bottom of the stalk. Note that before this time no mature axons exist (Fig. 30). During the fourth and fifth days, differentiation progresses posteriorly and externally, and spreads throughout the membrane during the following days.

*As we show in Figure 30, this region is situated not at the center of the retina but eccentrically, as many embryologists, including Froriep[15] have recognized.

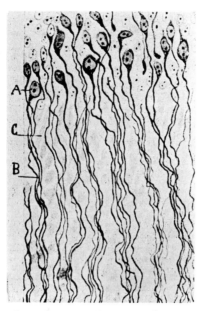

Fig. 29. A slightly oblique tangential section of the retina of a 5 day chick embryo. A) Ganglion cell; B) fascicles of axons from the layer of optic nerve fibers; C) series of feet of Müller's fibers.

The other retinal elements are not stainable at all; this is fortuitous, since it permits careful analysis of the development of the ganglion cells. We have already described elsewhere some interesting facts about the postembryonic development of the visual membrane.[163,169,177]

Before ending our essay on the development of cerebrospinal centers, we wish to mention a physiological fact which we will discuss at length in another work. From our investigations and those of Tello and Marinesco, it is known that the neurofibrillar framework can be greatly transformed by the influence of cold. Our recent experiments demonstrate that these changes can occur in embryos at the end of the fourth day of incubation. This transformation consists of the formation of large, black staining, undulating, smooth filaments in the interior of the cell body. The filaments are separated by long spaces of unstained protoplasm. This phenomenon is perceived in almost all young neurons of any category.

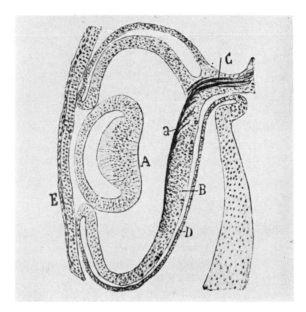

Fig. 30.   Horizontal section of the eye of an 80 hour chick embryo. A) Lens; B) bottom of the retina from where the optic nerve fibers leave; C) rudiment of the optic nerve; D) pigment layer; E) cornea; a) layer of optic nerve fibers.

To produce it, it is merely necessary to cool the egg containing the embryo for one hour at room temperature. It has seemed to us that such cooling before fixation in alcohol is always suitable for the study, for it lends a greater energy to the neurofibrillar staining. Be that as it may, the alteration under discussion is less apparent at the level of the dendrons and unnoticeable in the axon.

NEURONS OF THE SYMPATHETIC NERVOUS SYSTEM

Birds. The neurons of the paravertebral sympathetic system, as well as the clusters of sympathetic neurons of the heart, mediastinum, intestine, etc., can be impregnated between the third and fourth day of incubation. Unfortunately, at the time that these cells attract the metallic deposit the neuronal differentiation of the ectoderm and of the sensory ganglia is already terminated. It is therefore impossible to determine precisely the origin of the visceral sympathetic system. Only in an occasional preparation have we found traces of sympathetic cells uniting the paravertebral sympathetic ganglia with the plexuses of the heart, lung and intestine.

Whatever may be the origin of the sympathetic elements, their formation is very precocious. Even during the fourth day of incubation many of the prevertebral sympathetic cells have passed through the neuroblastic phase and show some diversity of shape, although fusiform and triangular shapes predominate. As may be noted in Figure 31, the cells possess diverse processes which travel in different directions and dichotomize numerous times. It may be noted in some cells that one prolongation (probably the axon) is more robust than the others, and that it terminates abruptly in a small, irregular enlargement (Fig. 31, a) similar to a growth cone.

Just as with sensory elements during these very early phases, the neurofibrillar framework of the cell body is still rudimentary and consists of a stainable bridge or ligament which unites the neurofibrils of the expansions. The nucleus is marginal and has several nucleolar clumps. Furthermore, these neurons do not yet form true ganglia and they appear intermixed among mesodermal cells.

For the moment we will not concern ourselves with the study of

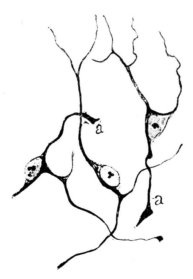

Fig. 31. Nerve cells scattered throughout the mesodermal region which will later form a sympathetic ganglion. a) Large process provided with a growth cone.

the cells of the visceral sympathetic ganglia. Let it suffice to say that during the fourth and fifth days of incubation a great part of the cardiac wall appears sprinkled with very embryonic neural elements: monopolar, bipolar and especially multipolar cells having long complicated expansions which form a tangled plexus. These neurons also lie around the intestinal epithelium and at certain points are so numerous that one might think them more abundant than the connective tissue cells. We will treat this matter more fully in another work. It is only important for us to record that the processes of the sympathetic neuroblasts, because they are free and lie in ordinary mesodermal tissue, are also produced by a mechanism similar to that of the axons and dendrons of central neuroblasts, i.e., by the growth and ramification of neurofibrillar trunks which arise from the neuronal cell.

Mammals. Impregnation of the neurofibrillar framework of sympathetic neurons of the rabbit embryo cannot be accomplished until late. In the 2.5 centimeter embryo the cell bodies of the superior cervical ganglion still fail to attract the metallic deposit, and the axons or fibers of Remak barely stain, while the axis-cylinders of the cranial motor nerves stain intensely.

It is important, in view of the question under discussion, to examine the composition of the nerves arising in sympathetic centers. We have carefully explored the structure of some visceral branches, especially the principal ascending branch of the superior cervical ganglion. Our result completely confirms the classical description of organization of embryonic nerves. At the outset, the sympathetic nerves of mammals are composed of naked axons without the least trace of intercalary nuclei (Fig. 32, C). Only in the nerve sheath do satellite cells appear. The latter completely resemble nearby connective cells. One interesting fact is that the intrafascicular and intraganglionic axons lack lemmoblasts or marginal elements, while the unbound fascicles which travel freely through the connective tissue or near arteries possess them, albeit in small number. They consist of elongated nuclei which have several chromatin granules and are surrounded by a small amount of transparent protoplasm which extends the length of the nerve fascicle (Fig. 32, C). The isolated fibers (Fig. 32, a) completely lack satellite cells be-

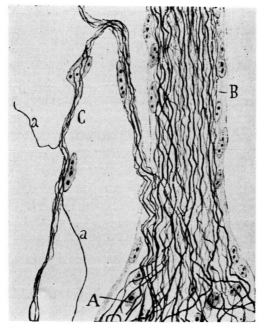

Fig. 32. Ascending trunk of the superior cervical sympathetic ganglion of a 2.5 cm rabbit embryo. A) Ganglion; B) mesodermal sheath of the ascending bundle; C) small visceral sympathetic nerve; a) isolated fibers lacking nuclei.

cause their formation is recent and perhaps there has not been sufficient time for the satellite cells to be attracted.

ORIGIN OF THE ADVENTITIAL CELLS OR LEMMOBLASTS

What is the origin of the lemmoblasts or Schwann cells? In different passages in this memoir we have mentioned their presence, during relatively early phases of development, around nerves, between bundles or nerve fascicles, or extending along the fascicles of free, intramuscular, or subcutaneous axons. They are elongated cells, not continuous with the conducting substance, and undoubtedly are identical with those elements which, through error of interpretation, have been envisaged by the polygenesists as being arranged in chains. It is equally doubtless that these elements, by multiplying actively during the final phases of development, penetrate into the thickness of the nerve fascicles and create an individual sheath for every axon, whether myelinated (fibers of the cerebrospinal system), or unmyelinated (sympathetic fibers).

Where do these cells originate? This question has been extensively debated for more than 30 years without a definitive and unanimously accepted conclusion being reached. Two principal hypotheses on this subject have been upheld with equal energy and persuasiveness. According to some embryologists, the adventitial elements of the nerve fibers simply represent misplaced mesodermal cells which are attracted by the chemotactic forces of the axons. They subsequently remain subordinate to the axon, protecting it by their protoplasm and constructing an isolating sheath for it (Schwann sheath). According to the polygenesists, and even some renowned monogenesists, these elements are of ectodermal origin, actively migrating across the mesoderm and ultimately taking part in the formation of nerves. But opinions are sharply divided about the precise portion of the ectoderm from which these cells emanate and the road that they follow. Bethe and others affirm that the peripheral neuroblasts derive from the spinal cord itself, while Harrison and Lenhossék prefer to invoke an extraspinal origin and believe it probably that these cells migrate from the spinal ganglia. Finally and very recently, Kohn, agreeing with Lenhossék, defends the ganglionic origin of the lemmoblasts. He claims they multiply actively in the sensory ganglia and then invade the territory of the centripetal and motor nerves.

We have no intention whatever of discussing, still less of resolving, a point shrouded in such obscurity. In our opinion, positive facts derived from observation are not available to definitively settle so ardently debated a question. Those facts which we do possess pertain purely and exclusively to late phases of neural development; whereas those which would be decisive for the subject in question (i.e., observations on the emergence and migration of the lemmoblasts), their site of origin, (ectoderm, spinal cord, ganglia), etc., are so questionable and open to such different interpretations, that in truth they lack any positive value. Let us state from the outset that, in spite of all our efforts, we have never been able, in routine preparations of the 2 day chick embryo, to perceive even the slightest indication of migration of intraspinal or intraganglionic neuro-blasts, and we believe that the facts of this kind described by Bethe and other authors are accidental, inconstant phenomena and diffi-cult to evaluate. The hypothesis of migration conflicts, furthermore, with numerous observations which, if not directly contrary, are at least quite puzzling. Let us cite among others:

1. The lemmoblasts are considerably more abundant and also appear sooner in the small peripheral nerve fascicles (muscular, vascular, sympathetic and cutaneous nerves) than in the trunks of origin. The mammalian fetus is very expressive in this regard; it may be demonstrated with the greatest ease that the trunks of muscular nerves lack intercalary cells at the outset. They only possess some superficial elements, while the plexuses of small fine nerves distributed in the muscles are garnished with relatively numerous lemmoblasts. In their entirety, the perifascicular cells of the peripheral nerve branches constitute a field considerably greater than that which may be observed at the level of the trunks.

2. The adventitial cells of embryonic chick nerves, at whatever developmental phase studied, never appear more abundant around the supposed sources of neuroblastic migration (ganglia, spinal cord, etc.) than in the peripheral regions.

3. As for the quantity of perifascicular lemmoblasts, one never notes any difference between the motor nerve trunks far away from sensory ganglia (e.g., hypoglossal, oculomotor, motor vagus and trigeminal) and the sensory nerves (vagus, glossopharyngeal, etc.). Lenhossék himself has described a long glossopharyngeal trunk in which no intercalary nucleus appears, in spite of the proximity of the nerve nucleus. This fact does not therefore support the hypo-thesis of an intraganglionic origin of lemmoblasts.

4. Our careful and substantiated observations on the origin of adventitial cells of isolated, slender peripheral axons and of sensory and motor nerve fascicles, have convinced us that these cells do not arise by mitosis and migration of pre-existing neuroblasts, but rather by a successive drawing together of mesodermal cells which, ap-parently under the influence of chemotactic attractions, end up by being precipitated upon the fascicles and surrounding them with their protoplasm. Examination of Figures 5, 6, and 21 is very in-

structive; it illustrates the appearance of the connective tissue cells in the neighborhood of the growing peripheral axons. We do not completely deny the possibility of multiplication of lemmoblasts. We only state that the mitoses do not occur primitively, and nuclear pairs arranged along the nerve, as if announcing a recent division, do not appear during the early phases of development.

5. As we have proved in another work,[178] during the regenerative process young actively ramifying axons travel naked across embryonic connective tissue. They progressively attract mesodermal cells which ultimately embrace the nerve fibers and end up by being transformed into lemmoblasts.

6. Finally, in preparations both of embryos and adult animals during nerve regeneration, all transitions of cellular form and nuclear composition between the embryonic connective tissue elements and the lemmoblasts appear clearly visible.

From what we have just stated, it is seen that we are inclined toward the classical opinion of Kölliker and His concerning the origin of the adventitial cells of nerves. At the same time we do not consider the question entirely resolved. Current techniques, useful in the differentiation of neural and neuroglial cells, for example, are not capable of any reaction which may distinguish a lemmoblast from a mesodermal element with certainty, or an intraganglionic satellite cell from a migrated connective cell. However, it would be rash to absolutely exclude the possibility that in the earliest stages of embryonic development (from the first to the second day of incubation) the mesoderm might undergo diffuse invasion by a great quantity of ectodermal cells (a kind of peripheral neuroglia). These cells could be attracted by pre-existing axons and form a kind of symbiotic relationship with them. We have described a similar relationship between adult sensory cells and their endocapsular satellite cells. But for the time being this possibility seems quite remote.

BOUTONS AND LATE GROWTH CONES OBSERVED IN THE MAMMALIAN EMBRYO AND FETUS

We have already noted that our neurological studies have preferentially dealt with the chick, both because of the ease with which very early embryos may be procured as well as because of the constancy and energy with which they may be impregnated by silver. In fact, the rabbit and cat embryos that we have obtained were found to be too advanced for study of the first developmental phases of the spinal and bulbar neurons. However, if we exclude the study of the motor and sensory nuclei whose organization is almost completed in rabbit embryos exceeding 2 centimeters and fix our attention upon association cells of relatively tardy nuclei, e.g., cerebellum, surface of the midbrain, acoustic nuclei, pons, etc., it is still possible to see neuroblastic cells and growing axons possessing a very apparent terminal swelling.

Even in the 6 centimeter cat fetus there are, in the above nuclei (Fig. 33, a, b), a considerable number of retarded cells and fibers provided with the afore-mentioned excrescences.*

Let us mention the superior and middle cerebellar peduncles, granular layer of the cerebellum, cerebellar olives, and acoustic tubercle as regions especially abundant in growth cones. Interestingly enough, the tardy cones wandering across the developing white matter do not present a conical appearance as do those belonging to neuroblasts, but rather the form of an olive or terminal button, in all respects comparable to the terminal mass recently found by us in regenerating adult nerve fibers. These masses present a somewhat variable appearance (ovoid, olivary, fusiform, etc.) and a very variable size which maintains a certain relationship with the diameter of the axons. Thus some very small masses and other relatively large ones are noted. In any case, the substance of which they are constituted seems homogeneous, stains strongly with silver, and is continuous with the terminal axon by means of a robust pedicle which thins progressively. Figure 33 shows some masses of diverse dimension taken from cerebellar white matter; note that they lack an enveloping capsule.

In general, the nerve paths formed by large association fibers, and especially by motor and sensory nerves (whose development is very precocious) do not show any axons terminating in a mass. In

---

*We now believe that these buttons and swollen masses are pathological phenomena resulting from the straying or detention of the young axons. (*Note for the French edition.*)

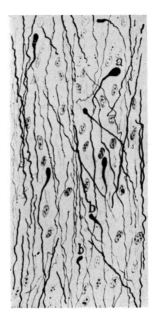

Fig. 33.   Fragment of white matter of the cerebellum of a 6 cm cat fetus. a) Large growth mass; b) small masses.

advanced fetuses all the axis-cylinders have probably reached their destination. We have found some exceptions which are worthy of being recorded, because they reveal some of the difficulties which the motor axons face in their progress across the white matter and perineural tissues.

The first case of retarded migration concerns the facial nerve. In the 6 centimeter cat fetus the immense majority of its roots have arrived rapidly at the periphery, not having been retarded at all during the complicated curve which the seventh nerve describes in the medulla. However, there are instances in which some fibers having attained the beginning of the first curve (beginning of the vertical intrabulbar portion) seem to hesitate and be detained; they occasionally describe an unusual detour and finally exhibit a stout terminal mass of arrest or detention. In one section we have observed four of these terminal buttons intermingled with other radicular fibers. Furthermore, the arrest hypothesis is not merely a conjecture suggested by the accidental observation of these masses and by their unusual volume (like the enormous excrescences of the retrograde fibers in regenerating nerves). But it is natural that this retarded migration could also be interpreted as a simple consequence of the physiological fact that certain neurons only develop very late in motor nuclei.

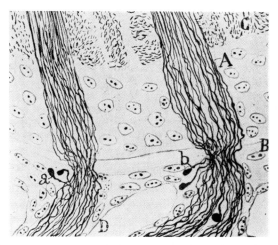

Fig. 34.   Vagus nerve roots at their emergence from the medulla of a 2.5 cm rabbit embryo. A) Roots; B) pia mater; C) white matter of the trigeminal nerve; D) neurilemma sheath of the nerve bundles; a) retarded sensory masses; b) motor masses.

The second instance of apparently retarded masses (Fig. 34, a, b) concerns the motor fibers of the vagus nerve (2.5 centimeter rabbit fetus). Note that all the terminal buttons are found outside the basal portion on the external connective tissue membrane (rudiment of the pia mater), where it appears as though the axons have run against some obstacle. In the same figure we also reproduce some sensory growth masses arrested in almost the same place (a). General rule: Every retarded mass, besides attaining a great size, is preceded by a long thickened portion which progressively diminishes in diameter proximally.

In Figure 35, A, we picture another peculiarity which may be related to the difficulties which the retarded axons find on their way. We allude to certain voluminous swellings which some as-

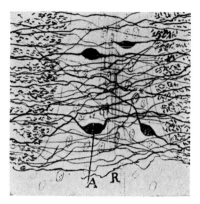

Fig. 35.   Region of the dorsal portion of the raphe of the medulla of a 2.5 cm rabbit embryo. A) Massive thickening along the path of an axon; R) raphe where a dorsoventral wall of epithelial cells exists.

sociation fibers show their path across the raphe. These swellings, which must not be confused with vacuoles or varicosities, are massive, strongly stainable, and formed by a sort of coiling up of the neurofibrillary framework. What is more curious is that most of these swellings are found near the epithelial partition of the raphe, i.e., near a barrier of rigid columns whose narrow interstices, which were filled in advance by earlier axons, probably constitute a serious obstacle to the migration of the slowest cones. In our opinion (based especially on recent observations of the growth of regenerated nerve fibers), every accidentally arrested terminal button grows inordinately and may degenerate unless part of the substance of the protoplasmic mass succeeds in filtering between the obstacles which have stopped it. After resorption of the mass, the part which has overcome the obstacle ultimately forms a new branch in continuity with the primitive axis-cylinder. Applying this doctrine to the case which concerns us, the gigantic spheres formed in some large association axons during their journey across the raphe purely and simply represent the residue of voluminous terminal masses of detention. Furthermore, we have also observed such pathway enlargements in other centers, especially in the cerebellar Purkinje axons. The rarity of this arrangement; the fact that it occurs preferentially at the level of the raphe; the fact that it appears in the best fixed preparations as well as in those impregnated without previous alcohol treatment; finally, its great resemblance to the wandering terminal buttons of regenerating nerves (buttons which also stain by other methods) cause us to reject the idea that it is an artifact.

CONCLUSIONS

1. As His demonstrated, and as has been confirmed by Lenhossék, Retzius, Harrison, and ourselves, every adult nerve cell arises from the transformation of a single primitive ectodermal cell or neuroblast.

2. Every adult axon purely and simply represents the result of the growth of the primordial process of a neuroblast.

3. Likewise, the bifurcations and the terminal branches of the axis-cylinder are nothing more than protoplasmic projections of the latter, which are formed without the assistance of any accessory element.

4. The dendrites of nerve cells are produced later than the axon and likewise arise by the growth of the somatic protoplasm without the intervention of foreign cells.

5. During its journey across the gray matter, the primordial axon possesses a growth cone, composed of a neurofibrillar axis and of an unstained cytoplasmic tip.

6. In the axons of the late pathways of the white matter, or in those retarded accidentally, the terminal cone is modified and converted into a button or terminal mass—an olive shaped organ with a smooth surface which is completely comparable to that which we discovered in regenerated nerve fibers.

7. In certain cases, i.e., when the central or peripheral axon is about to divide or has just bifurcated, the terminal button may be lacking, being replaced by sharp points or fusiform swellings.

8. The neurofibrillar network is already differentiated on the third day of incubation in the chick embryo. It begins to form at the level of the expansion of the rudimentary axon, and is propagated progressively throughout the neuronal cell body.

9. This neurofibrillar differentiation appears almost simultaneously in motor and sensory neurons and shortly afterward in the

large commissural and funicular cells. The neurofibrillar frame-work of bulbar motor and sensory nuclei arises at the same time as in certain organs of special sense (retina).

10. The intercalary cells appear later among the axons of the nerves. They arise from the mesoderm and are attracted by the chemotactic activity of the newly formed axons.

11. In agreement with many authors, all pathways of the spinal cord, medulla, midbrain, etc., be they sensory, special sense, or of association category, are composed initially of naked axons com-pletely devoid of nuclei. It follows that the neuroglia cells, which migrate later into the white matter, cannot intervene in the forma-tion and growth of the central axis-cylinders.

12. Finally, the error of the catenary theory by which Beard, Dohrn, Balfour, Bethe and others attempted to understand the for-mation of nerves and of nerve cells, is the result of the application of inadequate methods. These methods are incapable of correctly demonstrating the presence of embryonic axons among the meso-dermal formations or the morphology of the neuroblasts and young neurons.*

---

*These conclusions, as well as the principal observations recorded in this work, were recently stated before the Anatomical Section of the XVth International Congress of Medicine held at Lisbon, April 23-26, 1906.

Chapter 2

NEW OBSERVATIONS ON THE DEVELOPMENT OF NEUROBLASTS, WITH COMMENTS ON THE NEUROGENETIC HYPOTHESIS OF HENSEN-HELD [183]

SOME MONTHS AGO [181] we tried to refute the objections that the most adept authorities of the catenary theory raised concerning the neurogenetic concept of His and Forel. In this work we only criticized the arguments of the polygenetic school; this partiality in the critique, made necessary by the great importance that the old hypothesis of Balfour, Beard, and Dohrn has acquired in recent years, displeased our illustrious friend and learned confrère, Professor H. Held. He reproaches us very sharply [60] for having examined the question from too one-sided a viewpoint, without considering other theories—e.g., that of Hensen. These other theories, like the catenary concept, also merit critical examination and discussion.

Held is truly correct, and yet our actions have a very natural explanation. Because of the great authority of Apáthy, Bethe, and Dohrn (who are the principal defenders of the catenary hypothesis) this theory has recently become very threatening to the neuronal concept. It had acquired a great number of skilled, convinced and enthusiastic adherents. That is why it seemed very urgent for us to make some immediate effort to stop the progress of a theory which we consider very detrimental to the cause of scientific truth.

We do not fail to recognize Hensen's interesting and very ingenious hypothesis, which we consider definitively refuted by the old observations of His, Kölliker, Lenhossék, and Retzius. Nor do we disregard Held's theories. In recent years Held, by his great scientific prestige, attempted to support an almost forgotten conception, one scarcely mentioned by modern neurologists and embryologists. But as my eminent colleague will readily understand, the careful examination of Hensen's theory would have likewise necessitated the analysis of other neurogenetic theories, e.g., those

of Sedgewick, Joris, Besta, Fragnito and Capobianco, Pegna, Pighione, Cameron, and many others. All these theories, while agreeing
in general with the catenary doctrine, also possess certain individuality and merit careful discussion. Such a study would have exceed-
ed the boundaries of the outline that we had drawn up for the
paper—our principal aim having been to treat the question of
nerve regeneration—and it would have attained a length incompatible with the brevity imposed by the synthetic character of this
journal.

Before answering Held's observations we would have liked to
have been able to examine his pyridine-silver nitrate preparations
and thereby better appreciate the cause of our differences of opinion.
To our great regret we have not been able to satisfy our desire.*
In compensation he has generously sent us some excellent photomicrographs, some of which appeared in his last work.

Even such excellent photomicrographs as Held's unfortunately
do not shed light upon, much less settle, the questions under discussion. The best histological photographs offer only a pale re-
flection of the preparations. Save in the case of sections that present only a single focal plane (e.g., bacterial smears), they have
value only for those who have made them and are understood only
by those who have studied the original preparations. For example,
in Held's photographs it is impossible to decide whether a fiber
passes above, beneath or in the interior of a conducting cell (*Leit-
zelle*). It is likewise impossible to ascertain whether the fine appendages (*plasmodesmes*) which seem to connect the growth cones
with the neighboring mesodermal elements really ensheath the
nerve tip, or whether they merely run along its edge and cross it
without making any axonal contact other than that of contiguity.
These difficulties increase when one is obliged to use small apertures in order to observe the contours of the fibers better. As is
known, small apertures allow one to obtain equally sharp photo-
graphic images and details from different planes of the histological

---

*During a recent trip to Germany, we had the pleasure of examining Held's
excellent preparations. Just as we expected, they are very successful, and to our
great surprise, they show very much the same picture as ours. We will discuss
them when we analyze the neurogenetic opinions of this scholar.

section; this eliminates any possibility of distinguishing structures in one plane from those in another.

One must admit that histological photomicrography renders only very mediocre service as a means of demonstration. Nothing can replace direct examination of the preparation and the use of the fine adjustment, especially in the study of arrangements as complex and debatable as the structure and development of embryonic nervous tissue.

To avoid overly delaying our answer to Held's friendly observations, it becomes necessary for us to make use of our preparations. Nevertheless, desiring to avoid the accusation that the preparations which our previous researches and descriptions employed were incompletely impregnated, we recently devoted some months of work to making new preparations. For the most part we fixed the specimens in alcohol at 40° for 24 hours, then transferred them to 1.5 per cent silver nitrate for 6 to 7 days at 35° and reduced and embedded them in the usual manner. We impregnated chick and duck embryos from the fifty-second to the sixty-fourth hour of incubation. Thanks to these new trials, we have enriched our collection with more than 100 excellent or very acceptable preparations.

We have also employed fixation for one or two days in pyridine before immersion in alcohol. But the results obtained were not superior to those given by alcohol fixation alone. Alcohol fixation has the further advantage of staining the nuclei perfectly and of not exaggerating the agglutination phenomena which occur almost inevitably in embryos whatever method of fixation is used. However, we acknowledge that pyridine is essential under certain conditions, especially when one wishes to study only the arrangement of the neurofibrils in the neuroblasts and to exaggerate the contrast between the general background and the impregnated elements.

Although the main object of this article is to reply to Held's observations relative to His's neurogenetic theory, the present paper must also be considered as a new contribution to the knowledge of the mechanism of nerve formation. Above all, we intend to describe precisely the first phases of neuroblastic development and the details of the journey of the growth cones across the mesoderm. We do not intend to neglect the neuroglial framework of the embryonic gray matter, a framework to which Held has attributed great importance in the process of formation and orientation of nerve paths.

The neurogenetic concept of Hensen-Held, as it has been described recently by the learned Leipzig professor,[57,59] can be summarized in the following propositions:

1. The development of the embryonic nervous system is the result of the collaboration of two classes of cells, a) the neuroblasts which produce the axon and the neurofibrils, b) the conducting cells (*Leitzellen*) in whose interior the embryonic nerve fibers advance and grow.

2. The primordial axon, which is composed of a fascicle of neurofibrils, arises at a special pole of the neuroblasts (fibrillogenetic zone of the protoplasm) and terminates, as we and others have noted, by means of a growth cone. But neither this terminal swelling nor nerve fiber itself ever travel freely in the intercellular spaces as the proponents of His's doctrine believe. In reality these processes are contained in the interior of a system of pre-existing protoplasmic bridges, represented in the central nervous system by a network of spongioblasts (neurospongium) and in the mesoderm by the anastomotic processes (plasmodesmes) of stellate or conducting cells.

3. These last-mentioned conducting elements, which may be of ectodermal origin, would also have the function of nourishing and protecting the axons, ultimately becoming Schwann cells; nevertheless they would not be capable of producing neurofibrils.

4. Finally, neuronal independence can hardly be said to exist either in the first phases or in the adult, since the neurofibrils of one neuroblast frequently penetrate into the interior of another, producing diffuse networks. These networks could be modified in the adult but never disappear completely. Such anastomoses also exist between primordial axons.*

---

*During the writing of this work a new neurogenetic theory appeared based on results obtained with the modified Bielschowsky method. According to Paton [137] who has worked with embryos of Pristiurus, all cells of the embryonic spinal cord, without distinction as to neuroblasts and spongioblasts, constitute a continuous network. Furthermore, in agreement with Held, pre-established bridges are found which unite this plasmodesmal reticulum with the mesoderm-

———→

Unfortunately, all our efforts to verify this theory have, been fruitless. However, at least some of the facts described by Held correspond to real arrangements, but we believe that these arrangements are compatible with a simpler interpretation, one in perfect harmony with the classical doctrine of reciprocal independence of neuroblasts and the continuous growth of nerve fibers. Let us summarize the observations which are unfavorable to or completely incompatible with the concept of Hensen-Held.

I. In our preparations the neuroblast cell body and process are free, i. e., without anastomoses; the growth cone and the axon al-

---

al cells. As regards the nature of the uniting bridges, he does not declare himself hesitant to consider them as a true cellular prolongation, or rather as a special substance secreted by the spinal cells. Paton deviates from Held's concept concerning the appearance of the neurofibrils. According to this American scholar they do not originate from the fibrillogenetic zone of the neuroblasts and grow centrifugally, but they make their appearance in the periphery, outside of the cells, and they penetrate into the cord by way of the pre-established extramedullary bridges. They spread to the cells and plasmodesmes of the medullary tube by virtue of a differentiation *in situ.* In the embryo of Pristiurus they would appear almost simultaneously in the myotome, the ventral roots (pre-existent radial bridges) and the nerve cells of Beard. Finally, the initial neurofibrillar network of the neuroblasts described by Besta, Held, and ourselves would be considered artifact.

We do not have time to criticize Paton's bizarre hypothesis. It is in complete contradiction with the most incontestable facts revealed by the Golgi and silver nitrate methods. We will merely affirm that in this difficult sphere of nerve histogenesis there is but one indubitable fact: the neurofibrils form initially in the distal protoplasmic pole of the neuroblasts of His, and they progressively grow centrifugally from this fibrillogenetic zone.

We can only understand this singular concept of the American scholar by supposing that the process of silver impregnation he employed stains the primitive neurofibrils very incompletely. The colloidal metal deposited only on those fibers that had attained full maturity, fibers located in the portion of the axon far from the distal neuroblastic pole. Furthermore, in the figures appended to Paton's work one clearly notes arrangements contradictory to his theory (reticular appearance of the neurofibrils, independence of neuroblasts and nerve fibers, first appearance of the neurofibrillary network in the protoplasm of very primitive neuroblasts, etc).

In spite of the author's allegations, one also observes that, far from having stained the neurofibrils in a stage prior to that which Held, Besta and we had stained them, he has in reality stained them in a later stage when the neuroblasts are quite developed and the ventral roots are already large and long.

ways travel through the interepithelial or interneuronal interstices of the central nervous system. Before justifying this opinion, which has been upheld by a great number of histologists since His and Kölliker, permit me to recount briefly the results of our recent observations on neuroblasts.

For a long time we have applied the reduced silver nitrate procedure to the study of neurofibrillar development, succeeding in staining these filaments first in the nerve cells of the cerebrum and cerebellum of newborn mammals [174] and in the 10 day chick embryo.[175] This research, concerned only with cells already advanced in development, demonstrated that in neurons which are not yet mature at birth, the stainability of the reticulum begins in the periphery of the protoplasm.*

Besta,[12,13] who used our technique, deserves the credit for having been the first to recognize the great precocity of appearance and stainability of the neurofibrillar apparatus. According to his observations on the spinal cord of chick embryos, the neurofibrils already make their appearance during the neuroblastic phase at the end of the sixtieth or sixty-fifth hour of incubation. At this stage the motor cells appeared to him to be bipolar in form, with two radial processes, of which the peripheral is continuous with a nerve fiber. This last observation of Besta confirms another, almost forgotten one, made by us a long time ago [156] using the Golgi method. We had noted that the youngest neuroblasts, still bound within the zone of the columns of His, often exhibit an ependymal process.†

----

*Just as many authors have observed, neurofibrillar staining can be obtained well before the tenth day. It is therefore necessary to distinguish between the variability in neurofibrillar staining which depends on the silver formulas employed, and the pre-existence of these organs which are often difficult to demonstrate in their earliest developmental phases. There is still another source of error which only our recent studies have uncovered, namely, the action of cold temperature sometimes produces considerable alterations (agglutination, formation of fusiform bundles, rarefaction of the reticulum) in the embryonic neurofibrils. (*Note for the French edition.*)

†It seems that a long time ago Hensen [64] also recognized this initial bipolarity of the neuroblasts. Unfortunately his descriptions and figures do not enable us to learn whether he always succeeded, in the initial phases, in differentiating between the nerve cells and the epithelial elements. His radial fibers seem rather to belong to the spongioblasts of His.

The precocious appearance of neurofibrils has been denied by Fragnito,[42,43,44]* who succeeded in recognizing these filaments only at the end of the sixteenth day of incubation, and by La Pegna[91] who only saw them at the end of the tenth day. As for Pighini,[139] Brock[21] and London, scholars who also applied the silver nitrate process to the study of fibrillogenesis, they seem to have studied only neurons that were already multipolar. Furthermore, Besta's discovery has been confirmed by Held[57] and ourselves.[180]

But neurofibrillar differentiation occurs at an even earlier stage than that of the neuroblast. According to the very interesting research of Held,[58] the fibrillar reticulum is coarse and restricted to one locus in the protoplasm (fibrillogenetic zone of Held) at first. This reticulum first appears in the primary neuroblastic phase, i.e., before the appearance of the polar processes. The filaments grow progressively away from this fibrillogenetic zone and are arranged in bundles which give rise to the primordial axon.

Our recent researches, which were performed on duck and chick embryos of 25 hours incubation, permit us to confirm the well-founded observations of the Leipzig histologist. In our opinion the phases which the rudimentary nerve cell goes through include: 1. germinative cells of His; 2. apolar or polygonal cell; 3. bipolar cell; 4. unipolar cell (neuroblast of His); 5. multipolar cell.

Germinative Cell. This cell corresponds to the germinative corpuscle of His and is characterized by the presence of conspicuous signs of proliferation. Its finely granular protoplasm does not attract the silver precipitate.

Apolar Cell. This is the primitive neuroblast of Held. Judging by his pictures, Held studied it especially in the trigeminal ganglion of bird embryos. According to our observations these elements, already capable of fixing silver, are very abundant in the retina and in the forebrain vesicle of the 50 to 60 hour chick embryo. Let us state first that the apolar cell is not the germinative corpuscle of His, but is a special phase of the rudimentary nerve cell, during which phase the latter, having completed its cell division, begins

---

*In opposition to the incontestable observations of Besta, Held, Paton, and ourselves, Fragnito has recently insisted on the late appearance of the neurofibrillary apparatus.[41]

to migrate and prepares to form a neurofibrillar framework. Ordinarily the apolar cell is located in the same row as the germinative
cells, i.e., very near the adjacent ventricular cavity (Fig. 36, A).
Sometimes it is a little further away; very rarely it is found at a
great distance from the internal limiting membrane (Fig. 37, D,
and Fig. 38, A, D). Perhaps those apolar cells which are far from
their site of origin correspond to the displaced elements which
show extraventricular mitoses, as described by Merck, Buchholz,
Schaper, Paton, and Hamilton.

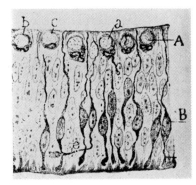

Fig. 36.   Section of the wall of the anterior vesicle of a 3.5 day chick embryo.
A) Apolar nerve cells; B) bipolar nerve cells; e) growth cone.

In addition to the absence of processes and the rounded or polygonal shape, the apolar cell is characterized by the existence of a
completely localized neurofibrillar network (fibrillogenetic zone of
Held) in the distal portion of its protoplasm (Figs. 36, b, c, and 37,
A). Furthermore, the shape, richness, and extent of this network
vary. Very often this neurofibrillar framework consists of a small
number of undulating fusiform, anastomosed strands, located in a
distal lobule or excrescence of the protoplasm (Fig. 37, A). Other
times it is reduced to a simple, variably-directed neurofibrillar loop,
from which some barely visible filaments emerge. The latter become lost in the unstained portion of the protoplasm (Fig. 36, C). It
sometimes takes the form of a circle or a variably-oriented ellipse
which is often perpendicular to the direction of the future axon.
Very delicate ascending fibers which surround the nucleus occasion-

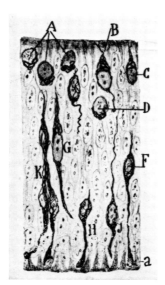

Fig. 37. Retina of a 2.5 day chick embryo. Cells copied from several sections. A) Apolar nerve cell; B) bipolar nerve cell; C) neuroblast with distal prolongation; F) more advanced bipolar neuroblast; K) agglutinated neuroblasts simulating anastomoses; a) growth cone.

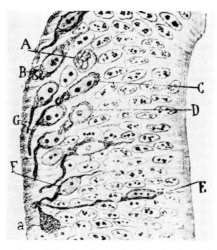

Fig. 38. Dorsal portion of the lumbar spinal cord of a 3 day chick embryo. A, B) Apolar cells with fibrillogenetic zone; C) rudimentary bipolar cell; E) more advanced bipolar cell; G) cells in the neuroblastic phase of His; a) gigantic growth cone.

ally emanate from this rudimentary skeleton (Fig. 36) and, during this stage or during the transition to bipolarity, it is not rare to observe fine descending trabeculae which penetrate among the spongioblasts and terminate in a mass (Fig. 36, a).

In Figures 37 and 40 much the same configuration is found in the retina as in the forebrain vesicle. Our preparations of the spinal cord show this appearance less frequently because the spinal neurons have generally attained the bioplar or monopolar phase before they are mature enough to attract silver. However in Figure 38, A, C, we show some very characteristic ones which are similar to those found in the retina. Note various rudimentary neurofibrillar frameworks that are either circular (Fig. 38, D), or in the form of a figure 8, or arranged in fine complicated networks.

Moreover, this apolar phase is also seen very frequently in sympathetic neurons of the paravertebral chain as well as in those of the visceral ganglia. Among the latter sympathetic cells we shall refer especially to a great cellular agglomeration which lies ventrad to the abdominal aorta between the two leaves of the rudimentary mesentery (Fig. 39, D). By migration and transformation, this mass will probably give rise to the pre-aortic ganglia and perhaps also to those of the intestinal plexuses of Meissner and of Auerbach.

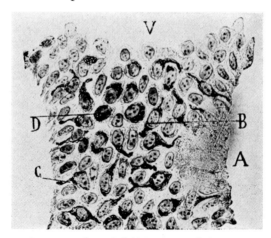

Fig. 39. The midline mesodermal fold in front of the Wolffian body of a 52 hour embryo. A) Peritoneal cavity; B, C, D) apolar, bipolar and monopolar neuroblasts of the visceral sympathetic nervous system; V) vessel.

Furthermore, these rudimentary sympathetic cells resemble (except that they may be slightly smaller) those described in the retina and in the forebrain vesicle. But lacking orientation, their fibrillogenetic zone lies on either side of their protoplasm. It is also noteworthy that besides cells which have a single neurofibrillar nucleus, other elements exist which possess two and even three such nuclei lying in certain protoplasmic excrescences (Fig. 39, B).

During all these transformations of the apolar cell, the nucleus does not seem to be modified appreciably; we have not succeeded in verifying Cameron's [24] recent assertion that the substance of the cellular processes and the neurofibrils is derived from the nucleus.

Phase of Bipolarity. Not constantly but very frequently the apolar nerve cell is transformed into a bipolar cell by the simultaneous, or almost simultaneous, formation of two polar prolongations. This modification is produced while the cell migrates progressively from its juxtaventricular location toward the layer of neuroblasts (medullary plaque of His). We do not know whether purely protoplasmic prolongations (perhaps made up of a network which does not attract the silver deposit) exist before the appearance of the polar neurofibrils. All that one can affirm with certainty is that the cell processes result at least in part from the progressive growth of the neurofibrillar network, which, after having wound around the nucleus, overflows at the two poles of the cell. In Figures 37 and 40 we show the most frequent arrangements in the retina and brain of the embryonic chicken. Note that in most instances the distal process, or primordial axon, is larger, darker, and richer in fibrils than the proximal prolongation, although the converse is not extremely rare. Futhermore, while the former terminates at a variable distance from the external limiting membrane, either in a rounded mass or a brush-point, the internal process, ordinarily shorter, terminates in a fine pale point which extends just to or a little beyond the ventricular surface.

Until now the two prolongations seem to have much the same properties but at this time they very clearly become differentiated from each other. As the bipolar neuroblasts gradually approach the external limiting membrane, the axon rapidly increases in diameter and length and, at its extremity, presents a thickening which is the

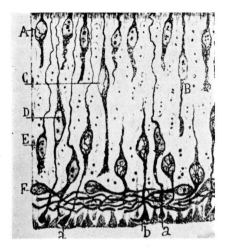

Fig. 40   Retina of a 4 day chick embryo. Cells copied from 2 successive sections. A, B, C) Various phases of the bipolar cells; D) bipolar cell whose axon, provided with a growth cone, touches the internal limiting membrane; F) neuroblast of His; a, b) growth cones.

growth cone. The proximal expansion, on the other hand, becomes paler and shorter and progressively atrophies (Fig. 40, D, and Fig. 38, F). In the 4 day chick embryo, therefore, almost all the bipolar cells in the anterior third of the retina show a proximal appendage which is very small and difficult to recognize. Nevertheless exceptions are found and, in Figure 40, D, we reproduce some bipolar elements whose ventricular prolongation still terminates at the epithelial border. These facts can be verified in the spinal cord.

Thus, as we have noted in another work,[179] the retina very clearly shows some interesting stages in the progress of the growth cones. One stage, which is represented by a palisade arrangement of the cones, throws considerable light on the mechanism by which the primordial axons advance across the retina. In reality, as can be seen in Figure 37, a, the immense majority of bipolar neuroblasts possess a growth cone which terminates immediately beneath the internal limiting membrane, parallel to the direction of Müller's fibers. Some cones seem to be wedged in and immobilized between the terminal feet of the epithelial fibers. In our opinion, only after the tip of the cone has struck against the limiting membrane does the axon assume a tangential direction and become an optic nerve fiber. Sometimes, however, the change of route occurs a little sooner, probably because of the impenetrability of the mass of more advanced nerve cells (in the unipolar phase) which lie very near the internal limiting membrane. The tardiest cones rebound against this solid mass. It is not rare moreover to see cones, repelled by an obstacle (epithelial feet, etc.), bifurcate and give rise to a point or secondary branch which is destined to atrophy (Fig. 40, b).

Growth cones arranged in palisade fashion and wedged beneath the limiting membrane occur very frequently in the bulbar and spinal motor nerve nuclei of 52 to 64 hour embryos. They are most readily found in lumbar region of the spinal cord since development of this region is always delayed considerably as compared with other segments of the spinal axis (Fig. 41, a). They often have an elongated form reminiscent of a barley grain, and they possess a pale tip, which sometimes leans against the limiting membrane and sometimes against the terminal feet of the epithelial cells. Bifurcations of the growth cones, in adaptation to the shape of the interstices, are not rare in the cord; one of the branches, generally the more robust, can be seen to slip away longitudinally in the furrows that the epithelial feet delimit within the basal membrane (Fig. 41, b).

All these facts (change of direction provoked by mechanical obstacles, the axons' search for epithelial interstices, axonal bifurcations induced by obstacles against which the cones abut) suggest a freedom movement of neural protoplasm which is contrary to Hensen-Held's theory of pre-established intracentral pathways. We will return later to these very important facts.

Phase of Monopolarity. Having described this stage in detail in our previous publications, we will not dwell on its mode of origin or its morphological varieties. We will only add that this phase ordinarily results (as can easily be seen in Figure 40, F), from the successive atrophy of the proximal prolongation and the growth of the axon. Let us note in the retina (5 to 6 day embryos) that most of the cells that have attained this developmental stage lie near the layer of optic fibers; furthermore the neurofibrillar network, instead of occupying only one side of the cell body as is usual in bipolar cells, completely surrounds the cell body with a very compact network. These horn-shaped neuroblasts were seen and drawn by His [71] a long time ago. In our first research on the retina of newborn mammals [163] in which we used the Golgi technique, we confirmed His's description regarding this point.

Such phenomena of migration and transformation are noted in the medulla, spinal cord, and brain. Thus, in the spinal cord the unipolar cells ordinarily lie in the periphery, although some exceptions are found (such as pyriform neuroblasts near the epithelial zone). Finally, the resorption of the ventricular prolongation, a phenomenon which induces the pear shape, is often omitted in the cord and in the medulla; the nerve cell thus becomes multipolar without having passed through the classical form of the neuroblast of His. Similar exceptions are also encountered in the paravertebral and visceral sympathetic ganglia, where nerve cells sometimes pass directly from bipolarity to multipolarity (Fig. 39).

Up to now we have described, without any theoretical consideration, the first developmental phases of neuroblasts and the growth of axons within nerve centers. Let us now disclose some facts and some reasonable inferences that are unfavorable to the Hensen-Held theory.

(*a*) *Absence of Interneuronal Anastomoses.* Let us begin with a negative observation. In these studies, which were based upon about one hundred very successful preparations, we hardly ever found the interneuronal anastomoses that Held described in the primordial neuroblastic and subsequent phases. In our sections two arrangements are encountered: either the neuroblastic protoplasm is barely or not at all impregnated, in which case it is impossible to recognize the true arrangement of the cellular contours, or else the protoplasm is sufficiently stained and shows very clear limits which are often in contact, but never in continuity, with the neighboring cells.

Let us add that when the growth cones are well situated for observation they always seem to travel freely in the interstices of the epithelial framework. Such independence of movement is observed both in the depths of the neural tube as well as in its peripheral sub-basal border (where the marginal layer, the first rudiment of the white matter, will ultimately make its appearance).

Naturally some fibers or nerve cells occasionally seem agglutinated because of the transforming and coagulating action of the reagents. Alcohol, osmic acid, sublimate, are all very poor fixatives for embryonic nerve tissue and produce a great number of artifacts.* Thus in Figure 37, K, we show three seemingly fused retinal neuroblasts. However, in the locations where they are intensely stained and sufficiently remote from epithelial fibers or neighboring nerve cells one can be very easily convinced of their individuality. Thus we believe that Held's intracentral plasmodesmas and neurodesmas, as well as his interneuroblastic anastomoses, are artifacts brought about by the reagents and exaggerated further by some accident of preparation. Perhaps pyridine provokes interstitial coagulation of some albuminoid, and the resultant filaments (which are especially apparent in paraffin sections) have succeeded in misleading Held.

---

*At the time of our recent visit to Held's laboratory we examined the anastomotic sensory neuroblasts (trigeminal ganglion of the 3 day duck embryo) described by this scholar. In truth, careful observation of these elements produced the impression of fusion or partial continuity of the neurofibrillar reticulum of two or three neighboring neuroblasts. But, even admitting that these images are not artifacts, they would not seem to have the great importance that Held (in his very natural desire to find arguments to support this theory of incrustation) has given them. It is necessary to take into account the following indisputable observations. First, fused sensory neuroblasts are so rare that in several dozen successful sections of the trigeminal ganglion of the 3 day chick embryo (fixation with alcohol or pyridine) they are almost always lacking, the ganglion cells preferentially being bipolar and perfectly independent. Secondly, in Held's preparations the immense majority of the sensory cells of the ganglion are bipolar and not anastomotic. We could not interpret this lack of substantial unions as the result of incomplete impregnation since all the monopolar or bipolar cells were very energetically stained. Thirdly, after the fourth or fifth day of incubation fusions are completely lacking. Consequently, even if it is true that accidental deviations from the normal autotrophic tendencies of neurofibrils can lead to a certain plasmodial or syncytial state among neighboring embryonic neurons, this state is transitory. This argument would not serve in the adult in support of the supposed intraprotoplasmic penetration of the neurofibrils of terminal nerve boutons (boutons of Held-Auerbach). One must not forget that in fully developed ganglia a direct communication is never found between the pericellular nervous nets and the protoplasm of the ganglion cell.

(*b*) *Absence of an Epithelial Reticulum.* The epithelial cells, like the neuroblasts, are free and do not show the least trace of any reticular arrangement (neurospongium of His) that might serve as a path for the growth cones. This negative fact, which we have stressed many times, is especially evident in the embryonic retina, where the primitive epithelial cells are seen to be perfectly smooth throughout their course from the external to the internal limiting membranes. And this arrangement is just as constant in the retinas treated by the Golgi method as in those studied by means of dissociation (retinas of the mammalian fetus and of the 5 to 12 day bird embryo).

But in the brain and spinal cord, as in the visual membrane, the primitive epithelial framework appears smooth from the very first. The short epithelial spines found between the neuroblasts never anastomose; they are simply placed in reciprocal contact (Golgi, Cajal, Lenhossék, Retzius, Athias, Sala, Kölliker). As we show in Figure 42, the radial fibers are perfectly smooth at the level of the marginal layer, a region traversed by embryonic axons.

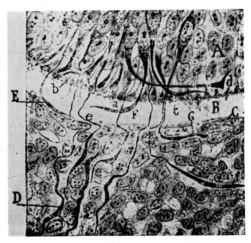

Fig. 41.   Lumbar spinal cord of a 70 hour duck embryo showing the first indication of the motor roots. Cells copied from 2 successive sections. A) Spinal cord; B) perimedullary space; C) meningeal limiting membrane; D) bifurcated growth cone; E, F) growth cones in the perimedullary space; G) strayed cones which travel dorsad; a) cones in palisade; c, d) cones traveling ventrodorsad beneath the basal membrane; e) fibers arranged in steps.

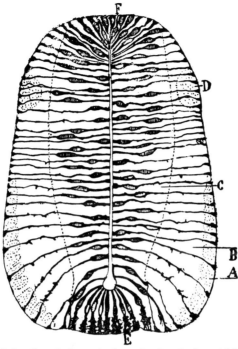

Fig. 42. Epithelial cells of the spinal cord of a 3 day chick embryo. Golgi method. A) Region of the ventral horn; D) round bundle of His; E) ventral epithelial vault.

One could perhaps reply that silver chromate only stains a portion of the primitive neuroglial network and that many components of embryonic gray matter escape its action. We would answer that even in ordinary preparations, i.e., stained by hematoxylin or aniline dyes, only an indistinct plexus — not a network — can be discerned between the neuroblasts. This plexus may be composed of the radial fibers, by their processes in contact, and by the axons which are lodged in the interstices and which often cross the epithelial cells at a right angle. Furthermore, when it is a matter of interpreting disputable appearances, it seems more prudent to accept, at least provisionally, the clear and selective revelations of the Golgi method rather than to refer to pictures that are confused, variable, misleading, and without selective staining (such as are furnished by routine techniques).

(*c*) *Growth of the Axis-cylinder.* As we have just said, in the retina, spinal cord, medulla, and cerebrum the intracentral advance of embryonic fibers occupies two successive mechanical phases: first, the cones travel radially following the orientation of the epithelial cells and without experiencing the least resistance; second, after having struck against the external limiting membrane the axons take a direction perpendicular, or almost perpendicular, to the epithelial fibers and glide longitudinally beneath the limiting membrane.

In the retina this tangential route leads to the forebrain vesicle; for a great many spinal neurons (commissural ones) the route is dorsoventral and leads to the raphe. Occasionally, especially at the level of the raphe, some dorsoventral commissural fibers of the spinal cord deviate somewhat from the external limiting membrane. This deviation results from the fact that the tardiest terminal nerve excrescences find the sub-basal space already occupied by the fibers which have preceded them. They are consequently forced to place themselves immediately beneath the latter. Naturally, on carefully studying the preparations one may find some exceptions to this law of growth, which seems to prove that the terminal nerve cone is capable of changing direction when it is repulsed by seemingly impenetrable nervous or epithelial masses.

(*d*) *Gigantic Growth Cones and Misplaced Axons.* In general, the neurofibrillar portion of the intraspinal growth cone is fine and terminates in a pencil point or small brush point. But at times this axonal end hypertrophies, becoming triangular, ovoid or semi-lunar and even thicker than the neuroblastic cell body. Very often these colossal swellings belong to misplaced axis-cylinders which were seemingly arrested *en route* by some unexpected obstacle. In Figure 43, i, we sketch a motor neuroblast whose axon, provided with a hypertrophied mass, is directed through error towards the ependyma. Such elements are also observed in the medulla oblongata (Fig. 44, F).

In our opinion these facts merit discussion. We have seen that the obstacle formed by the limiting membranes very often decides the definitive route adopted by the growing fibers. Also we observed that disoriented cones are sometimes arrested or caused to stray by obstacles and that the cones thereby acquire dimensions greater than those of the epithelial cells and their appendages. Finally, in the first stages of intracentral axonal growth, the terminal cones seem to advance freely in the path of least resistance, utilizing the interepithelial and sub-basal interstices as passage way. In view of the foregoing facts, what purpose is served by invoking the existence of a pre-existent directive reticulum?

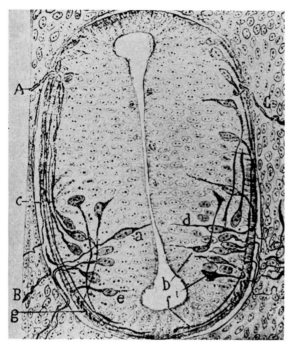

Fig. 43. A 58 hour chick embryo. The cells of this figure have been copied from 3 successive sections. A) Dorsal motor fibers; B) ventral roots; C) sensory fibers terminating in a mass; a) bipolar cell; b, i) cells possessing giant masses; e, d) bipolar cells arranged in a palisade; f) commissural fibers; g) rudiment of the ventral funiculus.

(*e*) *Inverted Neuroblasts and Cells Accidentally Fallen into the Ventricular Fluid.* Under the name of inverted neuroblasts we designate certain cells that we have recently found in embryos which, perhaps by some accident, have undergone an initial polar inversion. As a consequence of this disorientation, the growth cone, instead of proceeding towards the external limiting membrane, is directed towards the internal one, while the ependymal process takes the contrary direction (Fig. 44, D, E).

Naturally this inversion, if real, is produced in the first developmental phases, when the embryonic nerve cells are not yet susceptible to impregnation. When they can be impregnated (from the fifty-fourth to sixty-fourth hour of incubation) they already show a well-delineated fibrillar reticulum and two polar processes of which the more robust, i.e., the axon, is already quite long.

Two varieties of these cells, probably corresponding to two different developmental phases, can be recognized. In some elements the centripetal progress of the growth cone is arrested by the internal limiting membrane. The growth cone then slips tangentially externally and after describing a wide arc it becomes centrifugal and is reunited with its congeneral motor fibers (Fig. 44, C). In other cells the growth cone pushes energetically against the basal internal

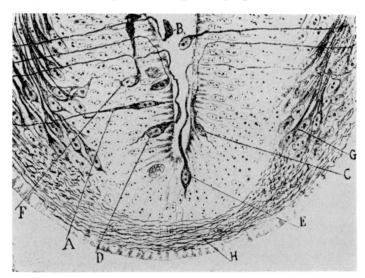

Fig. 44. Basal portion of the medulla oblongata of a 4 day chick embryo. These cells were copied from 3 successive sections. A) Displaced bipolar neuroblast; B) neuroblasts which have fallen into the ventricular cavity; C) tangential or subventricular neuroblast; D, E) neuroblasts whose peripherally-directed axon crosses the ventricular fluid; F) neuroblast possessing a giant cone; G) motor nucleus of the vagus nerve.

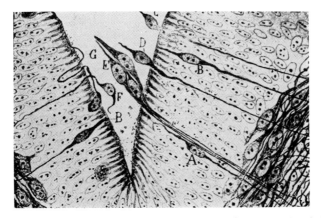

Fig. 45.   Section of the basal region of the medulla oblongata of a 4 day chick embryo. These cells were copied from 2 successive sections. A, B) Displaced bipolar cells; C, D) neuroblasts fallen into the ventricle; E) cluster of neuroblasts in the ependymal fluid; G) neuroblast whose disoriented axon traces a curve in the epithelial wall.

membrane which it perforates. The growth cone then grows freely in the ventricular fluid. At another point some attractive influence of the epithelial wall (E, D) causes the growth cone to re-enter the neural tube. The strayed fiber returns to the corresponding motor nucleus and joins its congeneral fibers definitively. We designate the elements of the first variety, which are the most common, as *cells making a sub-basal arc,* to distinguish them from the second, which we call *cells making an intraventricular arc.*

Striking examples of these two neuroblastic varieties are represented in Figures 44 and 45. Note that almost all these cells are bipolar and that the initial portion of the axon of the intraventricular arc cells is often very large and varicose (Fig. 44, D). Finally, some centrifugal ependymal processes are undergoing atrophy, just as in similar nonmigrated elements. In Figure 45, G, we show a cell making an intraventricular arc which is very remarkable and interesting from the point of view of the mechanism of axonal growth. This unipolar element possesses an axon which, after having tried fruitlessly to re-enter the gray matter has recrossed the epithelium and fallen anew into the ventricular cavity. Unfortunately, as this axon was cut, we do not know if it had the fortune to succeed in its attempt to find its path.

These singular inverted cells are undoubtedly pathological. Nevertheless, they are fairly frequently encountered in 3 to 4 day embryos. They abound in the medulla, especially at the level of the nuclei of the vagus and glossopharyngeal nerves (dorsal motor nuclei) as well as at the level of the hypoglossal nucleus. It is also notable that they demonstrate a preference for the ventricular angle of the raphe. They are never observed in the lateral regions of the medulla (*Flügelplatte of His*).

(*f*) *Intraventricular Neuroblasts.* His mentioned these cells a long time ago and we possess an original photomicrograph by this scholar in which the entire soma of one of these cells appears submerged in the ependymal fluid of the spinal cord. Other authors, e.g., Lenhossék and Held, also found them in preparations stained by routine methods. But, as these elements were not impregnated by plasmatic or neurofibrillar methods, one could doubt whether they were living growing neuroblasts.*

---

*Inverted and intraventricular elements may be identical, representing different topographical phases of a misplaced neuroblast which has accidentally fallen into the ventricular fluid. Thus, instead of believing that the inverted cell extends its axon towards the ependymal cavity, one could equally well imagine that it is the neuroblastic cell that is displaced. The cell first reaches the internal limiting membrane and then enters the ventricle. Finally, after a more or less complicated detour, the unsettled cell would penetrate the epithelial wall, definitively becoming a sub-basal arciform neuroblast.

This hypothesis would have the advantage of subordinating all the described types to a unique, simple mechanism. But, accepting this conception makes it necessary to attribute to the soma an ameboidism and a capacity for chemotactic orientation equal or even superior to those attributed to axons and growth cones. It would also be necessary to attribute a considerable slackness and mobility to the epithelial wall, by virtue of which the interstices could enlarge very easily at the least entreaty of the unsettled cell or of its ventricular prolongation. The absence of cells whose soma is just re-entering the epithelium or of displaced neuroblasts fallen into the ventricular fluid after a complicated journey across the epithelial wall are the reasons which have prevented us from unreservedly accepting the unitary hypothesis.

Futhermore we do not consider the question settled. Further research is still required. Impregnation of the primordial phases of the supposedly inverted cells, i.e., before their growth cone arrives at the ventricle, would be very significant. The absolute lack of these elements would be equally significant.

Some intraventricular neuroblasts which we recently stained with silver nitrate seem so normal, as regards structure and stainability, that it is impossible not to consider them as living cells, in spite of the abnormal environment in which they are found. Like the inverted neuroblasts they lie preferentially in the inferior bulbar region at the level of the basal plate of His (the site of origin of the ventral motor column). Thus, as is seen in Figure 45, C, D, most of these cells are bipolar; nevertheless some are frankly unipolar or at the stage of the neuroblast of His. They completely lack plasmodesmas or radial appendages. In this case no doubt can be expressed concerning the arrangement of the neuroblastic soma because it stands out perfectly against the transparent and colorless background of the ventricle. Sometimes one notes a group of two, three, or more intraventricular cells which give rise to a fascicle of axons which is probably continuous with the fibers of the vagus nerve root (dorsal motor nucleus?). However this wholesale emigration is very unusual and, although it occurs in spontaneously displaced elements found beneath the internal limiting membrane, it seems probable that various mechanical influences, perhaps following operative manipulation (handling the embryo, cutting with the scissors, etc.), have contributed to its production.*

The continuity of the axon of these elements with the radicular fascicles of the corresponding motor nuclei can be readily verified in isolated cells (Fig. 44, B). This prolongation seems composed of a compact fascicle of neurofibrils which is quite normal in appearance. The fact that intraventricular neuroblasts possess an axon similar to that of nondisplaced congeneral elements proves that the migration and the intraventricular sojourn is relatively innocuous.

The length of the axon is variable. It is generally very short, but the free portion of the axon at times attains several hundredths of a millimeter. In the latter cause the axon, bathed by the ventricular fluid, is a little swollen and even undulating (Fig. 44, E).

---

*In a case in which the embryo was accidentally squeezed between the blades of a forceps, a great number of neuroblasts were found to have fallen *en masse* into the ependymal fluid of the medulla. Could this be a simple coincidence? In any case we believe it necessary to repeat this accidental observation in order to determine to what extent the phenomena with which we are concerned are influenced by traumatic factors.

Every transition form is found between the intraventricular neuroblasts and those which are normally situated. The most interesting
is that represented in Figure 45, B. It shows displaced cells which
lie very near the ventricle and which possess two processes (phase
of bipolarity): an ependymal expansion, which extends just to the
internal limiting membrane, and another expansion, the axon,
which travels centrifugally toward the corresponding motor nucleus
(Figs. 44, A, and 45). In our opinion it is those elements located in
the neighborhood of the ventricle which accidentally fall into the
cavity of the latter.

All these facts are not in harmony with the theory of Hensen-
Held. They suggest a freedom of movement and behavior of the
soma, growth cone, and primordial axon that is not easily reconciled with the supposition of a system of interneuronal bonds (plas-
modemas and neurodesmas), nor with the hypothesis of a framework of pre-established pathways along which the young nerve
fibers must travel. Quite the contrary, in accord with the classic
doctrine of His, it shows us the great facility with which the axons
and even the cell bodies glide through the interepithelial interstices
and even fall, by error or by accident, into the ventricular fluid. All
this occurs without appreciable loss of neuroblastic vitality since
the axons are still capable of giving rise to definitive nerve fibers.

These facts must be compared with Harrison's observations of
axons growing freely in the peritoneal cavity after transplantation
of larval fragments. They must also be placed beside Perroncito's
and our own recent experiments which demonstrate the ability of
growth cones of regenerated nerves to cross blood clots and pathological exudates despite the complete absence of Schwann cells.
Furthermore, a long time ago Vanlair demonstrated that regenerating fibers from the central end of a cut nerve even push across
Haversian canals of interposed osseous fragments. Finally, we have
occasionally noted the existence of nerve fibers accidentally crossing the ependymal cavity in the spinal cord of the newborn dog
and cat.

Some of these observations have already been cited and discussed
by Held, who claims to reconcile them with his theory in two ways.
First, by invoking a property of the fibrillogenetic zone of pushing

the embryonic axon even across the most unfavorable terrain by a kind of *vis a tergo*. Second, he claims that arguments based on pathological or abnormal anatomical facts are not valid. But these arguments are not sufficiently convincing.

Let us note first of all, that the *vis a tergo* hypothesis by which Held attempts to explain the growth of axons in the ventricular fluid or in abnormal organic environments, is basically a concession to His's concept. *Vis a tergo* of the fibrillogenetic zone and ameboid growth of the terminal nerve cone imply the same idea and assume that the propulsive force of the nerve fiber is constant and subject to internal conditions, i.e., to conditions which reside within the very cell body of the neuron. We agree with this interpretation which we accepted a long time ago, following His, to explain the growth of the terminal cones; but, since this explanation supplants the plasmodesmas and pre-established pathways for certain pathological cases, we cannot understand why Held does not venture to generalize it to the normal case to which it applies equally well.

Nevertheless, His's conception of continuous growth across mechanical obstacles is not sufficient. One must also acknowledge that growth cones, normal or aberrant, are affected by influences (possibly chemotactic) which come from the nerve nuclei, the extramedullary epithelium, and the motor plate. Only in this way can one understand the cases which we have just cited, e.g., the fact that the misplaced axons in the cerebrospinal fluid ultimately succeed in refinding their way and in forming ordinary motor fibers.*

We consider Held's prejudices regarding inductions drawn from pathological nerve development as being very exaggerated. In our opinion, it is precisely in the domain of abnormal development of the nervous system that we must search for evidence of great value to the solution of neurogenetic problems. By experimentation (ablation, nerve transplantation, nerve transection, etc.) one endeavors to separate out some possible components of a phenomenon, in order to understand the cause and the mechanism. Also, in the de-

---

*In the hypothesis that inverted cells and those fallen into the ventricular fluid are identical, it would be the soma which is affected by the chemotactic substances and which seeks its path across the epithelial wall independently of the supposed pre-established intracellular paths.

velopmental deviations of the central nervous system nature accomplishes some very delicate and very interesting experiments, in which the suppression of one supposedly necessary condition notably simplifies the problem and permits us to make rational hypotheses on the true causes of developmental phenomena. For example, when an axon accidentally enters a cavity, or when axons regenerate across a blood clot, they grow in the absence of *Leitzellen* (or Schwann cells). This experiment in nature suppresses one element (the Schwann cell) hitherto falsely considered essential to nerve outgrowth. We must not forget, furthermore, that pathological-anatomical phenomena are nothing more than normal processes slowed down, exaggerated, or inopportunely provoked. These processes are sometimes abnormal, but they always bring to bear the same forces and the same principles as physiological phenomena.

II. The growth cones are completely free in their passage across the perimedullary vaginal space.

The term vaginal or perimedullary space is applied to the circular empty space which surrounds the embryonic spinal cord. It is bounded by the external limiting membrane and the first layer of flattened connective cells which will give rise to the meninges (*membrana limitans meningea* of His) This gap, which His describes as being very large in human embryos, may be narrow or even nonexistent in the living condition where, like connective tissue spaces, it may be reduced to a potential cavity. Such an enlargement is probably produced by the fixing reagents which condense the medullary tissue more energetically than the mesodermal framework. We must note that in this perimedullary lacuna we have never found the slightest trace of the uniting fibers that Hensen described nor have we found prolongations of *Leitzellen* in continuity with the supporting apparatus of the spinal cord. Let us now carefully examine the progress of the growth cones across the vaginal space. In Figure 41 we represent the principal varieties of and location of spinal motor fibers of the 3.5 day duck embryo. Let us first note that all the terminal nervous excrescences, once arrived at the perimedullary space, glide to the surface of the *membrana limitans meningea* where they seem to grope blindly for a path.

Some find their path immediately, whereas others only encounter it after considerable wandering. Some disoriented cones which have become lost in the perimedullary lacuna travel dorsoventrally or vice-versa for considerable distance. They ultimately retrace their steps and finally worm their way between the mesodermal cells (Fig. 43, C). Other more fortunate fibers have only to describe a short path before arriving at the mesoderm. The axon, like the growth cone, appears perfectly naked and possesses no cellular escort during this intravaginal journey.

We are therefore faced with an argument identical to that previously cited with reference to inverted cells. During the intravaginal journey the fibers are capable of locating their route without the aid of *Leitzellen* and even after having temporarily lost their way. This suggests that the mechanism of fiber orientation is not mechanical in nature, but is chemical. Perhaps we should look for the possible presence of positive chemotactic substances whose diffusion towards the cord across the connective tissue interstices excites neural ameboidism.

III. The nerve fibers travel across the mesoderm, availing themselves of the cellular interstices. The *Leitzellen* and their anastomotic expansions are always located beside the axons which, because of the disturbing action of the reagents (pyridine, alcohol, etc.), appear fused or partially struck to the mesodermal framework.

In our recent works on neurogenesis we believe we have faithfully represented the arrangement of the motor and sensory root fibers in the 64 hour chick embryo. Inasmuch as the purpose of these drawings was to demonstrate the innate continuity of nerve fibers, we did slightly neglect the details of the relationship between the mesodermal cells and the growing nerve fibers. As will readily be understood, these relationships are of prime importance to Held. That is why this scholar accuses us of not having copied the microscopic preparations faithfully and of having ignored the *Leitzellen* and their plasmodesmas which he believes completely surround the growth masses and axons and guide them toward the periphery. Figures 46, 47, 48 and 49 are completely incompatible with this point of view; they show nerve fascicles located in the intercellular spaces.

Furthermore, we believe Held's criticism does not have merit. Our illustrious friend seems to forget that a histological drawing is never an impersonal copy of everything present in a preparation. If that were true, our figures would be far too complicated and almost incomprehensible. By virtue of an incontestible right, the scientific artist, for the purpose of clarity and simplicity, omits many useless details. He suppresses those things which are only of secondary importance or which, on the contrary, have sufficient worth to merit being reproduced separately. In our opinion, the requirements of nonschematic scientific figure is not that it show everything, but that it should not include subjective elements, and that its author should not have been led, by prejudiced ideas or theories, to falsify the representation of nature. And we must declare that if our drawings at times omit details, in compensation, all details that they show have been copied with the utmost fidelity. In order to decrease the number of figures artists are sometimes forced to combine objects which are scattered in two or three successive sections. We are very far from considering our drawings as flawless, but we prefer to sin by omission rather than by excess; we prefer to neglect the less important parts or those which are observed very readily for example, rather than scrupulously reproduce images which could be judged by a somewhat severe critic as accidental arrangements or as artifacts of preparation.*

But let us now examine the progress of nerve fibers across the mesoderm and see what connections these fibers have with the connective tissue framework.

Movement of Motor Fibers. In Figure 46 we reproduce as exactly as possible some very young radicular fibers of the lumbar region of a 52 to 56 hour chick embryo. In such intensively impregnated sections the protoplasm of the connective cells has a chestnut hue and the nuclei are perfectly stained.

Let us note first the form and the position of the growth cones which have invaded the mesoderm. These excrescences, which

---

*In our opinion most of the errors committed recently in the study of the fine structure of gray matter result precisely from neglect of this rational principle of interpretation: one must draw and consider as real only that which appears constantly and clearly with the aid of selective methods.

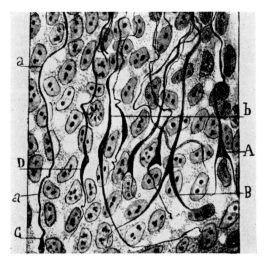

Fig. 46. Growth cones arriving at the myotome. Nuclear staining by thionine. A) Bifurcated cone applied to a connective tissue cell; B) division of a cone travelling through cellular interstices; C) terminal bouton; a, b) free portions of the axons in the mesodermal lacunae.

appear coffee-colored and finely striated, vary slightly in shape both in accommodation to the connective tissue interstices and because of the variable rate of their advance. They may take the following shapes: oval, pencil-point, brush or reversed cone, but the most frequent shape, judging from our preparations, is that of a barley-corn grain having a sharp and, at times, very pale point. Moreover, the shape and the dimension of the terminal mass varies according to the obstacles which it encounters in its progressive movements and whether it remains undivided or whether it is about to give rise to a branch. When the cones do not find obstacles in their route they elongate and become fine, pale and barely undulating. Contrariwise, the presence of an obstacle, which transiently arrests the ameboid movement, often produces large cones or intensely stained terminal buttons at the peripheral end (Fig. 46, C). It is not rare to find fibers which, in the face of insurmountable obstacles, wander and become lost. In Figures 41, G, and 47, E, we reproduce two disoriented masses which advance by error, towards the vicinity of the spinal ganglion. Bifurcation occurs frequently in radicular fibers which are several hundred millimeters away from their point of emergence. At the point of bifurcation the mass becomes quite increased in volume and takes the form of a corner whose basal angles give rise to short appendages (Fig. 47, F). Sometimes these appendages are very long, fine and pale (Fig. 46, B). Very often one of the divided branches or appendages is stouter than the other and takes the shape of a horn. It is not rare, moreover, to observe bicornuate masses (Fig. 46, A) which merely represent the initial stage of division. Finally, we have frequently observed that division of growth cones seems to result from obstacles in their path. As we show in Figures 46, A, and 47, F, D, G, one or two connective tissue cells are always found in the angle of division.

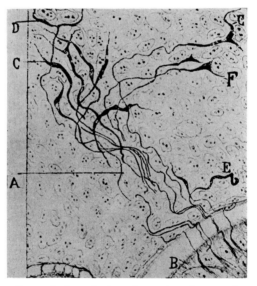

Fig. 47.   Motor fibers of the spinal cord crossing the mesoderm in a 58 hour embryo. Nerve fibers copied from 2 successive sections. A) Ventral root; B) spinal cord; E) wandered and coiled mass.

It is noteworthy that the axons, during the first period of their development and in proportion as they lengthen, decrease progressively in diameter. Thus the fibers first emerged from the spinal cord are relatively stouter than those that have reached the myotome, and are especially stouter than those which, during the fourth and fifth days of incubation, are arranged in very compact fascicles. That seems to indicate that the initial lengthening of the axons occurs in a certain measure at the expense of the very substance of the young nerve fiber.

Naturally the first axons that migrate into the mesoderm appear isolated. They advance making great detours to avoid the connective tissue cells, and they run along the edges of the latter (Figs. 41 and 46). But when the number of fibers arrived at the mesoderm has increased (from the third to the fourth days) the most recent among them profit from the path already marked out by their older companions. In this way the primordial nerve fascicles are formed, the fiber richness of the fascicles increasing considerably up to the sixth and seventh day of incubation. One fact to which we must draw attention is that the very fine nerve fibers are in intimate contact with each other in the interior of these primordial fascicles. Thus one cannot perceive any connective tissue process between them nor any sheath around them. The adventitial cells (*Leitzellen* of Held, lemmoblasts of Lenhossék) always lie between the fascicles, to which they are sometimes very tightly bound.

Let us now consider those axons which travel in isolated fashion. In thin sections they lend themselves especially well to the study of the relationship between the nerve fibers and the connective tissue framework.

In Figures 41 and 46 we have faithfully reproduced these relationships as found in our best sections upon examination with the oil immersion objective and by making use of the diaphragm to appreciate the cellular contours better. Let us first note that the cells adjacent to the nerve fibers (*Leitzellen* of Held) vary greatly in shape, being polygonal, fusiform or stellate. They have a tangential nucleus, i.e., are surrounded on one side by a fine layer of protoplasm. Many of the cells present an almost smooth contour which is bounded by contact with nerve fibers and with congeneral neighboring cells. Others possess polar processes which seem anastomosed, forming meshes in which one clearly observes spaces or lacunae. During life these spaces are probably occupied by a more or less coagulable liquid. As for the orientation of these elements with regard to the nerve fibers, one also notes some variations.

Often they are arranged lengthwise, either among the nerve fascicles or beside them; at other times they seem indifferent to the presence of the nerve fascicles, since their principal axis is transverse or oblique to the direction of the axons. These differences in the orientation of the mesodermal cells suggests that they are not in any genetic relationship with the nerve fibers. They only respond passively to the presence of nerve fibers, becoming more compact and often changing their direction to become more or less parallel to the embryonic nerve fibers. Naturally this inertia is not maintained later.

But let us reveal one fact which is very important to the controversy: whatever may be the abundance and the proximity of the connective elements which extend along the axons, with a good objective it is always possible to convince oneself that the only relationship between nerve fibers and connective tissue is that of contiguity. In many places and often over long distances the nerve fibers can be observed to be completely isolated from adventitial cells (Fig. 46, b). Furthermore, the extent of these free segments varies according to the preparations, the regions examined, and the degree of alteration (agglutination, dislocation, coagulation) produced by the fixatives and the embedding procedures. In the vicinity of the myotome we have found such free segments of more than 0.04 millimeter length. At other times (Fig. 46, a, b) the free distance seems shorter.

Another very troublesome observation for the theory of Hensen-Held is that even in places where adventitial cells or their protoplasmic prolongations (plasmodesmas) seem to lie along the axon, one side is always perfectly free (Figs. 46, a, and 41, D). That shows us that the axon is supported and embraced by the cells but is not lodged in their interior. The protoplasmic appendages sometimes accompany the nerve, but more often they cross the nerve fibers at various angles without effecting any relation with them other than that of contact.

The same views may be expressed concerning the relation of the terminal masses to the connective tissue framework. The growth cones travel freely in the interstices, at times running along the edge of the cells and their appendages. There is no possible doubt about this point; our preparations leave nothing to be desired (Fig. 46, D).

Since such a good observer as Held has described cells perforated by cones or cones bound within protoplasmic cords, some objective arrangement must have existed in his preparations which gave rise to these interpretations. By carefully studying our sections, especially those prepared according to Held's fixation procedure, we encountered some arrangements which, on less careful examination, seem to lend support to Held's theory. We show them in Figures 46, B, and 47, F. But they are easily explained by supposing that the growth cones, especially when dividing, lean upon and even adhere to the protoplasm of the connective tissue cells. Thus in Figure 47, F, we see a cone whose base has two fine expansions which are applied so intimately to the protoplasm of a mesodermal element that it seems as though the neurofibrils have penetrated into the cell body. In other instances the cone ends at the level of a cell and, when the cone is either above or below the cell, the illusion of an intraprotoplasmic passage results. Sometimes one notes a cone terminated by a hook upon the very edge of an element which it seems to have run against (Fig. 41, D). Finally, it is not rare to find very elongated cones which, after having followed the contours of a cell, terminate by means of a pale point which seems encrusted in the surface of a protoplasmic appendage. The risk of mistaking extracellular nerve fibers for intracellular fibers is all the greater since the nuclei of connective tissue cells are often very superficial and one could say that the axon is in contact with this nucleus. But, we repeat, all these arrangements, and even others which are encountered in good preparations, can be interpreted simply and without recourse to Held's theory. One must simply bear in mind that, in their movement of growth towards the periphery, the nerve fibers must skirt the edge of all the obstacles which oppose their progress. It is the reagents that often transform this appearance into that of veritable incrustations.

Movement of Sensory Fibers. Having already examined the structural development of the sensory neurons and the mechanism of formation of the dorsal roots in our last work on neurogenesis, we will merely add some details about the mode of entry of these roots into the cord and the first phases of their terminal division.

In 54 to 56 hour chick embryos the lumbar cord almost completely lacks sensory roots and, consequently, the rudiment of the dorsal funiculus (round column of His). But immediately beneath the external limiting membrane, slightly ventrad to the ventral root, the first outline of the white matter appears, represented by some longitudinal fibers (Fig. 43, g). Careful research into the origin of these fibers reveals that they are nothing more than the continuation of commissural axons. That demonstrates that the system of commissural fibers develops almost simultaneously with the motor roots and that the sensory fibers penetrate the neural tube shortly after the initial differentiation of the white matter.

However, in spinal ganglia of these 54 to 58 hour embryos, two or three bipolar cells as well as some radicular fibers were in the process of perforating the external limiting membrane (Fig. 48, D). It is interesting to study the stages of this penetration. Let us first note that some dorsal root fibers terminated by growth cones have not yet arrived at the vaginal space. Other fibers have fallen into this lacuna, make detours, and seem to search blindly in

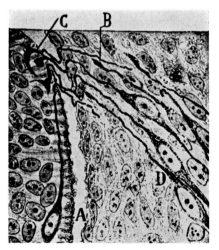

Fig. 48. Portion of a transverse section of the spinal cord and spinal ganglion of a 56 hour chick embryo. The cells of this figure have been copied from 2 successive sections. A) Motor cell of the dorsal root; B) growth cones of the sensory cells; C) bifurcation of the axons in the spinal cord.

the epithelial palisade of the cord for an accessible interstice. Finally, some sensory cones have attained their objective and appear within the external limiting membrane in the form of a voluminous mass, a kind of protoplasmic reserve from which the terminal division will emerge.

In Figure 48, C, which illustrates these sensory masses, one can also appreciate the mechanism of bifurcation. The terminal excrescence is transformed first into a triangular protoplasmic mass which later bifurcates, giving rise to two points which grow progressively. One of them becomes a robust fiber which travels dorsoventrad immediately beneath the external limiting membrane, while the other, often finer and shorter, progresses radially at first and ultimately becomes the descending branch. These branches, disoriented and often tortuous at the outset, progressively become oriented and adopt a longitudinal direction. This is as though, after hesitation and groping, they end up by feeling the effects of some directing chemotactic influence. All this occurs as though Held's supposed preformed pathways did not exist, the initial advance of the growth cones occurring irregularly and in the path of least resistance.

During the third and fourth days of incubation a great number of sensory axons penetrate the cord, profiting from the paths marked out by the first nerve fibers. Thus very compact fascicles are formed which strike against the mass of commissural neurons and against the palisade of dorsoventral nerve fibers within the cord. The sensory fascicles are consequently forced to lie immediately beneath the external limiting membrane. The fact that the nerve fibers are grouped in dense fascicles in the embryo, without intervention of cells, is a general phenomenon in the nervous system. This phenomenon suggests the existence of a certain reciprocal attraction of similar nerve fibers (reciprocal homotropism); but it also testifies to the spirit of rigorous economy which reigns over all organic processes: in developing nerve pathways, by virtue of the law of least effort, the late-arriving fibers seek to follow the pathways marked out in advance by the earlier ones. This is especially true when the tissue to be crossed is very compact and rich in cells.

In spite of all efforts, we have not succeeded in noting the slightest trace of pre-existing paths in the sensory ganglia, in the vaginal space, or in the sub-basal medullary region where the sensory fibers pass.

The peripheral sensory branch grows by the same mechanism as the motor fibers, from which fibers it may be distinguished, especially in the duck embryo, by its greater thickness and its darker coffee color hue.

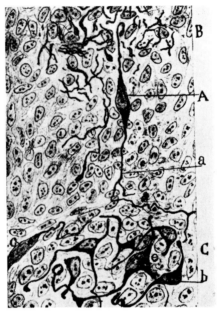

Fig. 49. Portion of a longitudinal section of a 3.5 day chick embryo. A) migrating sympathetic cell; B) section of a spinal nerve; C) sympathetic ganglion b, c) developing communicating nerve.

Movement of Sympathetic Fibers. Developing later than the motor or sensory axons, the sympathetic fibers can be studied very easily in longitudinal sections of the chick or duck embryo from the fourth day of incubation on. The longitudinal cords forming the prevertebral chain are very favorable for this study; these cords appear early in the form of a nerve plexus mixed with migrating nerve cells. As can be seen in Figure 49, the terminal masses are especially abundant. They often adopt the form of free masses, sometimes accidentally leaning against connective tissue cells.

Migrated Sympathetic Cells. The origin and mode of formation of the paravertebral and visceral sympathetic cells have been discussed enough. Whereas certain authors such as His Jr., Onody, Romberg, and Rabl believe that the sympathetic cells of the principal chain emanate from the sensory roots from the spinal ganglia, other scholars, e.g., Kohn,[77] are inclined to believe that they originate from the spinal cord and represent migrated Schwann cells (lemmoblasts of Lenhossék, neurocytes of Kohn).

According to Kohn, the young sympathetic cells arise from the cellular chain of the corresponding nerve pair and are arranged syncytially at first. After a complex process of multiplication, migration and differentiation they form the *primary ganglionic mass* (Kohn).

Opinions also differ regarding the visceral ganglia. According to His and recently Kohn, the principal sympathetic chain is the site of origin and the source of the visceral sympathetic cells; but many scholars still favor the direct ectodermal origin of these elements. Held appears to concede a medullary origin to the visceral sympathetic cells.

Our observations are not yet sufficient to allow us to take a stand in this important debate. All that we can affirm is that at the fifty-second hour of incubation in the chick (Fig. 50) the sympathetic cells of the paravertebral ganglia are already in place outside the aorta and in front of the thoracic cord. Moreover, at this same stage, the fold which supports the future intestine in the coelom already

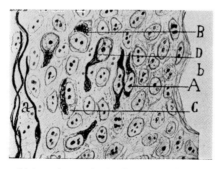

Fig. 50. A 52 hour chick embryo. A, B, C) sympathetic cells of the paravertebral chain.

contains some very compact agglomerations of apolar neuroblasts (Fig. 39). These agglomerations are most prominent in the lumbar region at the level of the wolffian body.

Nevertheless, if we are obliged to express an opinion, we would rather adopt the view which attributes a spinal origin to the sympathetic cells of the principal chain, and which supposes that they migrate along the same route as the ventral roots. Of course, we do not feel that these motor neuroblasts correspond to the neurocytes of Kohn but rather to true motor cells of the spinal cord. Their migration probably takes place before the emergence of the ventral roots, at which time migrating sympathetic cells are in the apolar or the earlier germinative phase. It is clear that such an exodus of motor cells cannot be observed in our preparations, for most apolar elements do not yet possess affinity for deposition of colloidal silver. However one sometimes sees retarded cells, i.e., which have emigrated after the fifty-fourth hour (and even after the third day) in which the neurofibrillar framework and its processes begin to show some affinity for silver. These elements are generally bipolar.

We have encountered these migratory elements both in the spinal and cranial motor roots as well as in the sympathetic rami communicantes. The most typical and developmentally advanced ones ordinarily lie in the afore-mentioned trunks, as is shown in Figure 49. In this figure may be seen a bipolar element, A, whose central process, which is slightly thickened near its extremity, terminates in a curved hooklike button that seems to disengage itself from the spinal nerve. The peripheral prolongation of this element divides and terminates in the vicinity of the corresponding sympathetic ganglion.

Those migratory bipolar cells which lie near the central nervous system within the motor roots are especially abundant in the vagus nerve, the motor root of the trigeminal, the facial, and the sensory branches of the trigeminal. They are customarily less advanced developmentally than those of the rami communicantes, and their neurofibrils, when present, are only found in the polar prolongations. Some bipolar cells are already so advanced that their peripheral process shows bifurcations.

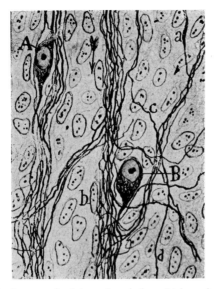

Fig. 51.   Trigeminal nerve fascicles of a 4 day chick embryo. A, B) Sympathetic cells.

But the largest and most easily stained migratory elements lie in the branches of the trigeminal. As we show in Figure 51, A, B, these cells already contain a very apparent somatic neurofibrillar reticulum. This reticulum condenses to form expansions which are quite long and parallel to the neighboring nerve fibers. One of these cells, (Fig. 51, B) is already unipolar.

It is also very easy to verify the migration of sympathetic cells along the longitudinal trunks which unite the paravertebral ganglia. Study of longitudinal sections of the ganglionic region reveals, as Kohn observed, that well-delimited ganglia do not yet exist; only agglomerations of neurons united by a plexus interspersed with bipolar or unipolar nerve cells are found. Very often the soma is almost colorless, save for an intensely stained protoplasmic mass from which the nerve process emerges. Sometimes, in the unipolar elements, the demarcation between this neurofibrillar coagulum and the rest of the protoplasm is so clear that on less careful examination one could believe that its fiber actually terminates in the depths of the parent cell body by means of a mass (Fig. 52, B). There is

yet another arrangement which appears questionable; in some
sympathetic cells, especially in those which have been submitted
to the action of cold prior to fixation, the neurofibrillar framework
appears concentrated and is restricted to one portion of the protoplasm. It thus simulates a cord which perforates the cell and unites
two cellular processes. An unforewarned observer might, because
of this arrangement, take for granted the existence of connective
tissue cells traversed by axons.

Let us dwell a bit here upon the morphology and the misleading
structural appearances of the migratory sympathetic cells. In our
preparations these are the only elements which under certain conditions might suggest the idea of a growth of neurofibrils through
the supposed *Leitzellen*. Are these equivocal images the ones that
Held erroneously took as objective proof of his theory? Knowing
the wide experience and the critical acumen of the Leipzig neurological scholar, we do not dare to attribute such an error to him
unreservedly.

From the objective facts which we have just described concerning
the development of the axis-cylinders and neuroblasts, the His
doctrine reappears as an inevitable postulate. The growing axon
tips cross the mesoderm, always availing themselves of cellular
interstices and traveling by roads which least resist the impetus of

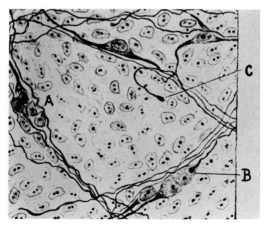

Fig. 52. Longitudinal section of the region of the neck of a 4 day chick embryo.
A, B) Agglutination of sympathetic cells; C) growth cone.

the ameboid cones. In order to account for the connections established between the neurons and the peripheral organs or between certain classes of neurons, one must acknowledge the existence of tropisms, i.e., chemical influences very similar to those which direct the activity of motile cells (leucocytes, spermatozoa, etc.).

These facts and deductions are irreconcilable with the theory of Hensen-Held. But besides the facts that we have just described, there are also a great number of reasons of experimental or speculative nature which argue against this theory; we will succinctly mention some of them.

(a) The growth masses are sometimes larger than the lattice work (plasmodesmas) of the connective tissue and, consequently, is is very difficult to accept that these latter are perforated and dilated by them. This disproportion is observed especially in axons of the sympathetic nervous system and in mammalian axis-cylinders that are retarded in development.

(b) According to our observations and to those of Held himself, the bipolar sympathetic nerve cells leave the spinal cord and migrate with the ventral roots. Since these migratory elements are more voluminous than the *Leitzellen*, how could they enter the interior of the latter? Perhaps Held will respond that, according to his observations, these cells and their polar processes travel freely through the cellular interstices, or rather that the cell bodies migrate along the interstices while the processes take advantage of the plasmodesmas. Both of these solutions are very difficult to accept and the former would only be an indirect way of admitting that the supposed preformed pathways have no objective reality. If nerve cells are capable of emigrating by virtue of ameboid movements, and of reaching their normal peripheral location without detours and without errors, then why cannot we ascribe the same power to the axons which must also encounter the same obstacles *en route?*

(c) Numerous observers (Kölliker, Lenhossék, Harrison, Retzius, and ourselves) have recognized that, excluding isolated nerve fibers, embryonic nerves are composed mainly of compact fascicles, without interposition of cells or cellular prolongations. This fact constitutes, in our opinion, a great difficulty opposing the theory of

Hensen-Held. In fact, according to this conception, one must choose between two alternatives: each new axon about to be added to a fascicle either penetrates the same preformed intercellular tube, or each axon possesses a special cellular sheath. Examination of preparations with powerful objectives proves, as many authors have noted, that neither of these two opinions is tenable. On the one hand, individual sheaths surrounding constituent axons of a fascicle are never seen and, on the other hand, the perifascicular membrane, far from being formed by a single cell, is actually composed of a great number of individual, more or less flattened, elements.

(d) Carefully considered, the theory of Hensen-Held does not clarify question of the orientation of nerve paths and the peripheral connections of nerves, notwithstanding Held's improvements on Hensen's primitive conception (notion of the shortest path and neurofibrillar *vis a tergo*). It only serves to alter the problem by moving it to a new terrain. From the point of view of this theory the question is reduced to these terms: In the young embryo prior to the appearance of the axons, what physicochemical conditions produce direct and perfectly congruent roads between all the organs that ultimately join in anatomical and functional connection? The hypothesis in question unfortunately does not reveal anything exact or well-founded about this transcendental point which is, in essence, the heart of the problem.

(e) Our observations and those of several authors have demonstrated a great number of highly variable and useless axonal detours and even temporary or definitive straying during axonal outgrowth. To cite only one example, we reproduce (Fig. 53, C) an arrangement of the trochlear nerve roots which occurs very frequently in the newborn rabbit. The axons farthest away from the point of emergence of the nerve are disoriented, and they descend within the dorsal longitudinal column, describing some curves and finally find their true route which permits them to join the ordinary radicular fibers.

In this case (as in similar ones that we could mention) must we accept, in accord with the theory of Hensen-Held, the existence of pre-established aberrant and useless pathways? And if so, how can we explain how the strayed fibers abandon the wrong road and reach their destination?

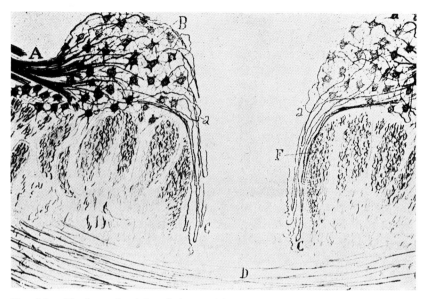

Fig. 53. Nucleus of origin of the trochlear nerve of a several-day-old rabbit. A) Nerve: B) motor cells; C) strayed fibers which, after an arciform detour, return to the nerve roots.

(f) Finally, almost all the facts of pathological regeneration discovered by Perroncito, Marinesco, Nageotte, Lugaro, Tello, and ourselves, militate against the theory of Hensen-Held just as they do against the theories of Balfour, Dohrn, Apáthy, and Bethe. We cannot describe them here in detail. We will only recall that in its most primitive stages every new nerve fiber that is formed under pathological influences lacks a cellular sheath and travels freely in the cellular interstices (ball phenomena, creation of nerve nets and dendrons by transplantation as discovered recently by Nageotte and by Marinesco, Perroncito's phenomena). To understand the value of these observations which are so irreconcilable with the hypotheses of Balfour and Hensen, we beg the reader to refer to the figures in our works on nerve degeneration and regeneration and especially those of our recent monograph on this subject.[182] These figures not only show young naked axons traveling without *Leitzellen* across connective tissue, but even show isolated, newly-formed neurofibrils which wander and ramify both within the necrotic segment of injured axons as well as beneath the Schwann membrane. These fibers describe circles and spirals of extraordinary complexity. Furthermore, His's neurogenetic doctrine has been recently accepted by Dohrn in a very interesting work in the development of the trochlear nerve.[31]*

We will terminate this long critique with these conclusions:

1. Embryonic nerve fibers are the result of the continuous growth of the principal prolongation of the neuroblast of His.

2. The neurofibrillar framework differentiates, i.e., becomes stainable, before the neuroblastic phase. Thus, as Held noted, the neurofibrils initially form a network in the distal pole (fibrillogenetic zone) of the rudimentary nerve cell and then grow centrifugally to give rise to the axis-cylinder. There are some exceptions.

3. This principal prolongation possesses a thickened free end or growth cone which is variable in shape. It glides between the cellular interstices in the embryonic neural tube as well as in the depths of the mesoderm. In addition to a neurofibrillar skeleton, the primordial axon and terminal cone also possess an unstained neuroplasm and a fine limiting membrane.

4. The supposed penetration of growth cones into the interior of the epithelial cells of the spinal cord (neurospongium) and into the mesodermal cells (so-called neuroblasts, plasmodesmas, etc.) is an artifact due to agglutination of the embryonic axons and the neighboring epithelial or mesodermal cells. The interneuroblastic anastomoses described by Held either represent accidental cellular fusions produced by the reagents or an abnormal arrangement. Even admitting that in a certain number of cases these anastomotic appearances are real, they cannot account for the supposed interneuron-

---

*While studying the development of the trochlear nerve in Pristiurus embryos, Dohrn observed that this nerve completely lacks cellular chains and nuclei during the first phases of development. At this stage it possesses only naked axons which grow towards the periphery across an almost acellular mesenchyme. Moreover, he did not succeed in finding the pre-established pathways supposed by Held, whose theory of growth in the shortest path is in disagreement with the very complicated path of the vertebrate trochlear nerve.

al anastomoses in the adult because these rare and inconstant fusions disappear completely after the fifth day of incubation.

5. Although the mechanical factors described by His help explain the mechanism of growth of the primordial axons in the central nervous system, they do not suffice to explain the later growth of nerve fibers across the mesoderm or to clarify their relations with the myotome and epithelium. As we declared a long time ago, to explain the relationship between nerve and muscle or between central nervous system neurons placed some distance apart we must invoke the presence of specific chemotactic processes. There probably are substances secreted by the myotome, the epithelium, or the nerve cells themselves which excite the ameboid activity of the growth cones while orienting them towards their terminal apparatus.

Moreover, the chemotactic doctrine, first formulated by us in 1892, is no longer a simple unverified hypothesis. On the contrary, there are already numerous observations and experiments that argue in its favor. Setting aside the well-known experiments of Florssman dealing with the tropisms of the central end of regenerating nerves and those which Lugaro and we reported in studies on nerve regeneration, we will mention only the following:

(a) According to Tello,[220] motor plaques regenerate (after sciatic nerve transection) following the arrival of an embryonal fiber possessing a ball or growth cone. This ball, which is the continuation of an unmyelinated nerve branch, is attracted by some substance secreted by the old degenerated plaque. It abandons its pre-existing orienting sheath and travels freely towards the nuclear mass of the muscle fiber where it disperses in a free terminal arborization in contact with the nuclei. We have confirmed these observations.

(b) In his very beautiful research on the transplantation of sensory ganglia, Nageotte[121] often noted that newly-formed nerve branches are greatly attracted by the mass of satellite or subcapsular cells of the neighboring necrotic nuclei, around which they form extremely complicated terminal nets. This fact, of such great theoretical importance, as well as all the recent fundamental discoveries of the French scholar, have been confirmed by my assistant,

Dr. Cardenal, who actually repeated this work on the interesting question of ganglionic transplantation and neuronal metamorphosis.*

The questions Held raised regarding the neuron doctrine requires publication of a separate work, one in which we would examine all the reticular theories (and there are almost as many such theories as there are antineuron theorists). I hope to be able to explain, in accord with the doctrine of neural unity, certain morphological and structural facts that Held, Wolff, and Bielschowsky have presented against the neuron doctrine. We had noted many of these facts in our first research on neurofibrils, but we had passed them by in silence because we had considered them as artifacts produced by the reagents, and we consequently felt them to be devoid of value for the solution of the problem of interneuronal connections. In this work we will try to prove that the diverse neurological schools are separated not by differences of technique, but by divergent scientific logic and philosophical tendencies.

Furthermore, for all the readers who are not theoretically inclined and who know how to exclude doubtful and controversial facts, the positive results of Held's interesting research coincides with ours perfectly. One has only to compare our respective figures showing the unity of origin of axons, the initial phenomena in the growth of neurofibrils, and the early neuroblastic phases to realize that we are confronted by the same objects. Some complementary notions, introduced in the original theory by the Leipzig scholar, e.g., the principal of the shortest path and the supposition of the *vis a tergo* of the fibrillogenetic zone, are even perfectly compatible with the neuron doctrine.

Madrid, November, 1907

---

*We now acknowledge that other hypotheses are plausible. The chemotactic and catalytic explanation which we proposed[198] is only a provisional theory. The reader should examine the alternative hypotheses recently suggested by Harrison, Dustin, Heidenhain, Nageotte, Marinesco, Tello, Ariëns Kappers, and Boeke. (*Note for the French edition.*)

Chapter 3

SOME OBSERVATIONS CONTRARY TO THE "SYNCYTIAL" HYPOTHESIS OF NERVE REGENERATION AND NORMAL NEUROGENESIS [193]

T HE LAST 15 years' research with methods selective for nerve proto-plasm (performed by Purpura, Lugaro, Krassin, Perroncito, Marinesco and Minea, Dustin, Tello, Poscharisky, O. and H. Rossi, Deineka, Ortin and Arcaute, Boeke, and ourselves) have definitively resolved the problem of the origin, growth, and multiplication of the nerve sprouts which penetrate into the peripheral end of transected or avulsed nerves. However in spite of the energy expanded in clarifying all the phases of the regenerative process, some points still remain controversial. These include the origin of the protective sheaths of the newly-formed nerve fascicles which cross the scar and the mechanism of production of new Schwann cells, peritubular membrane of Retzius, and myelin sheath.

Finally, there are several points which we believe definitively resolved, e.g., the initial nudity of the sprouts emerging from the central end and the orienting action produced by the liberation of catalysts at the peripheral end. These catalysts or neurotropic substances excite the outgrowth of nerves. These are points which have recently been revised and discussed by authorities including Boeke, Nageotte and Marinesco, Scaffidi, and Viale.

We do not intend to consider the entire complex problem of nerve regeneration, inasmuch as we have published numerous works on this subject. Moreover, the controversial matters have been discussed in our "Regeneración y degeneración del sistema nervioso,"* result of 6 years of persistent work. Partly because it was in Spanish and partly because it was published during the sad period of the world war, this monograph has attracted little or no attention

---

*Last year an English edition[108] was published under the auspices of Oxford University. (*Note for the French edition.*)

from neurologists, who were naturally absorbed in deep and anxious preoccupations.

For the moment we propose to treat succinctly only one aspect of the large problem of nerve regeneration and neurogenesis. We wish to examine Nageotte and Marinesco's assertion that the recently formed fibers are incapable of traveling alone across the scar and that they require, for orientation, a pre-established pathway of neuroglial fibers (proliferated Schwann cells or apotrophic cells of Marinesco). We hope to ascertain whether it is still legitimate to acknowledge (in spite of the dictum of these scholars) that the initial sprouts travel and are oriented absolutely independently of any ectodermal sheath.

We will therefore deal almost exclusively with the syncytial concept of Nageotte and Marinesco. The exceptional authority which these scholars enjoy, the brilliant neurological discoveries for which they are justly honored (and that we are the first to proclaim and admire), lends a singular transcendence to their opinions. This is the justification for our preference.

Fortunately, our differences are only secondary; they are not absolutely irreconcilable, provided that the syncytial theory is slightly modified. We are pleased therefore to recognize that with regard to the fundamental problems of nerve regeneration and neurogenesis we are in complete or nearly complete agreement. But before opposing the neuroglial syncytial theory by some precise and unequivocal facts gathered both from recent as well as old studies, let us first examine the views of the new supporters of the syncytial concept.

I believe that Boeke [17] was one of the first scholars who, inspired by Held's hypothesis of *Leitzellen* and plasmodesmas, sought to give it an objective foundation in the field of regeneration. But Boeke, who is an excellent observer, only expressed it cursorily and without details in one of his interesting monographs dealing with the experimental union between the lingual nerve (peripheral end) and the hypoglossal (central end). What interests us at the moment is his statement that the nerve sprouts, both those which are dammed up as well as those which are free and wandering in the midst of the scar, always travel by means of a syncytium.

Nageotte has defended the syncytial theory most zealously, persistently and with greatest conviction. He has devoted several interesting communications [123-128] to the process of nerve regeneration and related problems. All these communications contain a multitude of new facts and viewpoints as ingenious as they are suggestive. We shall describe and criticize them later. For the time being it is merely fitting to note the observations related to the theme of this article, condensing them into propositions.

1. When one cuts a nerve the two ends are separated, as is well-known. At the superior end is formed a *neuroma* which is a network of nerve fibers enclosed by a system of neuroglial trabeculae or tracts. Another network of neuroglial tracts, *the glioma,* is formed at the inferior end. The glioma grows until it reaches and blends with the neuroma of the superior end. Later these tracts or bundles are neuritized by the nerve sprouts; the latter never travel freely but are always enclosed in these tubular structures. These neuroglial tubes are of ectodermal origin and result from the proliferation of Schwann cells from the two ends.

2. When one avulses instead of cutting the sciatic nerve of a mammal, in order to prevent neuritization of the peripheral end, in a few days the peripheral end develops a purely neuroglial nerve whose hollow cells lack neurites. This neuroglial nerve advances unceasingly towards the central end. After 15 days, the peripheral glial stump, devoid of axons and made up of tubular anastomotic cells, is already 5 millimeters long.

3. From the preceding it follows that the free progress of the axons through the scar and the peripheral end is purely apparent. Nageotte's neurogenetic formula is categorical: "The neuroglia constructs the nerve and neurites reside there."

4. In Nageotte's drawings and descriptions the neuroglial tracts, stained by iron hematoxylin, appear robust, tubular and longitudinally arranged. They undoubtedly correspond to those demonstrated in a paler fashion by ordinary methods or by neurofibrilllar methods following the seventh and eighth days after transection. Each neuroglial cord or tract may enclose 4, 5 or more young neurites within its intraprotoplasmic sheath. This resembles the arrangement of bundles of sympathetic fibers, each of which is found in-

cluded, according to Nageotte, in a matrix of common protoplasm. Basically, therefore, the process of growth of the nerve bundles across the cicatrix represents a symbiosis between the neurites and the syncytial neuroglial protoplasm.

5. The new fibers emerging from the central end never enter into contact with mesodermal elements, i.e., with so-called fibroblasts; a prematurely and previously differentiated neuroglial sheath is always interposed between them. This type of mesodermal abhorrence is a constant feature in the architecture of adult nerves and in every isolated nerve fiber traveling towards its termination.[127] This French scholar believes that the neurites are naked only when they penetrate the ectodermal epithelium (the interior of the cornea, for example).

6. As corollary to the preceding doctrine, neurotropic or chemotactic influences would be superfluous in the innervation of the peripheral end of interrupted nerves. Granting that the neuroglial nerve necessarily precedes the neuritic one and that no sprout can escape from the confines of the precocious bands or syncytium produced by the migration of the Schwann cells, then the neuritization of the peripheral end becomes automatic. To penetrate into this end, the neurites have need only of being endowed with a great growth capacity; they would move smoothly along in the fashion of a train on its rails, or better, like the water through a conduit.

7. For the same reason it is useless to invoke the action of stereotropism, noted by Harrison, Dustin, Marinesco, Tello, and ourselves. At best, one could acknowledge an intraneuroglial or intratubular stereotropism.

8. Nageotte invokes the same principles for ontogeny: "Regeneration essentially repeats ontogeny." Only recently, cited later, does he speak of it further: "This law is general . . . except, perhaps, for the case of the emergence of the ventral roots during a very brief period of embryonic development."

In his studies on regeneration, Nageotte preferentially studied transverse sections of nerves. His material was generally fixed in Laguèse's fluid and stained by iron hematoxylin and other methods. For silver impregnation he preferentially fixed the specimens in chloral hydrate.

In general, Marinesco [112,113] confirmed Nageotte's results and he accepts the afore-mentioned formula: "The neuroglia constructs the nerve and the neurites reside there." Following some praise for our work on regeneration—for which we thank him sincerely—Marinesco acknowledges that there are gaps or weaknesses, among which he mentions "that we have not observed the Schwann sheaths (or embryonic neuroglia) which surround the young neurites penetrating into the scar." (We will discuss this later.)

According to the illustrious neurologist from Bucharest, every newly formed fiber is enveloped by certain anastomosed cells which derive from the proliferated Schwann cells and which precede the appearance of the nerve sprouts. These elements (the neuroglia of Nageotte) are the apotrophic cells described many years ago by Marinesco. The interstitial pathways which orient the fibers in the cicatrix according to Dustin's theory of odogenesis,[32] are replaced by the intraprotoplasmic spaces of the Schwann or apotrophic cells from the central end. In this way, as we have said above, neurotropism is unnecessary. However, Marinesco does not absolutely deny the existence of neurotropic sources, but he claims that in most cases it is the Schwann syncytium which acts to orient the newly formed fibers and to assist their nutritive exchanges. Only in the nerve terminations (motor plaques, sensory apparatuses, etc.) would neurotropism play a role. The Rumanian scholar is thus inclined towards the opinions of Harrison and Heidenhain.

Although favoring Nageotte's theory in principle, Marinesco does not formulate it in such absolute terms, nor does he generalize to normal neurogenesis. "Ontogeny," he says, "is not the same as nerve regeneration." He bases his very prudent reservations on Tello's observations of regeneration in the retina and the brain, in which the sprouts evidently travel freely, and on *in vitro* nerve culture experiments (Harrison and his students). Marinesco himself, while substantiating this disparity between neurogenesis and regeneration, recalls that in his experiments with cultures of ganglia, the new fibers travel freely in the plasma, often adhering to filaments of fibrin or to cells of uncertain origin. The interesting tissue culture experiments of Levi with chick embryos [101] could also be cited in support of his reservations. The Italian scholar has seen neurites grow freely by means of an ameboid movement (already suspected for a long time by Lenhossék and ourselves). These cultured neurites are sometimes united in such a way as to give an anastomotic appearance, and they also can emit collaterals which grow without the assistance of guardian cells.

Marinesco then comes to grips with a very interesting series of questions which constitute the most interesting and provocate portion of his work: 1. Are differences of electrical potential between the central and peripheral end a determinant of the advance and orientation of the sprouts? (In this regard one should recall the experiments of Scaffidi and of Viale, cited by Marinesco, as well as the suggestions of Ariëns Kappers's school which attempt to clarify the phylogenetic displacement of the bulbar nuclei.) 2. What are the transformations in the fine structure of the neurofibrils during the regenerative process? 3. What is the role of the oxidases contained within the neural protoplasm, and what are the possible trophic influences of the catalysts* elaborated by the Schwann syncytium or neuroglial tracts of Nageotte? We will discuss these fascinating questions elsewhere.

Since we desire to be brief and to avoid repetition of facts and arguments already stated in previous works, we will examine the principal assertions of the above-mentioned scholars without further preamble.

1. Identification of the proliferated Schwann cells as neuroglial cells. We are perhaps faced by a semantic question. Although "a rose by any other name would smell as sweet," there are occasions when excessive generalization of a word can lead to confusions and ambiguities that should be avoided.

It is evident that Nageotte identifies, or at least homologizes, the Schwann cell of normal peripheral nerves with the ectodermal neuroglia of the central nervous system. He also considers the sheath of the nerve bundles or fascicles appearing in the scar as

---

*We too have supported, as a provisional hypothesis, the supposition that neurotropic substances may only be catalysts whose function is to accelerate the assimilation and growth of the sprouts which have penetrated into their radius of diffusion.[198]

being glial and, therefore, ectodermal. Marinesco designates these enveloping elements as apotrophic cells.

The morphologic and structural features which distinguish the glial cells of the central nervous system from the true Schwann cells are so numerous and well-known that repeating them here in detail would fatigue the reader. I will limit myself to recalling that none of the specific methods devised for staining the neuroglia of the central nervous system (those of Weigert, Anglade, Alzheimer, Achucarro, our gold with sublimate, Rio-Hortega's ammoniacal silver carbonate, the modifications of the Bielschewsky procedure, etc.) stain the Schwann elements or the perifascicular syncytium of the cicatrix of cut nerves. Permit me also to note that the glia of the central nervous system, whose soma is very poor in protoplasm, encloses a rudimentary Golgi apparatus (visible only in young animals), whereas the nucleus of the Schwann cell is surrounded by a reticular apparatus of great extent and richness. For brevity we omit many other quite fundamental differences.

Since the term Schwann cell seems improper even for adult fibers (as well as from the historical viewpoint) and since that of neuroglia does not seem appropriate either for the adult phase or for the components of the syncytium of the scar, then why should we not adopt the word lemmoblast (proposed many years ago by Lenhossék) or any other designation which simply describes its peculiar morphology as perineuritic sheath without presupposing still problematical functions? Among other terms which could be accepted, I propose that of symphonocyte and, better yet, that of choleocyte (from Χολες, sheath).

2. During the first developmental phases, every isolated sprout arising from the central end of a cut or avulsed nerve travels freely, either across exudates, among connective tissue cells, or along embryonic fibroblasts, by virtue of the well-known phenomenon of stereotropism. This is clearly observed during early regenerative phenomena (phenomena studied by Perroncito, Marinesco, and ourselves) before Nageotte's syncytial tracts are yet differentiated. In this way do we answer the friendly objection of the Bucharest neurologist "of not having noted apotrophic cells which premature-

ly precede and accompany every neurite penetrating the cicatrix."
How could we have noted them if their presence is not demonstrable
(from the second to the fifth day after transection) by any method
including the one Nageotte preferentially used? Nageotte's method
only clearly outlines the tract at a relatively late stage.

In Figure 54 we reproduce a nerve whose neurilemma has been
crushed by the pressure of forceps. The pieces were fixed in pyridine two days after the operation. The afore-mentioned perineural

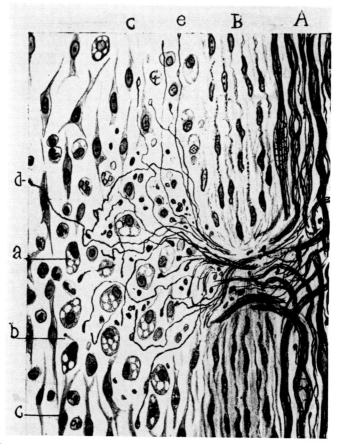

Fig. 54. Peripheral portion of a nerve crushed between forceps (semi-
schematic figure). Young cat killed 2 days after the operation. A) Tangential
axons in a productive phase; B) perineural exudate through which many axonal
sprouts travel; a) granular cell; b) neurite seen end on; c) fibroblast.

inflammatory exudate still persists. Many leucocytes, some granular cells (a), and several embryonic fibroblasts (c) are clearly delineated. There is not the slightest trace of a synctium. Across a crack or fissure in the neurilemma, rush a multitude of exploratory fibers as well as several bundles of neurites arising from stimulated axons of the central end of the nerve. Note that all the precocious neurites, without exception, travel freely across the inflammatory exudate, and that some of them terminate in small masses (d). Many of the growth *boutons* are free during and after crossing the neurilemma, thus illustrating the phenomenon of nervous autonomy of which we have spoken in previous publications. Since within two days the Schwann cells have not yet multiplied, and consequently the giant neuroglial sheaths of Nageotte are not yet formed, we consider it indisputable that the sprouts travel freely in the region of the injured nerve. Focussing with the oil immersion objective on a fiber seen end-on (b), it is impossible to perceive any trace of syncytial protoplasm around it.

Figure 55 is also highly suggestive. It is from a rabbit whose sciatic nerve has been completely cut, after a loose ligature had been previously placed a short distance above the lesion. This ligature has not been an obstacle to the production of sprouts traveling across the scar; it has only succeeded in slightly retarding the outgrowth of the first exploratory fibers. The animal was sacrificed 4.5 days after the operation, i.e., before the appearance of Nageotte's large orienting sheaths. A remainder of inflammatory exudate separates the young fibroblasts (A) which are stained an intense brown tone by silver. This separation greatly facilitates tracing the sprouts through the mesoderm (b, c, e). On studying the preparation with oil immersion objectives, *it is not possible to recognize any protoplasmic sheath around the exploratory axons,* and the same is true when the examination is performed without diaphragm as well as with one of the larger ones. In general, the fibers travel perpendicularly to the direction of the fibroblasts, frequently hurdling long protoplasmic spaces (b). However, from time to time some stereotropic phenomena are noted (Fig. 55, a, g). Occasional examples of autoneurotomy are also observed.

There are regions where stereotropism is considerably more

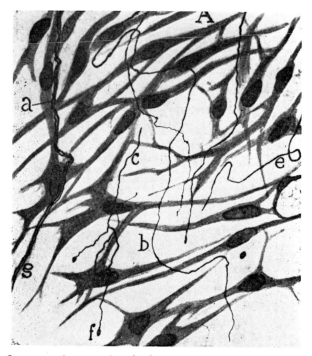

Fig. 55. Scar near the central end of a transected nerve which was ligated a short distance from the transection. The animal was killed 4.5 days after the operation. A) Fibroblasts; a) neurites which travel along fibroblasts; b, c, e) other naked neurites which travel through the plasma; f) fiber terminated by a small mass.

frequent (Fig. 56). Some neurites travel along the two sides of a fibroblast or of pairs of fibroblasts (a, c). In f, b, is seen a fiber which, after having flanked a connective tissue cell, turns backwards to accompany another traveling in a retrograde direction. Along its path the fiber presents a detention thickening. Finally, in e, is noted a neurite with a degenerative ball.*

In reality, a more or less complete cicatrical syncytium is seen in the preceding two preparations but, let us repeat, this syncytium composed exclusively of ordinary fibroblasts. It is impossible to perceive continuity of such fusiform or stellate cells with the

*In a recent work[196] we demonstrate the complete independence of the nerve sprouts up to 5 days after nerve transection.

Schwann elements of the two nerve ends. The interior of these cells do not exhibit any indication of cavitation. We therefore consider it infinitely probable that all these cells represent proliferated connective tissue cells and not the progeny of migrated neuroglial or Schwann elements.

3. The neuroglial sheaths of Nageotte are late formations, appearing only from the sixth to the eighth day after nerve transection. At this time the cicatrix has been invaded not only by exploratory fibers but also by sturdy fascicles of neurites which arise, as we have demonstrated, from the unraveling of the nerve branches of the cut axons.[198] The sheaths therefore do not precede the bundles but, on the contrary, are the result of the formation of the latter. All of our research on regeneration confirms this opinion

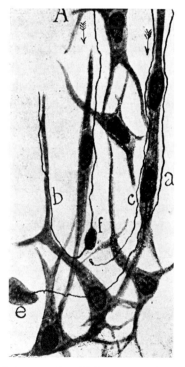

Fig. 56. A region of the scar in which stereotropism was evident. A) direction of the central end; a, b, c) neurites resting upon fibroblasts; e) mass of detention; f) thickening along the pathway.

which, as is known, has been subsequently defended with more or less abundant proof by Ranvier, Vanlair, Perroncito, Dustin, Marinesco (in his first studies), H. and O. Rossi, Sala, Tello, and ourselves. My recent experiments show moreover, that when the fascicles invade the scar precociously (from the second to the fourth day) they still lack a protective sheath. The sheaths appear at the seventh or eighth day and are as well revealed by Nageotte's methods as by certain reduced silver nitrate formulas.

Our opinion does not differ greatly from Nageotte's as regards the differentiation and origin of the neuroglial sheaths and tracts. We shall cite what we initially wrote about this problem (the most obscure one of the regenerative process in our opinion) in our now frequently cited work on Degeneration and Regeneration. [198] After having described the hypothesis that the sheaths in question derive from the mesoderm, we said, in support of Nageotte's ectodermal hypothesis:

"Let us confess, nevertheless, that the unitary (neuroglial) theory has the advantage of simplicity. Both theories explain the facts well but, lacking categorical objective proof, the mind is always led by a desire for unity. Let us therefore see how one can imagine the production of periaxonal sheaths by this hypothesis. As a rule, the Schwann cell of the central end gives rise to a great number of daughter cells. Some of the latter would be dedicated to initiating the myelin reabsorption, perhaps dying after fulfilling their mission. Others would be restricted to augmenting the number of cells which now make up the Schwann membrane of the interior of the old nerve. They would line the limiting sheath of the fascicle and, by migration, the sheath of the bundles traveling across the scar. Others, finally, still less abundant, would multiply rapidly and intertwine with the nerve sprouts and, migrating with them across the mesodermal formations, would be converted into Schwann cells of the axons in the cicatrix. Thus there would be two migrations: one *external,* perifascicular, giving rise to the sheaths of the bundles in the scar; the other, *internal* or intrafascicular forming the sheaths around each fiber."

However, despite the important contributions of Nageotte and Marinesco, I acknowledge that my doubts about the origin of these cells are not entirely dissipated. I have increasingly less faith in the histogenetic specificity of the germ layers, especially in view of my own observations and those of Tello.* In the mesoderm of the 3 day chick embryo many visceral nerve cells are differentiated at the level of the pleuroperitoneal endothelium. Dogiel showed that some of these cells possess dendrons and a true neurite. I would not therefore be surprised if some author succeeded in demonstrating that the Schwann cell and its allies (the cicatricial syncytium of Nageotte or the apotrophic cells) were merely simple mesodermal structures which have arrived at an extreme degree of differentiation because of their symbiosis with the neurites. It is certainly true that the mesoderm gives rise to several specific cell types which differ structurally and functionally, e.g., muscle fibers, fibroblasts, red blood cells, ova, and sperm.

4. Once fasciculation has begun and, consequently, the sheaths have formed, the neuritic contingent increases by the arrival of new fibers from the central end. These late neurites are incorporated into the pre-existing fascicle either by originating from the same axon and becoming encased by the same sheath, or by ramification of the pre-existing intrafascicular neurites, or by a type of attraction exerted by every axon over nearby errant axons. We have termed this phenomenon *reciprocal neurotropism;* it is perhaps merely a modality of stereotropism.

But even at this late stage when the immense majority of fibers, ensheathed or not, are arranged in fascicles protected by a membrane, some denuded errant axons are found undergoing turgescence or divisory irritation. We illustrated several examples of these in our first work on nerve regeneration. In order not to dwell on this point too much, let it suffice to reproduce a figure published in 1905 which shows that only the bundles of neurites and not the recently formed twigs possess an enveloping sheath (Fig. 57).

5. In embryos the initial exploratory fibers also travel in isolated fashion through the mesoderm. Only later, when other neurites are added by virtue of reciprocal stereotropism, is the enveloping sheath differentiated, as has been well described by Lenhossék,

─────────────

*Work in progress by Tello in which he refutes the old hypothesis of the ectodermal origin of the visceral sympathetic system.

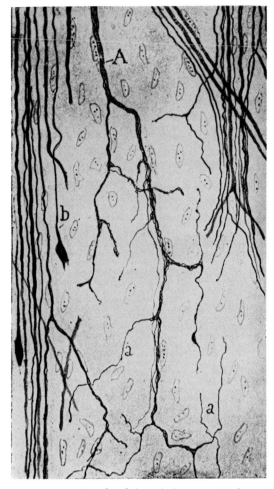

Fig. 57. Scar between the 2 ends of the sciatic nerve 10 days after nerve transection and ligation of the central segment. Note how the fascicles (A) possess enveloping cells, while the fine terminal filamaments (a) in the cicatrix do not possess them.

Held, and others. As proof of this statement we could cite almost all of our neurogenetic observations made on the 12 to 14 day old chick embryo. The reader who is interested in this point should consult the figures and descriptions published in our work refuting the theory of Hensen-Held,[179,183] the admirable neurogenetic re-

search of Tello [223] on the differentiation of the sensory nerve terminations in muscles, tendons and Paccinian organs, and finally, our
recent observations on the genesis of intraepithelial sensory and
special sense nerve ramifications.[192] It would be equally useful to
read the older monographs of His, Kölliker, Lugaro, Grahm Kerr,
and Lenhossék.

Careful examination of the preparations utilized in the afore-
mentioned investigations reveals that every fiber seeking a terminal
territory travels absolutely denuded through the mesodermal interstices. Only in slightly later phases of development does the still
solitary neurite appear surrounded by a nucleated protective sheath.

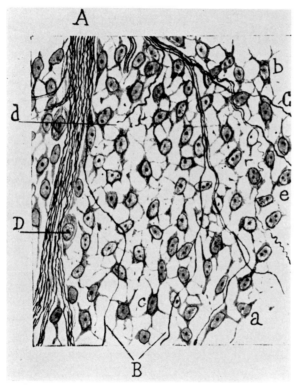

Fig. 58. Section of the trigeminal region in which the ophthalmic branch
is developing. Three day chick embryo. A) Voluminous fascicle; B) isolated
nerve fascicles travelling across protoplasmic interstices; c, e) anastomosed
fibroblasts.

The origin of this sheath is enigmatic. It is seen considerably before the differentiation of the Schwann cell and the myelin sheath (*vitreous sheath* of Vanlair).

To avoid repeating observations already described in works dealing with this fact, we will restrict ourselves to two new demonstrations. But first it is fitting to make certain technical remarks.

Sections impregnated with reduced silver nitrate generally have a serious inconvenience, especially when pyridine is employed as fixative. The neurites stand out strongly colored against a background of pale fibroblasts and a barely perceptible perineural sheath. On the other hand, in sections vigorously stained by hematoxylin or the anilines (and the same is true of iron hematoxylin after prior Laguèse fixation) the syncytial sheaths are outlined more or less correctly but the neurites are not seen at all or are only barely visible. It follows therefore that neither the first procedure, which Held used, nor the second, which His and the proponents of the catenary theory employed, furnish absolutely clear, unambiguous pictures.

But, fortunately, there are some instances in which the reduced silver nitrate vigorously stains both the neurites and the perineural web. These are the only preparations appropriate for clarifying this problem. Furthermore, the nuclear and protoplasmic staining of the fibroblasts and of the perifascicular cells can be intensified in a strongly selective hematoxylin bath.*

One other favorable condition from which we have profited is the looseness of the connective tissue across which the sprouts travel. In most regions this web, fashioned of fibroblasts, appears so compact and so intimately associated with the errant neurites that it becomes difficult to determine the true location of the neurites in relation to the fibroblasts or to the far-off migrating ectodermal cells (lemmoblasts of Lenhossék). Fortunately there are some regions in which the fibroblasts and lemmoblasts are scattered across

---

*A good nuclear and protoplasmic staining is very often obtained in sections fixed exclusively in alcohol or in chloral hydrate. However, we possess some sections in which the mesodermal cells appear stained even after pyridine fixation, provided that the mesoderm consists of a loose connective tissue web surrounded by an abundant interstitial plasma.

ample spaces filled with plasma. In such regions it is easy to determine the connections of the young neurites. These favorable regions are found especially in the places where the arachnoidal cavity will later differentiate or where noncartilagenous bone will be formed (e.g., region of emergence of the facial, trigeminal, ophthalmic and suborbital nerve). These propitious conditions are found in the sections copied in Figures 58, 59 and 60.

Figure 58 represents a section of the head of a 3 day chick embryo at the level of the termination of the trigeminal nerve. One perceives the very well stained embryonic connective web with anastomoses (*Leitzellen* and plamodesmas of Held) among which appear hollows filled with plasma (a,b). The nerve trunks of moderate caliber (A) undoubtedly possess a cellular sheath, perhaps homologous to that which Nageotte designates the neuroglial tract; but on the other hand, all the isolated fibers lack a cellular sheath and are independent of the neighboring syncytium (Fig. 58, B, C). It is especially important to note two peculiarities in this drawing: 1. It is impossible, even with the best objectives and employing a large diaphragm, to observe any indication of marginal nuclei or of a protoplasmic sheath beside the independent neurites, even though the enveloping cells of the nerve fascicles appear well impregnated. 2. The journey of the fibers, in great part free in plasma spaces, appears rectilinear or slightly curved, not sinuous or zig-zag, as would be inevitable if they were traveling across plasmodesmas. 3. Finally, it seems highly improbable that the fine expansions of the fibroblasts, some even as subtle as the young neurites, could contain an interior conduit that the best objectives are incapable of revealing.

Still more expressive are Figures 59 and 60 taken from a 2 centimeter cat embryo at the level of the emergence of the oculomotor fibers. The path and position of the neurites relative to the mesodermal syncytium is clearly and sharply revealed in Figure 59. Just as in the previous figure the early fascicles, rich in fibers, show some marginal nuclei, although it is impossible to state whether they constitute a continuous or discontinuous tube. On the other hand, all the neurites detached from the fascicles (a, b, and c) appear absolutely denuded. These isolated neurites cross the perime-

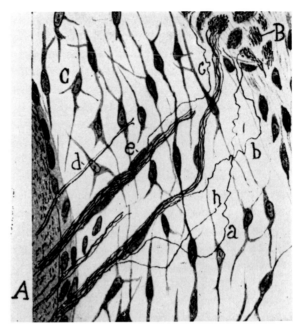

Fig. 59.   Site of emergence of the oculomotor fibers of a 2 cm cat embryo. A)
Pons enveloped by a rudiment of the pia mater; B) transverse section of the
oculomotor fascicles; C) fibroblasts; a, b, c, d) isolated naked fibers which become incorporated into the nerve; e) enveloping cells or lemmoblasts.

dullary web, becoming incorporated into the principal contingent
of the nerve, which appears cut in B. The oil immersion objective
does not enable us to discover any vestige of protoplasmic sheath
around them. It is important to note that we are not dealing with
strayed or lost fibers, but rather with solitary neurites which, although separated from the principal fascicles, end up by being well
oriented, since almost all succeed in being incorporated in the nerve
trunk. Finally, it is not superfluous to mention one highly significant
arrangement which also appears in Figure 60: There is no parallelism
between the direction of the connective cells and that of the wandering neurites. The latter preferentially travel perpendicularly to
the expansions of the fibroblasts. However, we do not wish to deny
the existence of some stereotropic phenomena.

Stereotropism is especially manifest in Figure 60, drawn to a larger scale than Figure 59. Note how some fibers upon leaving the pons (A) adjoin the walls of a wrinkled vessel (e). In this figure, which is also at the level of the oculomotor nerve, some isolated and absolutely denuded nerve fibers (a, b, c, d) are seen. Although they have traveled across plasmatic spaces, these fibers have not lost their route, since some of them become incorporated again into the most distal portion of the nerve fascicles. Furthermore, just as in the preceding figures, one notes the presence of marginal cells around some large bundles (g). Except for their orientation these cells are certainly not differentiated in any way from the other embryonic connective tissue cells. Let us add that a

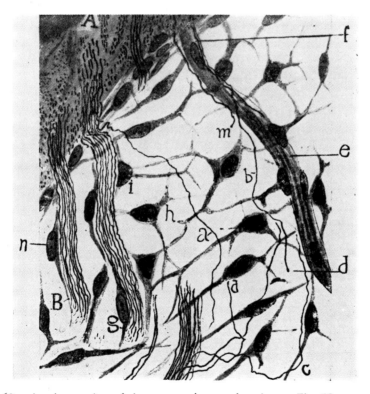

Fig.60. Another section of the same embryo and region as Fig. 59 at greater magnification. A) Pons; B) fascicles of the oculomotor nerve; a, b, d) isolated neurites; e) capillary; g, n) precocious lemmoblasts surrounding the fascicles; h) fibroblast; m) neurites which border the capillary.

compact layer of flattened cells is found around the pons, constituting the probable germ of the future *pia mater.*

6. After trauma to the central nervous system, especially to the spinal cord, the white matter frequently emits fibers which, without the assistance of Nageotte's neuroglia (proliferated Schwann cells) or of Marinesco's apotrophic elements, grow far beyond the pia mater or to the interior of the ependyma. In our book on regeneration [198] we cited numerous examples of axonal growth that is totally unrelated, at least initially, to the immediate orienting influence of Schwann cells. These instances are so significant and so conclusive that it is not without great astonishment, bitterness, and disillusion that we see the disdain and the neglect with which they are treated by the new catenary school. We prefer to believe that they have not read our works or the beautiful experiments of Tello, who has succeeded for the first time in carrying out the virtually impossible exploit of endowing the apathetic and inert cerebral neurites with enormous regenerative power. This oversight is certainly excusable, since the Spanish language is barely familiar to scholars. So far as we know, only Marinesco has paid some attention to these surprising facts.

We will not reproduce here in detail the theoretically important evidence to which we are alluding, for that would oblige us to lengthen this work indefinitely. I will limit myself to recommending to the proponents of the orienting syncytium and to the adversaries of neurotropism that they read the following: 1. the chapters of my work on regeneration [198] which describe axons of the dorsal funiculus that travel and ramify profusely across embryonic perimedullary connective tissue (Vol. 2, Figs. 217 and 221) and those sections which describe the innervation of the ventral roots by axonal branches emerged from the ventral funiculus (Fig. 61, e, b); 2. the afore-mentioned experiments of Tello who has induced cerebral axons to grow over great distances by using grafts of pieces of peripheral stump or pieces of mouse spinal cord impregnated with fluid extracted from the mature peripheral stump; 3. the no less expressive observations of Tello [221] and Ortin and Arcaute [135] (recently confirmed in birds by Urra), who have demonstrated that although retinal axons are ordinarily incapable of regenerating, they can grow enormously under certain conditions, crossing all the retinal layers and going beyond the choroid; 4. my observations on the production of artificial denuded sensory nerves in transplanted ganglia—the violence of growth of these nerves causes them to perforate the robust ganglionic capsule and spread

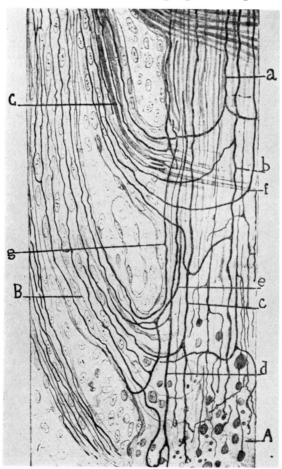

Fig. 61   Spinal cord of a young cat in which some motor root fascicles were injured by cord transection. Note how many of the fibers of the ventral funiculus ramify opposite the motor roots and send very long sprouts toward them. This fact, besides demonstrating the neurotropic power of degenerated ventral roots, shows that the sprouts can travel freely in the cord, without the assistance of Schwann cells.

across the scar (Fig. 63, A); 5. my works on retrograde motor innervation of the spinal cord after transection of the ventral roots
(Fig. 62, F, G).[186] In all of these instances, and in many others, the
syncytial or apotrophic cells are either absolutely lacking or else
lie so far from the region of emanation of the newly formed axon

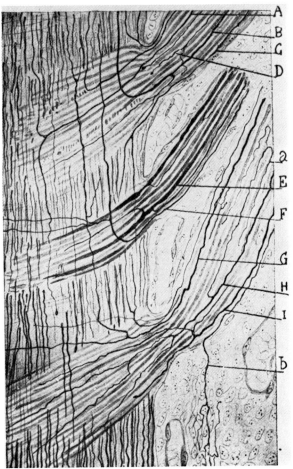

Fig. 62. Invasion of the spinal cord by retrograde motor collaterals arising
from the extraspinal pathway of the ventral roots. Several-day-old cat killed 4
days after spinal cord transection. A, B, C, D) Recurrent motor branches which
are invading the spinal cord. They arise from ventral roots which were transected not a great distance away. During regeneration, the ends of these roots
project sprouts both proximally and distally.

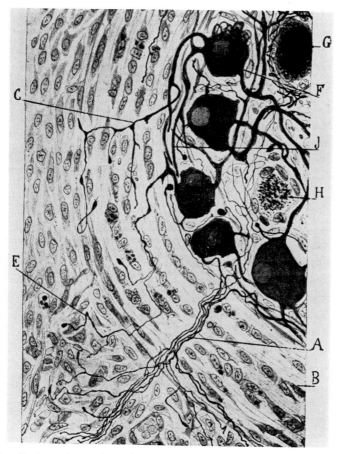

Fig. 63. Prolongations arising from the neurons of a grafted sensory ganglion. The recipient of the graft (young dog) was killed 5 days after the operation. A) Aberrent nerve which crosses the connective tissue capsule, without any cellular retinue, and is distributed throughout the cicatrix; B) capsule of the ganglion.

that it is necessary to invoke an action at a distance, either from the embryonic connective tissue or from the bands of Büngner of more or less degenerated nerves. The afore-mentioned facts demonstrate, moreover, that the young enlarging and growing axons possess an enormous power of penetration, in the face of which some obstacles, which would seem insurmountable *a priori,* often give way.

7. Within the peripheral end of cut nerves, a great number of the penetrating sprouts travel freely among the Schwann tubes, as we demonstrated many years ago (1905). The same is true of neurites invading grafts interposed in the nervous cicatrix. This is not only true for fresh grafts [198] but also for those preserved many days *in vitro,* as Tello [222] demonstrated. His interesting experiments on nerve transplantation confirm, in principle, experiments performed a long time ago by Nageotte.[122]

8. The young axons are capable of growing and ramifying across nutrient plasma without the assistance of any kind of satellite cells. All the nerve culture experiments of Harrison and his disciples, as well as those of Marinesco, Levi, and others indisputably demonstrate that neurites can grow and ramify in blood plasma. As regards growth across clots and exudates, that was demonstrated by Perroncito and by us a long time ago.

Concerning neuritic growth in ependymal liquid, allow us to recall that every time an embryonic neuroblast or axon falls by

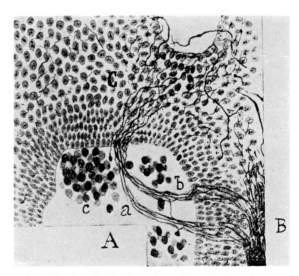

Fig. 64. Portion of a longitudinal section of a tadpole whose spinal cord has been transected. The animal was killed 12 days after the operation. A) Very dilated ependymal cavity; B) regenerating fibers of the ventrolateral funiculus; C) region of the spinal cicatrix crossed by the sprouts; a, b) newly-formed bundles which cross the ependymal fluid without becoming disoriented.

chance into the central cavity of the spinal cord and medulla, the functional process becomes oriented, in spite of some initial hesitation, and directs itself to its destination (Figs. 44 and 45). For the moment we will note that this is also true for batrachian larvae, as Lorente de Nó [103] recently demonstrated in my laboratory. After the spinal cord had been partially or completely transected, great ependymal dilatations were created (Fig. 64). Near the cicatrix (C) two fascicles of newly formed fibers, arising from the ventrolateral funiculus, cross the wall of epithelial cells, traverse the ventricular liquid which has been increased in quanity by the exudate, penetrate the cord and dispersed at the level of the cicatrix (C), where ramifications and balls of arrest are seen. In their route across the ventricle no cell accompanies the axons (the swollen portions of the latter are thickenings due to delays in growth). The axons are oriented as though they were attracted by some substance poured into the ventricle by the cicatrix or by the interrupted region of the spinal cord. We possess numerous sections made by Lorente de Nó which show similar phenomena of intraventricular straying followed by realignment more or less congruent to the lost route.

9. During the first phases of ontogentetic development in the central nervous system the axons grow and are admirably oriented in the white and gray matter without the assistance of Schwann cells or neuroglial elements. The latter and the former differentiate considerably after the basic architectonic plan of the nerve paths and principal interneuronal connections have been effected. It consequently seems extremely improbable that the congruent growth of neurites in the central nervous system would be effected without the aid of *Leitzellen* or of a Schwann syncytium, while the peripheral axons, endowed even in the adult state with an extraordinary capacity for growth and regeneration, require mechanical guardians in order to arrive at their destination.

Proof of the preceding doctrine can be found in almost all the neurogenetic works from the time of Golgi, Kölliker, Lenhossék, van Gehuchten, Lugaro, Retzius, Athias, and ourselves (all performed with the Golgi method) up to those performed with the neurofibrillar procedures.

GENERAL CONSIDERATIONS AND CONCLUSIONS

When investigators of great technical ability and thoroughly demonstrated neurological knowledge and experience maintain improbable interpretations, it can only be that their judgment, so lucid and shrewd on other occasions, must have been disturbed in one or more of the following three ways: utilization of inappropriate methods; misleading appearance of fortuitous facts; or, finally, fascinating attraction of some guiding hypothesis which lacks and distorts objective reality.

In our modest opinion, all three afore-mentioned disturbing influences have united in the syncytial concept. The seducing hypothesis has been the catenary theory which, driven from its first line of defense, now takes refuge in the trench of the *catena neuroglica* or syncytial Schwann cells, where it is protected by the great authority of Held and other scholars. It is only fair to note that in Nageotte's case the doctrine of the continuity of the Schwann cells of normal myelinated and unmyelinated fibers has greater influence on his present attitude than the rash lucubrations of Held.

This is not the occasion to examine this point which appears in the program of my future investigations. I will only note that up to now all my efforts to demonstrate the said continuity have failed, even after employing very vigorous and selective impregnation procedures. It will therefore be prudent for us to continue to retain the old concept of Ranvier inasmuch as this question has not been resolved definitively.

The methodological inadequacy or inappropriateness this time resides in the failure to have examined early regenerative phenomena in the central stump, or of only having given lesser consideration to these early phases. Under favorable circumstances some naked exploratory neurites (and even isolated fascicles) tipped by masses or fusiform enlargements, penetrate into the exudate as early as the second day after the lesion. This occurs prior to any migration of Schwann cells. And if these early phases of regeneration had been examined by Nageotte, could this scholar have been led into the error of taking a simple stereotropic phenomenon as evidence of an intraprotoplasmic or intrasyncytial position of young neurites? It is evident that such an illusion becomes impossible when the enormous syncytial tubes or fascicular sheaths are formed only after the seventh day following nerve transection.

Another possible cause of error has been Nageotte's excessive use of transverse sections, a misleading procedure which we employed, not without great risk, in our first studies on regeneration. Among other inconveniences, it has the very grave one of preventing one from discerning the origin of the nerve sprouts and perifascicular sheaths. Moreover, in view of the almost inevitable doubling back of the nerve ends and the difference in level of each fascicle (some descend more than others within the scar), it becomes very easy to consider bundles coming from the central end, or fascicles too high above the peripheral end, as a prematurely differentiated tubular syncytium. By that we do not mean to deny that as expert and wise an investigator as Nageotte did not make use of longitudinal sections and various known techniques as additional proof.

CONCLUSIONS

1. Both in ontogenetic development as well as in nerve regeneration, the first sprouts or neurites penetrating the mesodermal tissues (Harrison's exploratory axon) travel freely across cellular interstices.

2. By virtue of reciprocal stereotropism, each exploratory fiber is joined by several other similarly directed ones. In this way the nerve fascicles which wander across the cicatrix are formed.

3. After several days (3 or 4 in the chick embryo, 6 to 8 in the regenerative process) a nucleated membrane appears around the nerve fascicles. The origin of this membrane in the embryo is still unknown, despite the numerous investigations performed to clarify this question.* During the regenerative process, it could very well

---

*In agreement with His, Kölliker, Graham Kerr and other scholars, we defended the mesodermal origin of the Schwann cells during ontogeny.[179] In truth, the interesting experiments and observations of Harrison and of von Lenhossék later spread doubt in our mind. But now, in view of much more demonstrative preparations than those obtained earlier and those obtained recently in the chick embryo by Tello, we unreservedly take sides in support of the mesodermal origin of the *lemmoblasts* or *choleoblasts* (Schwann cells). They could well emerge, as Tello maintains, from the cellular sheath which envelops the central nervous system during the first developmental phases. These cells, once differentiated and infiltrated into the nerves, would perhaps constitute a specific type capable of proliferating indefinitely and of retaining the newly acquired properties.

arise from the Schwann cells which proliferate from the central stump, as Marinesco and Nageotte plausibly suggest.

4. This early sheath truly represents the rudiment of the laminar membrane (Henle's sheath in isolated fibers). Undoubtedly the tubular syncytium, revealed by iron hematoxylin and the neurofibrillar methods, corresponds to this membrane.

5. Some time after nerve injury (from 6 days on) or after the beginning of development (at the end of the third or fourth day), the isolated axons (not including the tardy fibers) also appear surrounded by a nucleated sheath.

6. The origin of the Schwann cells or of the individual sheaths of each fiber of a fascicle is a problem not yet definitively resolved. One can nevertheless accept the reasonable histogenetic mechanism recently described by Nageotte for regenerated nerves.

7. The regenerated fascicles provided with a nucleated sheath increase in thickness as do developing embryonic nerve fascicles. This is brought about by the arrival of numerous batches of tardy axons which, by homotactism or reciprocal stereotropism, make use of the prematurely differentiated sheaths.

8. We still question Nageotte's opinion that, with the prevention of the immediate union of the ends of a transected nerve, the neuroglial nerve always precedes the neuritic one. In our preparations, when the fiber tracts are clearly differentiated in the cicatrix or near to the distal end, the neurites in their interior are found to be proportionately more numerous as the syncytial funiculus appears thicker.

9. Nageotte's reducing theory in unquestionable in many cases, viz.: that every adult nerve fiber is separated from the mesoderm by a syncytial border of ectodermal origin. This theory could only attain the status of a law if one could demonstrate that all nerve arborizations (motor plaques, musculotendinous organs of Golgi, Paccini, Meissner, etc.) were surrounded by ectodermal formations. Our recent observations on the genesis of sensory terminations,[192] and the older ones of Tello seem hard to reconcile with this statement.

10. The results of the investigations of Nageotte and Marinesco are reconcilable in principle with our concept of the normal and

pathological neurogenetic mechanism, provided that one acknowledges that the syncytium is formed, not before the exploratory neurites, but somewhat afterwards, and that it adapts itself to the nerve
fascicles. The two views can be further reconciled by conceding
greater importance to neurotropic influences, in order to explain
the congruent growth and orientation of the sprouts and isolated
fascicles and their arrival at the peripheral end. It is unnecessary
to add that we do not claim to prejudge the physicochemical nature
of neurotropism, a question which only future biochemical investigations will be able to resolve definitively.

Madrid, February, 1921

Part II

PERIPHERAL NERVE
TERMINATIONS

THE MECHANISM OF DEVELOPMENT OF INTRAEPITHELIAL, SENSORY AND SPECIAL SENSE NERVE TERMINATIONS [192]

T HIS WORK, intended to describe the movement, growth, and genesis of intraepithelial terminations, can be considered a sequel to our previous communication.[191] From the point of view of neuro-genetic mechanism, it is complementary to the very important re-search of Tello [223] on the neurogenesis of motor plaques and cer-tain terminal sensory apparatuses.

We make no attempt to analyze all phases of the developmental process of nerve terminations, nor to describe their adult arrangement. The latter subject has been extensively studied by the staining techniques of Golgi, Ehrlich, gold chloride, and the various silver salt formulas. The following observations aim at gathering data concerning the mechanism of growth and orientation of the nerve terminations during the phase preceding their definitive formation. We therefore omit the initial and the final phases of nerve develop-ment.

At present the neurotropic theory is undergoing modification and improvement. Attempts to define this notion precisely in terms of specific physicochemical conditions are found in the relatively recent works of Kappers, Boeke, Tello, Scaffidi, Viale and Marinesco. In a very recent work on nerve regeneration, Marinesco [113] endeavors to relate the outgrowth of sprouts from the central end to the action of organic and inorganic ferments (iron, which can act as a catalyst, is included among the latter). In our review, *Degeneration and Re-generation of the Nervous System* [198] we noted the vague and equivo-cal nature of the neurotropic concept and tried to make it more ob-jective, comprehensible, and clear by supposing that the active sub-stances or elements which attract the nerve sprouts are enzymatic. "The substance of the growth cone and the neurotropic ferments of the tissues are perhaps comparable respectively—let us say—to the antigens and antibodies studied in bacteriology." In another work [186] we also assert: "As a tentative hypothesis, one could suppose that the substances contained in the Schwann sheath of the peripheral end may not be immutable . . . but are ferments or catalytic agents, stimulating the assimilation of the axonal protoplasm and incapable of being used up in the reaction with the nerve protoplasm (growth cone)."

Materials and Methods. Our neurogenetic observations have dealt with avian and mammalian (mouse and rabbit) embryos, especially rodent fetuses near term and at birth. In fact the intraepithelial nerve terminations are initiated in the period immediately prior or just subsequent to birth. Of all laboratory mammals, we have preferred the white mouse (used for some time now by London) because of the facility with which specimens in all phases of neural development can be obtained.

As specific impregnation procedure we have employed reduced silver nitrate after fixation in ammoniacal alcohol or in 70 percent pyridine (with subsequent alcohol treatment). In some cases, after ammoniacal alcohol fixation, we combined the metallic impregnation with routine nuclear stains. This is not absolutely necessary, as Tello has noted, since the impregnation procedure ordinarily stains the nuclei strongly and the protoplasm sufficiently selectively in the manner of a good hematoxylin preparation. Alcohol-pyridine fixation (pyridine, 3 parts: alcohol, 5 parts) also furnishes excellent results; with this formula the nuclei and young axons become visible simultaneously.

Finally, for some specimens we have made use of routine staining methods, including the specific ammoniacal silver oxide procedure of Bielschowsky and its variants. However this procedure is very difficult to apply to embryos and fetuses because it requires preparation of frozen sections. However, when good preparations are obtained with this procedure the results are in complete agreement with those obtained in preparations stained by reduced silver nitrate.

Naturally we have not reviewed all intraepithelial sensory nerve terminations. For our purposes we have considered it sufficient to analyze the late developmental phases of certain nerve arborizations.

This study can be divided into two parts: in the first we deal with sensory nerve terminations; in the second, special sense terminations.

DEVELOPMENT OF SENSORY NERVE TERMINATIONS

Nerve Terminations in the Cornea. We will disregard these terminations in the adult, which are well known today thanks to the work of Pappenheim, Hoyer, Cohnheim, Kölliker, and Ranvier, and which have recently been confirmed by Dogiel and ourselves with the methylene blue method. Our purpose, as we have already noted, is limited to studying the origin of the preterminal plexus and the development of the first intraepidermal twigs.

The process which gives rise to these nerve terminations consists of several phases. In the very early fetus, e.g., the 6 millimeter mouse and the 10 centimeter rabbit, we have been unable to perceive corneal nerves. It is true that the barely delineated corneal membrane still lacks connective tissue laminae (at least they do not appear in our preparations). In addition to the epithelium, the cornea is made up of a plexus of anastomosed fibroblasts, among which numerous plasma spaces are observed. This appearance of the embryonic connective tissue is also found in the 28 millimeter cat fetus.

The first corneal nerves penetrate the cornea before the fibrous laminae are formed. They originate from the sclera and appear as isolated fascicles terminated in a brush point. These fascicles, in great part rectilinear and deeply located, inhabit only the corneal periphery in this period. Some time afterwards they grow and overrun the entire area of the membrane. Because of their isolation and their small number they do not yet form a plexus. One could designate this first phase as the phase of isolated fascicles. During it the nerve fibers grow with especial facility since they do not run against any serious obstacles in their path. In our opinion, the isolated fascicles thrive in this embryonic tissue because they find favorable neurotropic conditions or substances there. The phenomena of attraction and growth of nerve sprouts that are regenerating into a cicatrix can be noted here during ontogeny with but minor variations.

Plexus formation is initiated shortly afterwards. In the cornea this represents the rudiment of the complicated fundamental plexus of the adult stroma. The first good impregnations of this plexus have been obtained in the fetus near term. Towards this time the quite thickened cornea still appears joined to the lens (Fig. 65) and in ordinary preparations presents a structure similar to that which it will show later except for the slenderness of the layers.

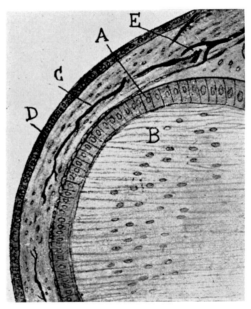

Fig. 65. Antero-posterior section of the ocular globe of a 1 cm mouse fetus. A) Anterior epithelium of the lens: B) prisms of the lens; C) nerves which besiege the corneal stroma; D) anterior corneal epithelium; E) scleral region from which the corneal nerves emanate.

In this stage of development the long isolated nerve fascicles still dominate. Their branches of bifurcation change planes and one still notes that the fibers near to the sclera predominate (Fig. 65). But by examining the latter in frontal sections one now notes that some small fascicles coming from various regions of the sclera converge and become reunited to form a rudimentary horizontal plexus (fundamental plexus). In any event, the fascicles tend to approach the anterior epithelium, near which they terminate freely in more or less fine brushes, often broken up into exploratory fibers. At this period, therefore, neither axon nor collateral penetrates into the epithelium. This is also true of 3.5 centimeter and 3 centimeter cat fetuses.

In passing, let us note a negative fact that is not unimportant. The fine nerve fascicles and, for better reason, the isolated exploratory fibers, still lack an enveloping sheath. This primary nudity of the initial fibers and fascicles is corroborated in sections of the corneal membrane stained by ordinary methods after fixation in aceticsublimate or formol-bichromate, in which preparations it is impossible to find marginal nuclei. Perpendicular sections, in which all the nuclei are arranged in parallel stages and belong to the fibroblasts of the stroma, are especially demonstrative. In the adult, as Ranvier demonstrated, these marginal nuclei, as well as the less numerous intrachiasmatic ones, are never lacking.

The last developmental phase is that of epithelial invasion. One must examine the newborn and especially the 3 and 4 day old mouse to be able to observe one or more exploratory nerve fibers within the epithelial covering. One can characterize such fibers as terminal fibers and collateral branches. The former cross the most superficial connective tissue strata obliquely and, virtually without detours, crowd around the subepithelial frontier directly. Once there, they are only occasionally disposed tangentially, and they form the rudiment of the subepithelial plexus that is so developed in the adult. In the great majority of cases these fibers border the integumental covering, bifurcating in the interior of the latter or immediately beneath it. Their branches travel more or less concentrically over long distances between the two epithelial zones and their terminal ends may ramify and reach the free surface. The collateral branches are of more theoretical interest. These fine filaments arise (Fig. 66, b, c) at right angles from the tangential fibers circulating beneath the epithelium. Having deeply penetrated the latter, they divide several times, the resulting projections always traveling in opposite directions. Often they gradually approach the corneal surface and travel tangentially to it for considerable distance (a). Let us again recall the unusual fact that some small nerve

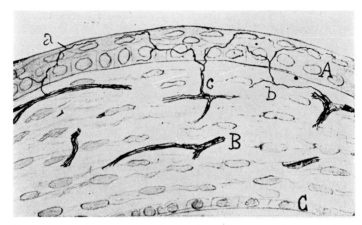

Fig. 66. Section of the cornea of a 2 day old mouse. A) Anterior corneal epithelium; B) fascicles of the fundamental plexus; a, b, c) epithelial nerve fibers arising at a right angle from the plexus.

fascicles penetrate the epithelium directly (Fig. 67, C), unraveling in the depths of this layer and orienting their fibers in opposite directions.

In spite of the proximity of the conjunctival space, one never observes a fiber falling into this oculopalpebral cavity. Nor does one find branches which return to the connective tissue after having assaulted the epithelium.

The following observations suggest the presence of neurotropic substances within the cornea: the presence of perforating collaterals which arise near the epithelium, the general tendency of nerve fibers to travel long distances between the connective laminae towards this ectodermal formation and the fact that they do not leave the epithelium but ramify greatly within it. These neurotropic substances or physicochemical states of analogous function would serve to activate the growth of the nerve fibers and to attract and retain them in the terminal territory.

In summary: the development of the corneal nerve terminations passes through four phases: 1. phase of isolated invading fascicles; 2. phase of the stromal plexuses, successively enriched by the addition of new fibers; 3. phase of small ascending fascicles

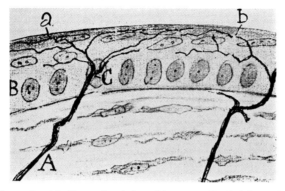

Fig. 67. Corneal epithelium of a 4 day old mouse. Copied from 2 small nerves lying in 2 successive sections. A) Nerve fascicle which, with all its nerve fibers, assails the epithelium; C) point of unravelling of its constituent fibers.

and of exploratory intraepidermal fibers; 4. phase of intraepithelial ramification of the latter. With the approach of adulthood one could add a fifth phase characterized by the extensive ramification of the intraepidermal filaments, the formation of the subepithelial plexuses, and the arrival of the late fibers which extraordinarily augment the fibrillar richness of the plexuses (Fig 68). It goes without saying that the development of the nerve terminations is intimately correlated with the growth and differentiation of the various corneal layers. There is no question that only a scanty contingent of fibers arrives at the cornea in the early phases and that the enormous extent of the adult plexus and arborizations must arise from the ramifications of the precociously arrived fibers as well as from the successive invasion of later developing axons which are for the great part incorporated into the primordial fascicles by reciprocal stereotropism or neurotropism.

Genesis of Cutaneous Nerve Terminations. Our observations have been on the skin of the chest, snout, lips, and eyelids of the mouse, rabbit, and cat fetus. Keeping to our plan, we will not describe all the facts observed, which are well known from the works of many authors (including Merkel, Krause, Klein, Ranvier, Arnstein, Retzius, van Gehuchten, Dogiel, Michailow, Ruffini and his school, Unanicka, Kohner, Regaud and Fabre, Botezat, Tello, Bielschowsky,

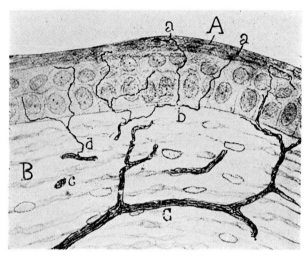

Fig. 68.   Corneal nerves of a 15 day old mouse. A) Epithelium; B) corneal stroma; C) trunk of the fundamental plexus; a) tangental intra-epithelial branches; b) origin of these branches; d) collateral fiber.

van der Velde, and ourselves). We will restrict ourselves to calling attention to those phenomena of location, direction, and ramification of the intraepithelial embryonic fibers which suggest valid arguments for the clarification of the neurotropic problem.

What we stated relative to the cornea is also true for skin of the mouse, rabbit, and cat fetus: The first nerve bundles to arrive at the terminal territories lie fairly deeply in the midst of an embryonic connective tissue composed of stellate cells separated by plasma spaces. For the most part these bundles are isolated, often bifurcated, fascicles which travel more or less parallel to the skin and terminate in a brush point. However, in different regions of the skin there are great differences in the richness of the plexus and in its proximity to the epidermis. Thus, in the 10 millimeter mouse embryo, while there are some territories where all the nerve fascicles are deeply situated and appear almost completely isolated, there are others, e.g., the skin of the thorax (Fig. 69) in which the plexiform configuration is not only evident but in which the primary sensory trunks send small fine fascicles to the vicinity of the epidermis, where the dispersion of the fibers is already being initiated. Note that exploratory fibers (a) arise both from the edges and the terminal ends of the small fascicles. This same arrangement is found in rudimentary eyelids and in other regions of the skin of the head and thorax of the 28 millimeter cat fetus (Fig. 70).

The developing plexuses become complex and extensive and the exploratory fibers increase proportionally as development advances. In the 5 centimeter cat fetus and 12 millimeter mouse fetus sometimes one can distinguish not only one plexus but two or more superimposed, wide-meshed ones. In any case, the complexity and the compactness of the cutaneous sensory plexuses does not ordinarily equal that of the similar plexuses described by Tello and others in the muscles of the trunk, limbs, and tongue.

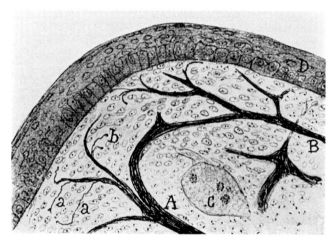

Fig. 69. Section of thoracic skin of a 1 cm mouse fetus. A) Primary sensory trunks; B) another bundle anastomosed with the preceding; C) vessel; D) cutaneous epithelium; a, b) isolated exploratory branches arising from the small secondary fascicles

In the skin of the snout and, in general, in skin provided with tactile hairs, the nerve bundles become unusually robust, dividing and subdividing several times and usually traveling in a radial direction. This orientation, almost perpendicular to the skin, appears clearly in the snout integument of the cat, rabbit, and mouse fetus during the time when the hair follicles are already formed. It is true that in the subcutaneous connective tissue there are no free spaces for nerves to travel towards the skin other than the more or less parallel interstices located between the hair follicles and the physiognomical muscle fascicles. We consider this radial arrangement a mechanical adaptation of the older nerve fascicles to the rudiments of the hair and glands. Do not forget that the largely horizontal cutaneous plexus greatly precedes the appearance of these epithelial derivatives.

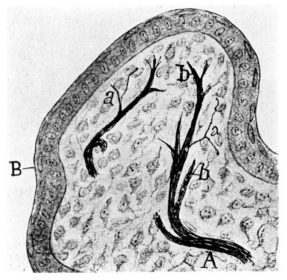

Fig. 70.   Section of the rudimentary eyelid of a 28 mm cat embryo. A) Primary fascicle; B) epithelium; a) exploratory fibrils; b) secondary fascicles terminating in a brush point.

Epithelial innervation is a late phenomenon. Intraepidermal nerve branches are still lacking in the 8 to 10 millimeter mouse fetus. The latter appear clearly only in the term fetus and in newborn animals. At this time the well-developed hair follicles receive a powerful stream of fibers, of which a relatively small portion deviates towards the epidermis, as Retzius observed a long time ago.

We are going to describe in slight detail the progress of the cutaneous nerve fibers prior to their epidermal invasion. In Figure 71 we reproduce the most common arrangement that is observed in the mouse. The disaggregation of the primary fascicles begins in the subcutaneous connective tissue. It is intensified and becomes more complex in the dermal papilla as though the neurotropic sources of the ectodermal formations act over great distances. In this way the considerably finer secondary fascicles are formed and spread across the dermal papilla and its environs. In its turn each secondary fascicle engenders tertiary fascicles, i.e., more and more delicate small fascicles. Finally, the fibers of these small fascicles are dispersed like a jet of water and then begin axonal dichotomizations which occur throughout the dermis. Moreover, as many authors have recognized, fiber dichotomization frequently occurs in the primary and secondary fascicles as well as in the chiasmas of the subdermal and dermal plexus.

Stereotropic phenomena are quite common during the ascending journey of the fascicles. Fibers and even small fascicles are frequent-

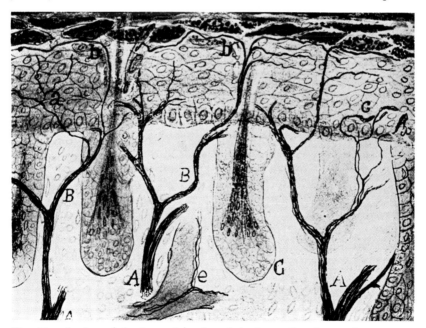

Fig. 71. Section of the internal border of the lower lip of a newborn mouse. Nerve fibers copied from 2 successive sections. A) Primary fascicles; B) secondary fascicles separated at almost a right angle; C) embryonic hair follicles; a, b, c,) intra-epidermal branches.

ly found traveling along capillaries penetrating the papillae, the divisions of these fibers coinciding with the vascular dichotomizations (Fig. 71, e). Not rarely, although less frequently, are small fascicles and fibers seen travelling along a cutaneous muscle fascicle (physiognomical muscle) or on a hair follicle (infraglandular portion). Finally, one sometimes also notes the growth of young fibers along a series of connective tissue cells when the direction of the latter is favorable. These stereotropic phenomena seem to be more common in the cat (fetus near term and newborn) than in the mouse.

Up to now, the observed nerve fascicles and fibers were restricted to the region of the subcutaneous tissue and the corium. At this moment epidermal invasion begins. It was already initiated in the term fetus but is easily recognizable only in newborn animals. Even though neurofibrillar methods can fail to reveal fibers because of the pallor of the impregnation, it seems probable that in the snout and lips of the newborn mouse vast regions exist in which only a small number of scattered twigs are observed.

In Figures 71 and 72 we show the arrangement of some of these intraepidermal fibers taken from the lips of the mouse. Note that most fibers do not give rise to branches upon arriving at the basal membrane but that they penetrate the Malpighian zone without dividing. They then cross the entire thickness of the latter either in a straight line or slightly obliquely. Finally, having ventured into the granular zone, they become arciform and even tangential, as if they had struck against an almost impassable object, and give rise to secondary branches terminating in fine spherules. Such a deviation, produced by the collision with the compact wall of granular cells, also appears in other pavement epithelium and suggests the idea that, *as soon as the neurotropic influences are lacking, the course of the nerve sprouts yields purely and simply to the impulse of continuous growth and to mechanical conditions.*

This is the usual behavior of intraepidermal fibers, but there are variations among different regions and even within the same region. One of these variations, admittedly unusual, is that reproduced in Figure 72, A. Instead of a single intraepidermal nerve branch, we see a small, thick, compact fascicle which crosses the epithelium

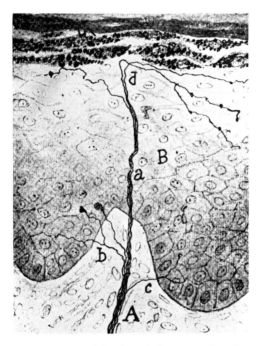

Fig. 72. Section of the internal border of the upper lip of a newborn mouse. A) Perforating fascicle; B) Malpighian cell; C) granular cell layer; a) course of the fascicle across the epithelium; b, c) branches attracted by the interpapillary epithelial eminences.

almost perpendicularly and disperses its fibers beneath the large cells of the granular zone, where some fibers assume a retrograde course. More frequently we have seen isolated fibers arborizing beneath the granular layer after having furnished fine twigs to the inferior zones during the first part of their journey. Some isolated fibers terminate beneath this stratum by means of a large sphere of detention (Fig. 73, d) from which an exploratory branch occasionally emerges. Collateral projections also arise from the tangential subepidermal fascicles. These twigs (Fig. 73, a, c) suggest the presence of epidermal neurotropic sources similar to those noted in the cornea, since the production of such twigs cannot be explained by the collision with any appreciable obstacle. Figure 75, d, also shows some collaterals which seem to imply the same attractive in-

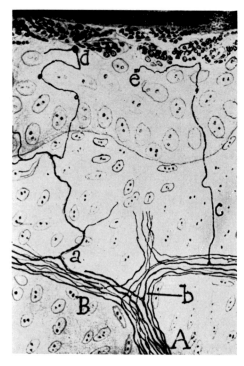

Fig. 73.   Details of the plexus and the origin of the intra-epidermal collaterals
in the eyelid of the newborn mouse. A) Primary fascicle; B, secondary fascicle;
a, c, collaterals; b, bifurcation of an axon in the midst of the fascicles; d) ball
from which an exploratory fiber emerges; e) small terminal spherule.

fluence that skin exerts over normal cutaneous fibers. Finally, some
fibers are slightly tortuous and provided with spherules along
their path, an unequivocal sign that must have undergone several
arrests in the course of their journey. We will dwell no more on
these arrangements nor on others which can be seen in Figures 71,
73, and 75, and which are common in the skin of the snout, lips,
and eyelids of the newborn mouse and rabbit. In all these arrangements one is struck by the fact that only very rarely do the highest
or most superficial branches venture beyond the granular layer.

If we now set aside the journey of the fibers and concentrate on
the area of their distribution, we will be struck by one fact that
histologists have noted but not yet sufficiently appreciated. *Each*

fiber is destined for an epithelial territory devoid of nerves, and there are no vast aneuritic spaces in some regions nor excessive collections of fibrils in others. One could say that after invasion of the epithelium a state of chemical equilibrium is created, by virtue of which the innervated territories are incapable of attracting new sprouts. Perhaps in such newly innervated epithelial areas the neurotropic agent is neutralized (at least temporarily) by substances from the neural protoplasm. Or perhaps (analogous to what has been observed in bacterial colonies) the fibers discharge ferments into the invaded territory which are paralyzing or inhibitory to their own growth. Virgin epithelium on the other hand, seems replete with neurotropic substances capable of exercising vigorous orienting and trophic influences over the small nerve fascicles which wander across the dermal papilla, and even over those which are farthest away from the subcutaneous connective tissues. The ascending jetlike branches (Fig. 74) are very suggestive of this action at a distance. Furthermore, many peculiarities and deviations of dermal and subdermal fibers become comprehensible by supposing that both the radially placed epithelial territories as well as the laterally located ones (including the interpapillary descending protuberances) act energetically on the errant fibers. Figure 74, B, C, is very significant in this regard. Note that the majority of the nerve fibers arising from the subpapillary sensory plexus are attracted by these robust epithelial protuberances; one very often perceives some fascicles which, apparently attracted by two neighboring protuberances, divide their fibers (generally by bifurcating) into two streams which travel directly towards the nearest epithelial masses. Some of these arborizations probably represent the embyonic phase of the hederiform terminations that were well described by Ranvier.

In view of the numerous obstacles along the path of nerve fibers and the disturbing influence of the hair follicles, it is obviously difficult to attribute all the arrangements to a single cause. Supposing that only epithelial neurotropic agents act on the connective tissue framework, and disregarding any disturbing mechanical obstacles, it would not be difficult to predict the probable path of the fibers. If we acknowledge that the fibers moving across the dermis

Fig. 74.   Section of the skin of the nose of a cat fetus at term. Nerve terminations copied from 2 successive thick sections. A) Primary fascicle; B) secondary
fascicles; C, D) tertiary fascicles attracted by the interpapillary eminences; a)
fascicle penetrating the epithelium.

are influenced by two attractive impulses, one direct or perpendicular
to the epithelial plane and the other tangential or parallel to it,
then each fiber would be forced to follow the diagonal of the paral-
lelogram of the actual forces. In fact this is the actual itinerary followed by the majority of the axons which arise from a nerve fascicle or from the branches of bifurcation of a radially oriented isolated fiber which is attracted by opposing interpapillary masses. Nat
urally we must disregard those direct fibers which are far removed
from the interpapillary protuberances. The latter could travel per-

pendicularly without dividing because of the reciprocal cancellation of opposed forces and the predominance of the radial direction. In every case, we repeat, the oblique and more or less arciform orientation of the branches predominates just as the theory demands.

It is clear that this explanation is only theoretical. The problem of the course and divisions of the fibers is extremely complex; several still unknown factors play a part.

The word "attraction" which we have employed in the preceding explanation is used figuratively. We are not seeking to prejudge the physical or chemical nature of the active conditions. We simply wish to suggest that the distribution and progress of the intradermal fibers occurs as though the afferent fascicle were convergently and simultaneously attracted by diverse epithelial regions, and that the route followed by each fiber represents the compromise (disregarding mechanical obstacles and stereotropic phenomena) among all the actual sources of energy.

In our research on the mouse, rabbit, and cat fetus we have also studied the mode of disaggregation of the fascicles in the vicinity of the midline (lips of the mouse and rabbit) and at the level of the epithelium of the closing apparatus of the eyelids (newborn mouse). Just as would be expected, and as some authors have noted, the fascicles of nerve fibers are not restricted exclusively to the homolateral territory; occasionally one or more axons or branches of bifurcation cross the midline to innervate nearby contralateral regions (Fig. 75). But, in any case, these strayed fibers are rare and, as is shown in Figure 75, they seem to stop shortly within the forbidden domain. The afore-mentioned aberrant fibers do not justify hypothesizing the existence of specific antagonistic neurotropic influences within each of the halves of the body or in each eyelid of the same eyeball. The fiber deviation could be explained by excessive rectilinear growth impulse or also by the accidental proximity of the contralateral epithelium with its not yet extinguished radial or tangential neurotropic forces.

In summary: In the skin and mucosa of general sensibility, neurotropic activity seems diffused throughout the Malpighian cells and is perhaps a little more intense at the level of the germinal zone than in the rest of the epithelial formation.

Genesis of Terminations in the Tactile Hairs. The older studies of Bonnet, Odenius, Jobert, Ranvier, Dietz, Sertoli, Renaut, Ostroumow, Symonowiez, Tretjakoff, van Gehuchten, Retzius, Lefébure, and the modern research of Botezat, Ksjunmy, London, and Tello have demonstrated that diverse forms of nerve terminations are found in the tactile hairs of rodents and many other mammals. In the mouse, rabbit, and cat the immense majority of the trigeminal cutaneous branches are attracted by the ordinary as well as the tactile hairs, the epithelium of the hair follicles seeming to attract the principal contingent of the growing sensory fibers.

In Tello's opinion,[218,224] four types of termination are found among the nerves of the tactile hairs: 1. longitudinally palisaded terminations, or those of tactile masses located above the glassy

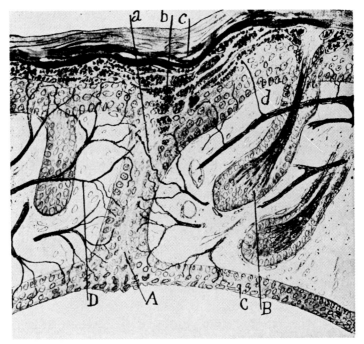

Fig. 75.   Vertical section of the point of union of the 2 eyelids of a newborn mouse. A) Intermediary epithelium destined to be resorbed; B) hair follicles; D) small nerve fascicles going to the internal epidermis a) perforating fiber which crosses the midline; d) collateral branches to the anterior integument of the eyelid.

membrane; 2. crescentric ramifications located among the most peripheral epithelial elements of the external sheath of the follicle (hypolemmal fibers of Ranvier); 3. ramifications lying beneath the first constriction of the hair, noted long ago by Bonnet; 4. those destined for the annular pad which apparently terminate in discs and masses.

In our opinion, the most interesting of these forms of sensory terminal arborizations are the discoidal or spatuliform ones, noted long ago by Dietz and Sertoli and masterfully described by Ranvier. Those terminal discs lie among the cells of the germinal layer of epithelium (external epithelial sheath of the follicle) and ordinarily arise from sturdy fibers which continue as the longitudinal palisade.

In the newborn and several day old mouse one can follow the complete development of these intraepithelial projections. In longitudinal sections of the tactile hair of a 4 to 6 day old animal it is seen that such branches are for the most part collateral in nature. They arise at a right angle from the palisade of fibers lying upon the basal membrane, cross this glassy membrane perpendicularly without stopping or retracing their steps, as though attracted by an irresistible force, and finally penetrate among the afore-mentioned germinal epithelial cells (Fig. 76, b, e, f).

At the outset (newborn mouse) these collaterals are rare, fine, short, nonbifurcated, and have either no terminal swelling or a very small one (Fig. 77). At 4 days, we have already stated, the fibers are longer, thicker, and almost all exhibit a small terminal nodule and, in some cases, a fusiform swelling (Fig. 76, B). At 7 or 8 days (Figure 77, f) these fibers show one or more bifurcations, the branches of which terminate in flattened dilatations possessing a neurofibrillar plexus. The form of a spatula, of a spear point, or of a swollen mass are very common. Frequently each fiber bends back within the limits of the *germinal layer,* climbing and descending without invading the deep epithelial strata as if the latter were a terrain unsuited to their growth or possessing insurmountable mechanical obstacles. Any fiber that succeeds in venturing into the interstices of the neighboring layer either shows atrophy of its terminal portion or else retraces its steps to reach

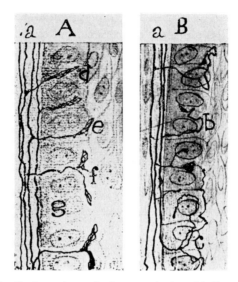

Fig. 76. Longitudinal section of the germinal epithelium of the external sheath of the root of the hair. A) Tactile hair of an 8 day old mouse; B) tactile hair of a 4 day old mouse; a) nerve fibers which travel along the vitreous layer; b. c) collaterals terminating in the region of the germinative cells; d, e, f) phases in the development of the terminal meniscus.

the previously innervated germinal zone, even though in its double journey it traveled through different levels. In time the divisions become more frequent, after which appear the classical arrangements of grapes, discs, and spatulas that Tello described so perfectly.

It is important for our purposes to analyze the initial form of the afore-mentioned dichotomous divisions. These divisions are much more readily observable in transverse than in longitudinal sections of tactile hairs. In Figures 76, f, and 78 of the 8 day old mouse we show some examples of the path taken by the daughter branches. As a general rule, they divide at an acute or right angle, usually in the epithelial zone, the branches traveling almost tangentially to innervate new arciform sectors of the germinal layer. It is evident that some branches do not travel in opposite directions and that some fibers even double lengthwise along the germinal layer and terminate by the well-known enlargement. Let us now add that some branches display the characteristics of terminal fibers, as Tello has demonstrated, possessing remarkable richness and variety of terminal ramifications.

The preceding arrangements are very suggestive. Note the following three most prominent and significant facts: 1. Almost all the branches terminating in laminar thickenings are collateral in character. 2. The secondary and tertiary branches ordinarily travel tangentially. 3. The afore-mentioned secondary projections only rarely stray from the germinal layer, the terminal plaque or spatula being found among the germinal cells.

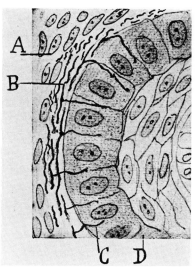

Fig. 77. Transverse section of the epithelial portion of the tactile hair of a 2 day old mouse. Fibers copied from 3 successive sections. A) Connective tissue covering; B) ascending nerve fascicles; C) collaterals.

The preceding facts seem to imply the existence of a neurotropic focus *located exclusively in the peripheral or germinal epithelial layer*. This source of trophic and orienting influence is so powerful that it induces the emission of collaterals in the palisade fibers and obliges the branches to surmount as formidable an obstacle as the glassy or basal membrane, which is absolutely devoid of fissures. Finally, the extensive growth of the germinal layer by mitosis suggests to us that the successive enrichment of the terminal arborization is the result of the appearance of new foci of attractive ac-

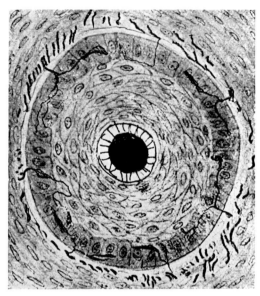

Fig. 78.   Transverse section of the root of a tactile hair of an 8 day old mouse.
Note the dichotomizations of the collaterals and the terminal swellings, all or
nearly all of which are in contact with the germinal epithelium.

tivity. In summary, the path of the primary branches of bifurcation (4 to 8 day old mouse), in accordance with what was already
stated relative to the skin, reveals that two active forces are also
found here: one radial, predominant in the beginning, and the other
tangential, which acts exclusively in the later stages of the developmental process. Thus one explains the rapid return of accidentally
strayed sprouts to the germinal layer. When all, or nearly all, of
the epithelial cells of the active region of the germinal layer enter
into union with a terminal nerve disc or paddle, the production of
ramifications definitively ceases. But this chemical indifference only
occurs in nearly adult animals.

Examination of the most embryonic phases of the tactile hairs
(28 and 35 millimeter cat) demonstrates that *besides the afore-
mentioned specific activity of the superficial epithelial layer of the
fully formed follicle, one must acknowledge another prior activity
which is diffusely spread throughout the ectodermal rudiment of
the hair follicle.* Without this primary orienting influence it would

not be possible to explain the convergent concentration of a multitude of scattered nerve fascicles. As we show in Figure 79, the entire epithelial rudiment of the root appears enveloped by an extremely complex sensory plexus, the richness and appearance of which varies considerably according to the degree of development of the hair. This is a purely expectant plexus (D), for the cells and connective tissues on which it will fix its future terminations are not yet developed. This plexus completely lacks intraepidermal fibers and its detached fascicles and fibers are intimately applied to the periphery of the rudimentary follicle. Numerous exploratory brushes which do not border the cutaneous plane all travel towards the top (Fig. 79, D). Laterally, some branches, detached from the sturdy trunk, are seen to be destined for the skin (C).

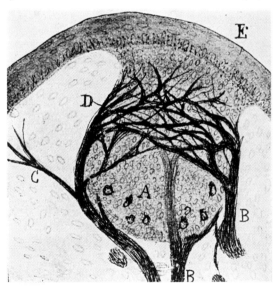

Fig. 79. Rudiment of a tactile hair of a 35 mm cat embryo. A) Epithelial rudiment; B) afferent fascicles; C) branch to the neighboring skin; D) expectant sensory plexus; E) epithelium of the skin; a) pigment cells.

In Figure 80 we show a still earlier phase of the tactile hairs of the cat embryo. The hemispherical epithelial rudiment is continuous with the integument. As though attracted by an irresistible impulse, several fascicles flock there and wander by the skin. Some

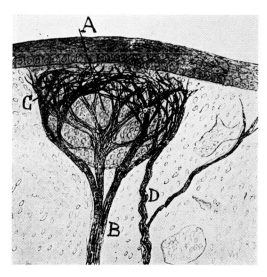

Fig. 80.   Rudiment of the tactile hair and its neural apparatus in a 28 mm cat embryo. A) Germinal epithelium emerging from the ectoderm; B) robust afferent nerve bundle; C) expectant nerve plexus; D) another bundle from which a cutaneous fascicle emerges.

days earlier these fascicles were arranged in a loose horizontal plexus. There is a tendency for the terminal plexus to be concentrated towards the base of the epithelial hemisphere, i.e., beneath the rudimentary integument. The compact meshes of the expectant plexus are largely tangential. Finally, these hair rudiments are also found in the snout of the mouse (8 to 10 millimeter embryo), where one often observes thick primary trunks furnishing bundles to three neighboring tactile hair rudiments. Let us note that well-delimited layers within the ectodermal rudiment are not yet differentiated at this time, nor does the regular peripheral epithelial zone, characteristic of young skin, exist. Therefore one could not speak of a specific attraction by cells which will only appear subsequently. The rich and tangled plexus which surrounds the epithelial rudiment is like an unformed depot of nerve fibers which, after ceaseless transformations, will form the future tactile terminations.

To recapitulate: two perfectly limited chronological phases are recognized in the innervation of the tactile hairs. During the first of these, coinciding with the development of the rudiment, the epithelium *en masse* strongly attracts the wandering subcutaneous bundles, breaking up the primitive plexuses and influencing the fascicles to construct the new peribulbar plexus. During the second, the skin and its newly-differentiated specific cells give rise to individual sources of neurotropism and neurocladism which create and model the nerve terminations. All these phenomena, we repeat, *imply the malleable and provisional nature of the primitive plexuses which, as was noted by Heidenhain as well as ourselves, furnish the necessary neural material for the structural development of the nerve terminations.*

GENESIS OF SPECIAL SENSE NERVE TERMINATIONS

Terminations of the Cochlear Nerve. It is well known that the cochlea is formed from an epithelial cul-de-sac which, in its turn, originates from the ectodermal otic vesicle. This sac, shaped like the finger of a glove, progressively elongates and then curves to form the first spiral turn around the external pole of the spiral ganglion (Boettcher). In the 7 to 8 millimeter mouse fetus the cochlear canal is still very embryonic, for the organ of Corti and neighboring structures (*basilar membrane, scala vestibuli, Reissner's membrane, spiral tunnel*) are still undifferentiated. As for the *scala tympani*, a mesodermal derivative, it is being formed by the successive removal of fibroblasts and elaboration of interstitial plasma. The rudimentary organ of Corti is thus merely a simple epithelial membrane in which two regions may be distinguished: a fine region, made up of a single layer of short epithelial cells, and a thick region, in which the organ of Corti will ultimately develop, formed of several rows of elongated neuroepithelial elements. This thick portion of the cochlear canal lies immediately above the spiral ganglion.* This rudimentary appearance of the cochlear canal

---

*Those desiring to orient themselves in the embryology of the acoustic labyrinth should consult the review works of Kölliker, the Hertwig brothers, and Retzius, as well as the excellent monographs of Boettcher, Denys, Baginsky, and especially Held.[61] The communications of Kolmer[96] and of van der Stricht[229] would also be very instructive. Finally, a good résumé of these studies will be found in Prenant's classical *Histologie*.[142]

is still maintained in the 1 centimeter mouse embryo (Fig. 81).

The spiral ganglion of 7 to 8 millimeter mouse embryos is intimately applied to the epithelium of the cochlear canal and its bipolar cells with their two processes, peripheral and central, can be clearly made out. The peripheral processes gather in the form of a brush (transverse sections) or, to describe it better, in the form of spiral crest with sharp corners (longitudinal sections of the cochlear canal). The ganglionic nerve fibers are very compact; the longest or apical ones (which can be considered exploratory) touch the epithelium, but none of them yet penetrates into the depths of the later. They appear stationary, as though awaiting the future changes that the thick portion of the spiral canal will undergo.

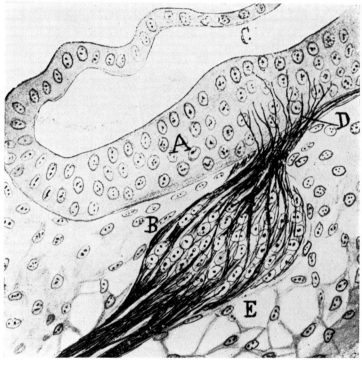

Fig. 81.   Section of the cochlear canal of a 1 cm mouse fetus. A) Epithelium which will form the organ of Corti; B) spiral ganglion; C) cochlear canal; D) some fibers which penetrate the epithelium; E) connective tissue spaces which will ultimately form the scala tympani.

A complete neurotropic inertia is observed in 22 millimeter cat embryos. In Figure 82, copied from a section almost parallel to one spiral turn, we note that the processes arising from the neighboring spiral ganglion form a compact plexus beneath the cochlear epithelium. There are a few tangential and oblique fibers, many of which run, as though strayed, for long distances, growing incessantly and superfluously. That proves that fiber assimilation has not yet ceased, in spite of the absence of neurotropic sources. The many windings, backward journeys, and plexiform arrangements could easily be explained by Held's *vis a tergo* or continuous growth of nerve protoplasm.

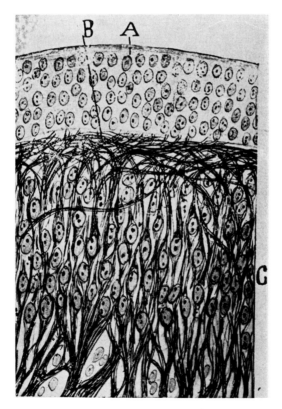

Fig. 82.   Section parallel to the cochlear canal of a 28 mm cat embryo. A) undifferentiated cochlear epithelium; B) subepithelial nerve plexus; C) spiral ganglion.

Conditions have already changed in the 10 millimeter mouse fetus. The supraganglionic portion of the epithelium has noticeably increased in thickness and several rows of nuclei are perceived. In some parts is noted a region that has thickened considerably, forming a mound or raised edge in transverse sections (Fig. 81, A)— the internal swelling of van der Stricht and Denys. Differentiation of the hair cells very possibly begins in this phase, even though they are far from their definitive state. Silver preparations are not sufficiently clear in this regard.

In any case, at about this time of development we have observed a fairly large contingent of exploratory fibers and fascicles within the epithelial wall. Such an invasion, *en masse,* takes place at the surface of maximal thickness or internal margin of the barely outlined organ of Corti. Most of these acoustic fibers cease to be stainable towards the deep half of the epithelium but there are a few which extend almost directly to the first row of cells without yet forming a cuplike arborization. Bifurcations are seen but rarely. In summary: *the immense majority of the cochlear fibers are applied strictly to the inferior* plane of the epithelium and terminate freely without penetrating the latter.

One detail whose theoretical importance will not escape the reader is found in these sections of the mouse fetus. The rare intraepithelial acoustic fibers (i.e., the peripheral branches of the spiral ganglion) before invading the superposed epithelium, glide as though groping beneath the latter. Having found the favorable region, the fibers describe a right or obtuse angle and attain their destination. It follows that neither the principle of rectilinear growth (Harrison) nor that of the shortest path (Held) are applicable here. If some attractive influence from the acoustic epithelium did not enter into play, one could not understand why the fibers in question would not continue to glide beneath the cochlear canal in the midst of the connective tissue. It is equally curious to note that of the entire extent of the thick cochlear epithelium, only one very restricted area of the latter (corresponding to the internal margin) attracts the peripheral processes of the spiral ganglion and gathers them into small compact perforating fascicles (Fig. 81, D). Penetration of the external margin takes place sometime later.

In the mouse fetus at term and especially in the newborn, the hair cells are already differentiated from the sustentacular cells. These two elements are found both in the internal and the external margins. We will not go into details about the structure of the organ of Corti at this developmental stage; these details would be superfluous in view of the excellent drawings and descriptions of van der Stricht, Denys, and especially Held. Held has particularly studied the rabbit fetus at term, beautifully analyzing the fine structure of the hair cells in the various spirals of the cochlea, the formation of the tectorial membrane, and the creation of the pillars and tunnels of Corti. In these figures, even though based on the iron hematoxylin method, this author reproduces penetrating nerve fibers destined for the two margins of the acoustic epithelium, although he is unable to describe their mode of termination in detail because of the technique he employed.

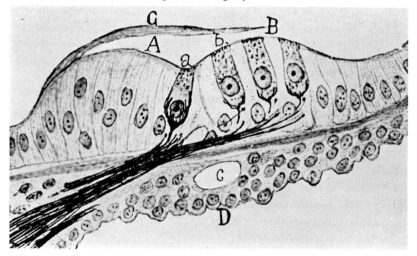

Fig. 83. Section of the epithelium of the organ of Corti of a mouse fetus at term. A) Internal margin; B) external margin; D) scala tympani; a) internal hair cell; b) external hair cell; c) spiral vessel.

The reduced silver nitrate method permits us to fill this gap. As we show in Figure 83 the nerve fibers divide into two series of fascicles: internal, destined for the epithelial margin facing the ganglion and terminating in a chalice of neurofibrils around internal hair cells (Fig. 83, a); and external which, after having traced some spirals among the external hair cells, terminate in a minute chalice (b). It is important to note that the internal chalices develop before the external ones. Both exhibit a compact network of pericellular neurofibrils intimately applied to the protoplasm of the hair cell but without substantial continuity with the latter. This is contrary to Kolmer's opinion. He misinterpreted some inconclusive appearances in reduced silver nitrate preparations of lower vertebrates. Furthermore, the nerve terminations in the organ of Corti of the newborn and several day old mouse were seen first and faithfully interpreted by the illustrious Retzius (Golgi method). His results were later confirmed by us and by van Gehuchten. Finally, the recent application of neurofibrillar methods to the examination of nerve terminations has given rise to numerous confirmatory and supplemental works (London and Perker, Kolmer, Bielschowsky and Brühl, and ourselves).

From the preceding studies one can conclude with all probability, that during the development of the cochlear epithelium two sources of neurotropic activity succeed one another: The first is of diffuse character and is localized throughout the entire region of the thick epithelium, perhaps especially in the cell bodies of the future sustentacular cells. The second is confined exclusively to the hair cells. Attracted by the first influence, the wandering fibers invade the epithelial wall and, attracted by the second, they are oriented and individually arranged around its afore-mentioned cells. We will now see that this double force also exists in the orienting mechanism of the vestibular fibers.

Terminations of the Vestibular Nerves in Birds and Mammals. The fibers of this nerve pass through the same phases as those of the cochlear nerve, but they organize and grow more precociously. In the 5 day chick embryo, as we noted a long time ago,[179] some ramified nerve prolongations are observed to penetrate into the cristae before the semicircular canals are formed. According to Held,[62] a ganglionic nucleus (acoustico-facial ganglion) is seen in the 3 day duck embryo uniting the otic vesicle with the medullary tube. The formation of this ganglion is also very precocious in the chick embryo. After 3 days and 7 hours of incubation, a nucleus of bipolar cells possessing internal and external prolongations already appears intimately applied to the inferior end of the otic vesicle (Fig. 84, B). This precocious differentiation was recognized a long time ago by Kölliker, His, Strecker, and others, although they did not use sufficiently selective methods.

The vesicular epithelium, which at this time presents 3 or 4 rows of nuclei, is not yet accosted by any nerve fibers. The immense majority of vestibular fibers form a flattened stream lying beneath the epithelium and presenting all the characteristics of the expectant fascicles or plexuses noted by Tello in muscles. All neurotropic activity therefore seems lacking. It is scarcely possible to discern crestiform epithelial formations or specific hair cells in such a precocious period of development.

After the fourth day, thick epithelial zones can be perceived, rudiments perhaps of the future cristae. Intraepithelial penetration by some vestibular fibers is now initiated. These exploratory fibers terminate in a point. The stream of vestibular fibers increases progressively and their branches, always located in specific areas of the epithelium, elongate and ramify profusely.

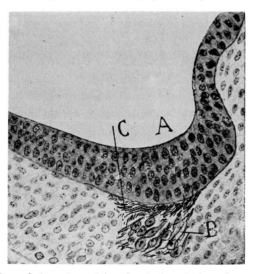

Fig. 84.   Section of the otic vesicle of a 3 day chick embryo. A) Interior of the vesicle; B) rudiment of Scarpa's ganglion; C) cut nerve fascicles beneath the epithelium.

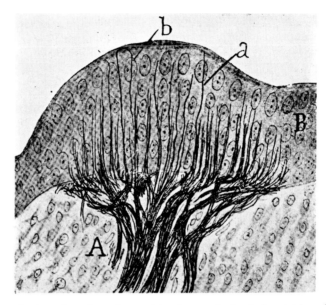

Fig. 85.   Section of a crista of a semicircular canal of a 5 day chick embryo. A) Fascicles of the vestibular nerve; B) epithelium of the crista; a) fiber arriving at the surface; b) fiber which, by turning back, forms an arc.

At the fifth day (Fig. 85), more and more elongated nerve processes reaches the zone of hair cells, which zone is quite advanced in differentiation. The excessive number of penetrating fibers causes us to speculate whether some of them may be resorbed later. In any event the majority of the nerve tips now touch the hair cells without yet forming the characteristic chalices.

After 8 or 9 days (Fig. 86) almost all of the vestibular fibers terminate by a bifurcation, the short and thick branches of which are located beneath the hair cells. The fibers are thicker and the terminal branches more robust toward the center of the cristae. Let us recall that this terminal ramification, which the Golgi method reveals as horizontal long branches, was observed and drawn by Retzius in the macula of the 11 day chick embryo.

Only at the thirteenth or fifteenth day of incubation does one observe true pericellular chalices and various types of fibers which are extremely diverse in thickness and mode of termination. We de-

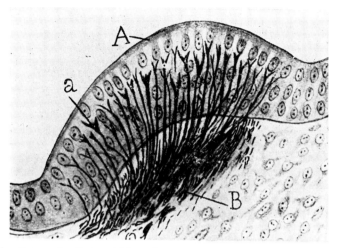

Fig. 86.   Crista of a 7 day chick embryo. A) Hair cells; B) section of a trunk of the vestibular nerve; a) rudiment of the terminal calyx.

scribed them in detail in a previous study using neurofibrillar methods.[175,184] Similar descriptions had been made very accurately many years previously by Retzius [202] in adult vertebrates, by Lenhossék [99] in young animals, and by Kolmer [85] in mammals.

The same observations can be made in the mouse, cat, and rabbit fetus. We have already noted that of all the special sense terminations the acoustic ones are the most precocious and, among the acoustic, the vestibular. Even in the 8 millimeter mouse fetus, these fibers have penetrated the depths of the epithelium, innervating the ampullar cristae of the semicircular canals and the rudimentary maculae of the saccule and utricle. It is possible that this penetration takes place during still earlier phases. These fibers divide in the depths of the epithelium and terminate in points which approach the region where the hair cells will differentiate.

In the 3.5 centimeter rabbit fetus the stream of vestibular fibers to the ampullar cristae, considerably more voluminous than in birds, also terminates by sharp intraepithelial points. Before reaching the ampullae, the vestibular fascicle is arranged in a complicated plexus separated by islets of connective tissue (Fig. 87, A). An even more marked plexiform arrangement is noted in the 25 to 28 millimeter

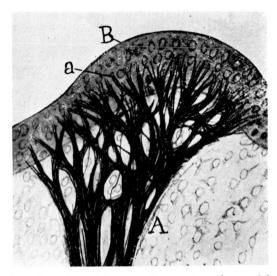

Fig. 87.   Section of a crista of the ampullar portion of a semicircular canal of a 3.5 cm rabbit embryo. A) Stream of the plexus of vestibular fibers; B) epithelium of the semicircular canal; a) brushes of the intra-epithelial nerve fibers.

cat embryo. The fibers destined for an ampullar crista are gathered into fascicles which, before accosting the epithelium, form a very complex plexus in which tangential or subepithelial fibers and fascicles predominate (Fig. 88). Some small fascicles and isolated fibers break loose from this plexus and, after having traveled along the sustentacular cells, are often arrested beneath the hair cells, although without yet giving rise to the chalicelike arborization. An occasional fiber however climbs up along the side of a hair cell. The formation of Lenhossék's intraepithelial horizontal plexus has already been initiated by many branches of bifurcation which travel tangentially beneath the hair cells (Fig. 88, b).

On examining these cat embryo preparations it is difficult to reject the idea that the first attractive impulse exerted upon the vestibular axons originates from the sustentacular cells and that the neurotropic and modeling action of the hair cells enters into play later.

In the mouse the first rudiment of the terminal chalice is seen in

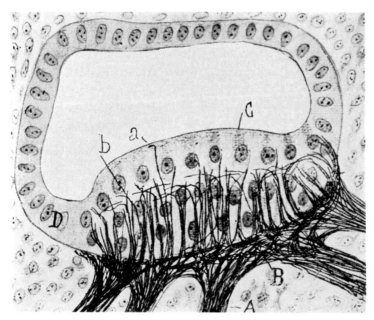

Fig. 88. Section of a crista of a 28 mm cat embryo. A) Vestibular fascicles; B) complex basal plexus; C) differentiating hair cells; a) fiber wandering in the superficial part of the epithelium; b) bifurcated fibers beneath young hair cells.

the 10 millimeter fetus. Towards this time (Fig. 89, a) the hair cells, which are nearly all fully differentiated, receive a minute arborization at their deep pole. This arborization is generally formed by only two relatively robust short branches which are intimately adherent to the covering of the receptor cell.

The nerve fibers or, more exactly, the peripheral branches of Scarpa's ganglion, come from far off. As though aware of the location of the rudimentary cristae and maculae, they travel towards both, approaching the hair cells either directly or circuitously. During this developmental phase (in the mouse or in the rabbit) there are no indications of the intraepithelial horizontal plexuses described by Niemach and by Lenhossék.

Finally, in the mouse fetus at term and, especially in the newborn mouse, the terminal chalices as well as the horizontal plexuses appear almost completely differentiated, as numerous authors have proved.

In short, the development of the vestibular terminations offers a very instructive example of a strict correlation between the differentiation of the neuroepithelial cells and the growth and arrangement of the terminal arborizations. Here also, just as was noted with regard to the cochlear nerve, it seems that there are some neurotropic substances which act initially and, later, certain attractive substances which are concentrated exclusively in the hair cells. It is unnecessary to add that neither in the connective tissue nor in the epithelium does one find pre-established orienting pathways. The metamorphoses undergone by the entire arborization and the changes and reshaping of the subepithelial plexuses preclude or render extremely improbable such an hypothesis. This hypothesis, moreover, is not in agreement with the relatively frequent instances of straying and turning back of exploratory fibers (Fig. 88, a).

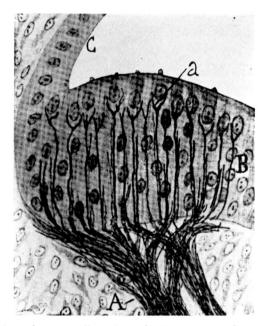

Fig. 89.   Section of an ampullar crista of a 1 cm mouse fetus. A) Fascicle of the vestibular nerve; B) sustentacular cells; a) bifurcation of a fiber beneath a hair cell.

Development of Sensory and Special Sense Terminations in the Tongue. The lingual nerve terminations subserving special and general sensibility have been the subject of numerous works. It suffices to cite the impressive names of Leven, Schwalbe, Rosemberg, Severin, Ranvier, Ehrlich, Arnstein, Fusari and Panasci, Lenhossék, Gehuchten, Jacques, Retzius and, among modern authors, Stahr, Cecherelli, Heidenhain (who has authoritatively studied the neuroepithelial cells of the foliate organ of the rabbit as well as the proliferation of the buds), and de Castro (who has studied the Golgi apparatus of the cellular types in these organs). It is not redundant to recall that the comparative anatomy of the gustatory apparatus and associated nerves has been greatly clarified by the contributions of Herrick, Johnston, Landacre, Sheldon, Kappers, Poulton, and Tuckerman. Finally, let us again cite Kölliker, who analyzed the nerve terminations of the lips, Bethe, who performed research on those of the palate, and Cutore, who studied those of the cheek.*

Again, we do not intend to analyze adult gustatory terminations. We will simply report some neurogenetic facts observed in mammalian embryos and fetuses. Our knowledge of this subject is still very incomplete, since the mammalian foliate organ has generally been studied by histologists who used inappropriate and capricious techniques.

We will discuss the preterminal plexus of the tongue first after which we will describe certain precocious phases of nerve development in the circumvallate papilla and foliate organ.

(a) Preterminal Nerve Plexus. As a result of the older research of Krause, Kölliker, Schwalbe, Fusari and Panasci, and the more modern studies of Rosemberg, Cecherelli, and Tello, we are not unaware of the fact that all the nerves of the tongue, before emitting their final branches, become organized into an exceedingly entangled diffuse plexus. The lingual nerve plexus, for example, which generally extends over the anterior two thirds of the mucosa,

---

*The reader who desires to acquaint himself with the current literature on gustatory terminations should consult the works of Heidenhain,[55,56] Sheldon,[215] Oppenheim,[134] and Kappers.[74] The older literature is thoroughly treated in the works by Retzius,[204,206] Lenhossék,[98] and Dogiel.[29]

assumes a surprising complexity. It lies in the depths of the subpapillary and adjacent muscle tissue and occasionally is arranged in 2 or 3 planes of small fascicles. The hypoglossal plexus is even more tangled and extends over a considerable area of the muscular portion. Its meshes are very compact initially (3 to 4 centimeter rabbit), but they enlarge progressively in order to accommodate an increasing number of muscle fibers.

We will confine our remarks to the lingual nerve plexus,* the formation of which is already very advanced in the 8 millimeter mouse and the 3 centimeter rabbit fetus. Analysis of its constituent fascicles reveals the presence of axons of two calibers, large and small. At the chiasms one notes both a change in size of the fibers and numerous bifurcations. Finally, each fiber possesses a cellular envelope, the rudiment of the future neurilemma sheath.

(*b*) *Formation of Ascending Subepithelial Branches.* As the development of the animal proceeds, the plexus becomes complicated by the arrival of new fibers which lodge themselves in the old sheaths and by the creation of new small secondary fascicles. However, the formation of exploratory ascending branches is initiated only in older fetuses (the 10 to 12 millimeter mouse, 4 to 5 centimeter rabbit). These branches, often isolated, arise at a right angle from tangential fibers of the plexus in question (Fig. 90, a). They travel across the zone of subpapillary embryonic connective tissue. They bifurcate several times on their way and approach the epithelium, the boundary of which stops them. Each fiber seems to travel separately, i.e., without an enveloping membrane, as though attracted by the superposed epithelium. Perhaps this attraction, represented by various lines of force, causes the afore-mentioned

---

*In rodents and in cats the lingual nerve probably furnishes sensory as well as taste fibers to the mucosa of the anterior two thirds of the tongue. The specific gustatory terminations probably arise from the facial nerve (geniculate ganglion) through the mediation of the chorda tympani, as most anatomists claim. Furthermore, the question of the relative participation of the glossopharyngeal, facial, and lingual (trigeminal) in these terminations is still debatable, especially when one descends from man to the inferior mammals, birds, reptiles, and fish. The reader desiring to inquire into this controversy should read Sheldon and, especially, Kappers.

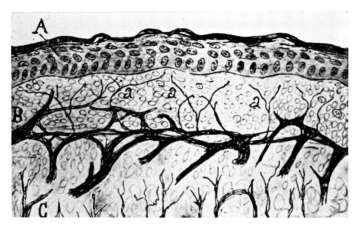

Fig. 90. Longitudinal section of the tongue of a 10 mm mouse fetus. A) Epithelium; B) sensory plexus formed by the lingual nerve; C) ascending hypoglossal nerve branches; a) exploratory branches arising from secondary fascicles of the horizontal plexus.

bifurcations. During this ascending journey of the isolated fibers, one notes some typical examples of stereotropism. Sometimes they travel along ascending capillaries, other times they accompany glandular rudiments, but most often they travel alone, as though breaking through the interstices of the compact wall of connective tissue cells of the dermis of the tongue.

(*c*) *Intraepithelial Branches.* There are two classes of branches, those of general sense and those of special sense (gustatory). The former are fully formed in the tongue of the newborn mouse. As is shown in Figure 91, fine twigs arise from the ascending fascicles or from exploratory fibers. They invade the epithelial germinal zone either directly or after one or more dichotomizations and travel up to the granular layer, where they usually terminate, after having bent tangentially. Some fibers bifurcate during their journey across the epithelium and a goodly number of them appear to terminate in a very small swelling. Here also, as in the skin, the granular zone constitutes an impassable barrier to the nerve fibers.

Sensory terminations occur quite precociously in the conical or filiform papillae. (In Figure 91, the direction of the section does not allow the connective-vascular axis of the papilla to be seen.)

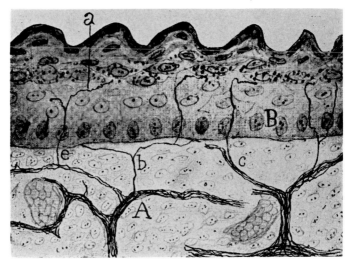

Fig. 91.   Longitudinal section of the tongue of a newborn mouse. A) Fascicle of the subdermal plexus; B) epidermis; a) ascending intraepidermal fibers.

In fact, the most lateral fibers terminating in the epithelium of the circumvallate papilla correspond to this sensory type (Fig. 96, a). In the cat the intraepithelial sensory fibers develop very precociously (4 centimeter stage or even earlier) when the epithelium begins to show pronounced foldings. These folds are the rudiments of the future papillae. Occasionally the fibers invading the lingual integument arrange themselves in fascicles which travel compactly to the granular layer, near which they unravel in a manner similar to that noted in the cornea and skin. The terminal apparatuses of Ruffini and other interesting types of terminations described by Cecherelli are not yet visible or, at least, are not easily recognizable in our preparations of early developmental phases.

It is probable that in the tongue, as in the skin, *the Malpighian cells in toto exert a neurotropic action which not only causes the nerve fibers to grow towards the epithelium and within it, but also produces the ascending ramifications within the dermal mucosa.* It is clear that mechanical obstacles may also intervene in this neurocladic phenomenon.

(*d*) *Gustatory Terminations.* In regard to this question, our preparations of the rabbit and mouse are a trifle incomplete. Reduced silver nitrate, which gives such excellent preparations of fibers of general sense, colors the fibers destined for the rodent foliate papillae only very palely or not at all. For this purpose colloidal silver is considerably inferior to the classical methods of Golgi and Ehrlich which have been employed by authors of the last century.

In the cat embryo, by contrast, the gustatory innervation of certain large papillae which are disseminated throughout the entire lingual mucosa and are concentrated especially along the edges and at the tip, is stained vigorously, consistently, and at early stages. Although the exceedingly embryonic configuration of these papillae in the embryo and fetus makes identification difficult, it seems probable that the well-impregnated papillae in our sections (Figs. 93 and 94) correspond to the circumvallate and, perhaps in some cases, to the fungiform types. It is possible that certain voluminous gustatory organs observed in the newborn cat represent still incompletely developed calciform ones.

The circumvallate papillae of the cat pass through several phases readily recognizable in the 28 millimeter embryo. In Figure 92 we illustrate these very precocious stages of these structures reproduced mainly from the edge of the tongue of a single embryo. The epithelium is constituted almost entirely of prismatic elongated cells covered superficially by one or two layers of flattened cells. The connective tissue core is completely absent or is only barely perceptible. The future terminal apparatus can be recognized in A, thanks to the presence of a compact plexus from which some exploratory ascending fibers emerge. These fibers have already reached the epithelium. In B, two ascending fibers have already succeeded in perforating the epithelial wall and travel directly towards the flattened cells. Finally, in Figure 92, C, the connective tissue core of the papilla is beginning to take shape and contains a very rich nerve plexus, composed of bundles which arrive from opposite directions. Note that three perforated fibers grow toward the surface in a nearly straight line. Figures 93 and 94 show more advanced developmental stages, in which both the fascicles of the nerve plexus as well as the intraepithelial fibers have attained

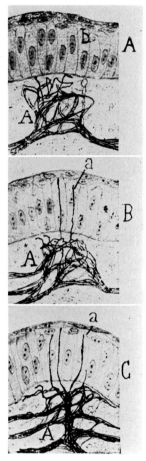

Fig. 92.   Developmental phases of the nerve terminations in the circumvallate papillae of the cat embryo. A) Expectant plexuses: a) intra-epithelial terminations; b) elongated epithelium of the rudiment of the papilla.

considerable development. Many of the filaments which cross the lingual epithelium are probably destined to be resorbed when the neuroepithelial elements are fully formed.

These terminal apparatuses can also be recognized, although with more difficulty, in the 10 and 12 millimeter mouse fetus (Fig. 95), where the papillary connective tissue is more developed than in cat embryos. Observe the formidable contingent of fibers which has arrived at the gustatory organ, the considerable thickness of the connective tissue core, and the abundant number of fibers which have succeeded in invading the epithelial cortex of the circumvallate papillae. These fibers terminate or bend just beneath the superficial flat cells.

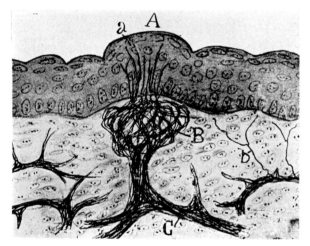

Fig. 93. Section of the circumvallate papilla of the tongue of a 28 mm cat fetus.

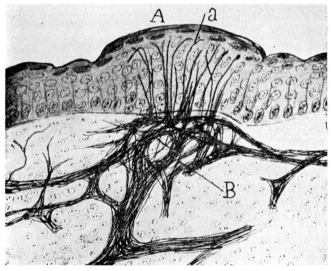

Fig. 94. Section of a lingual papilla of a 28 mm cat fetus.

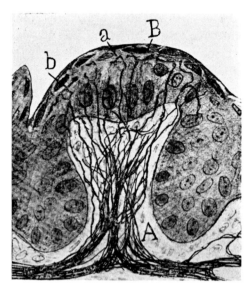

Fig. 95.   Circumvallate papilla of a 12 mm mouse fetus. A) Intradermal nerve plexus; B) superficial epithelium; a, b) intra-epithelial fibers.

The preceding observations reveal the interesting fact that *the gustatory fibers are attracted by a specific region of the tongue considerably before the neuroepithelial cells are formed and recognizable.* In fact, in the sections reproduced in Figures 92, 93, and 94 it is impossible to distinguish the true neuroepithelial cells from the other equally elongated cells of the rest of the epithelium. However, some distinction between these two classes of elements seems indicated in Figure 96.

It is necessary to study the cat fetus at term or the newborn cat in order to observe a clear-cut distinction between the ordinary lingual epithelium and the specialized neuroepithelial cells in the circumvallate papillae. In Figures 97 and 98 the taste buds are clearly shown. They consist of a peripheral zone composed of sustentacular cells and a central zone in which are found elements stained a somber brown. The latter are fusiform and lack or nearly lack a deep prolongation. Notice the elongated and well-developed connective tissue core of the papilla, the axis of which is traversed by a large nerve bundle instead of the complicated nerve plexus found in the embryos.

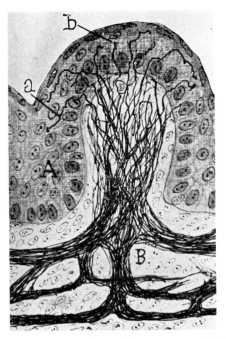

Fig. 96. Circumvallate papilla of a newborn mouse. A) Epithelial covering;
B) nerve plexus; a, b) intra-epithelial fibers.

Among the intraepithelial fibers, one readily distinguishes the
intragemmal fibers which are in contact with neuroepithelial cells
and the extragemmal fibers located along the outer rim of the papilla
and terminating in the ordinary epithelial pavement. Occasionally,
as in Figure 97, a, the extremities of the intragemmal fibers are
thickened and rough, a feature which we have not observed in all
papillae (perhaps because of faulty impregnation or for other reasons).

Finally, some gigantic papillae are ocassionally found in the cat.
On one of these papillae are seen twin taste buds oriented towards
the top of the epithelial mound (Fig. 98). A large axial nerve
fascicle divides towards the top and provides these taste buds
with appropriate nerve terminations. One occasionally notes twin
buds so close to one another that it seems to prove the interesting
process of proliferation of neuroepithelial corpuscles recently described by Heidenhain. In any case, these robust terminal appara-

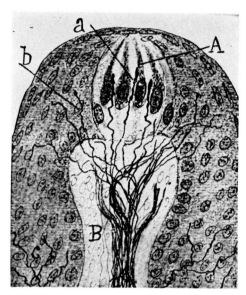

Fig. 97.   Circumvallate papilla of a newborn cat A) Taste bud; B) dermis of
the papilla with ascending nerve fascicles; a) intragemmal terminations; b)
extragemmal fibers; c) ordinary sensory terminations.

tuses do not possess a deep circular furrow. According to many
authors, and especially Retzius, the taste buds are located in the
walls of this furrow. In order to clearly identify the papilla in
question it is necessary to make a chronological study of these
papillae in the cat. We have not had time to perform such a study.

The nerves which penetrate the afore-mentioned papillae emanate from a very rich horizontal plexus which is occasionally arranged in two or three tangential layers above the muscle layer. Occasionally one can recognize the continuity of these plexuses with a
large lingual nerve bundle.

(e) *Rudiments of the Foliate Organ of Rabbit and Mouse
Embryos.* We have already noted that the neurofibrillar reaction
very often fails or gives excessively pale impregnations in the foliate organ of adult as well as young animals. However, preparations
of early fetuses (3.5 centimeter rabbit and 1 centimeter mouse)
have been obtained which show a very early phase of the development of the foliate apparatus. During this phase the epithelium,

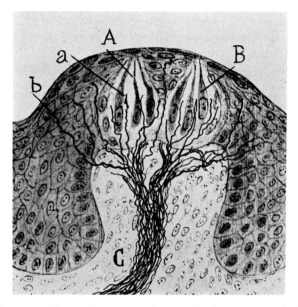

Fig 98.   Large papilla on the tongue of a cat showing two taste buds (A, B). C) Large fascicle of ascending fibers; a) intragemmal nerve fiber; b) extragemmal fiber.

in addition to lacking the characteristic foldings, does not show any indication of taste buds. This particular stage, readily recognizable in frontal sections of the posterior one-fourth of the tongue, is reproduced in Figure 99, B.

At the level of the thick lingual swelling, the glossopharyngeal nerve forms a very compact plexus, one of the richest and the most complicated plexuses of all nerve terminations. This plexus is composed of a deep portion of robust anastomotic fascicles and a superficial portion of fine fascicles. Many of the later are ascending and terminate by means of expectant brushlike endings. Some exploratory fibers terminated by a mass or growth cone emerge from the top of the plexus and plow through a large zone of embryonic tissue. These have not yet reached the epithelial frontier. Further anteriorly some tangential fascicles become separated from the superficial portions of the plexus and travel lengthwise along the dermis of the tongue. They terminate by expectant brushlike endings or fascicles (Fig. 99, b).

A similar picture is seen in the posterior one-fifth of the mouse tongue, but here the plexus is much less extensive and complicated than in the rabbit.

The comparison of the immobility, density and morphologic disorder of this subdermal plexus with the loose, ample and regular plexus characteristic of the adult animal constitutes a decisive demonstration that the embryonic plexiform arrangement represents a transititional state. The embryonic plexuses are storehouses of unformed fibers growing in all directions. Many of the branches of the fibers will be reabsorbed or radically transformed when the specific neuroepithelial structures become differentiated. The elaboration of the plexus and definitive terminal arborizations undoubtedly is a function of the epithelial organs with which the nerve fibers enter into conjugation or dynamic symbiosis.

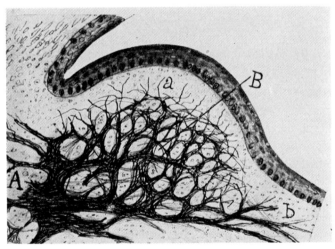

Fig. 99.   Rudiment of the foliate organ of a 3.5 cm rabbit embryo. The section is almost longitudinal and very lateral. A) Section of the glossopharyngeal nerve; B) compact plexus; a) exploratory fibers; b) fascicles directed forwards.

DISCUSSION AND CONCLUSION

Without further detailed examination of the neurotropic problem, the preceding neurogenetic studies permit us to establish the following statements as certain or at least as very probable:

1. The cutaneous mucosal epithelia and their derivatives,

the glands and hair follicles, exert a trophic and orienting action over the embryonic nerve fibers. This effect can be explained by the liberation of ferments or catalysts into the young connective tissue. These humoral agents stimulate assimilation of the growth cones. It is very possible that the germinal epithelium is the principal source of these influences.

2. In those epithelial organs which contain specific cells that are embraced by nerve fibers, it is necessary to acknowledge two successive influences. One is global or diffuse, localized throughout the epithelium, or perhaps in the sustentacular elements; its function is to attract the general stream of embryonic nerve fibers. The other is individual, emanating from specific elements such as peripheral elements of the tactile hairs, hair cells of the cochlea, vestibular maculae and cristae, and bipolar elements of the taste buds; its function is to establish an intimate symbiosis and a kind of selective attraction for strayed fibers. Occasionally the epithelial cell is almost surrounded by the terminal arborization, like a microbe by a leucocyte.

3. The afore-mentioned global influences of the young epithelium and its derivatives explain many facts concerning the orientation and ramifications of the embryonic fibers, if one acknowledges that the integumental mass exhibits tangential as well as radial attractive forces.

4. In general, every bifurcation not provoked by mechanical obstacles suggests the intervention of two or more neurotropic forces acting in different directions.

5. Once the epithelial mass or its specific cells is provided with a terminal arborization, the liberation of trophic and orienting substances ceases or becomes considerably attenuated. There are some cases (hair cells of the innervated vestibular and acoustic apparatuses) which suggest the idea of a negative chemotaxis: something akin to the repulsion phenomenon observed in the fertilized ovum. Thus could one explain why a mammalian acoustic hair cell, for example, almost always receives only a single terminal nerve chalice.

6. For the time being we do not guess at the nature and the mechanism of the orienting and trophic activities. As various authors

have suggested, their nature could be physical (e.g., effects of difference in electrical potential); but the specificity of the influences and their multiplicity in a single organic region seems to argue in favor of the hypothesis that enzymes or hormones are liberated by the epithelium into the adjacent mesodermal fields. For example, with the electrical hypothesis it becomes difficult to understand how, of the large nervous contingent arriving at the mammalian snout, some fibers travel without error towards the cutaneous muscle fibers, others towards the hair follicles, others to the epidermis and, finally, some to the tactile apparatus of the dermis. A similar multiple specificity is found in the tongue, where the hypoglossal fibers invade the muscle, trigeminal fibers innervate the ordinary papillae, and facial (geniculate ganglion) and glossopharyngeal fibers go to the gustatory papillae.

7. Our observations on the development of nerves, which agree in principle with those of Tello and other authors, reveal four successive phases: a) phase of small isolated or barely anastomotic fascicles terminating in more or less pointed brushes; b) phase of primary diffuse tangential plexuses; c) phase of small secondary ascending fascicles and of exploratory wandering fibers; d) phase of the assault of the epithelial structures. This is the most common order, but overlapping and exceptions exist among these stages and it is not rare to find exploratory fibers emitted during the primary plexus phase. One must not forget that these precursory fibers are even recognizable in early embryos when the formation of the nerve roots is initiated.

8. The essential difference between the adult and the embryonic plexuses is that the latter possess large meshes, because of the absence or rudimentary state of the muscle fibers, glands, and connective tissue, whereas the former appear more loose and regular, showing very ample meshes clearly filled with differentiated tissues. In the embryonic dog, in contrast to newborn animals, the dislocation of the fascicles can attain more than a millimeter.

9. Heidenhain's opinion [54] of the primary and secondary cutaneous plexuses seems very plausible. He considers them a reserve of fibers, in good part superfluous, which precede the appearance of the terminal organs and await the differentiation of the latter to

provide them with specific terminations. It is clear that many axon-al branches (not the axons) will be resorbed and that all the fas-cicles of the plexus undergo the most radical rearrangements and transformations as a result of towing effects of the growing terrain as well as the successive appearance of neurotropic sources.

10. Disregarding its physiological utility, the precocious forma-tion of the plexuses seems to us to depend on three positive and one negative condition. The first are: a) the incessant growth of the axons and their branches by which they invade the growing meso-dermal spaces; b) the reciprocal attraction or neurotropism of the fibers which induces them to seek each other out and gather to-gether in small fascicles; c) the precocious differentiation of a membranous bed around these small fascicles across which the new-ly arrived sprouts travel without encountering any obstacles. They travel in various directions, very often withdrawing from secondary fascicles to the primary ones. The negative condition is that neuro-tropic influences are lacking or very weak during plexus forma-tion because of the extraordinary tardiness of the development of the terminal organs (specific epithelial structures). What Harri-son* calls *specific reactions between nerves and terminal apparatuses* (equivalent to neurotropism) and Heidenhain cells *syngenesia* (simultaneous and co-ordinated development of organs and nerve arborizations) are real, but very late, processes. In reality, there is a very long period during which the young nerve fibers grow and ramify, even though the terminal apparatuses for which they are destined are not yet outlined.

11. The precocity of the peripheral nerve plexuses could easily be explained teleologically, by supposing that *only embryonic con-*

---

*Since there are many superfluous fibers in the plexuses and since many of the pathways are excessively long and even retrograde, one could not attribute any economic advantage to such structures. Futhermore, one could not accept as a general rule Tello's ingenious idea that the plexuses, upon arrival at an organ (a muscle, for example), surrender fibers deriving from different nerves. In reality, the plexiform arrangement is observed very early in the functionally homogeneous systems of the central nervous system. In fact, it is as common an arrangement in the central nervous system (among fibers of similar origin and function) as it is among the fibers of the vestibular or spiral ganglion of the acoustic nerve.

nective tissue offers mechanical conveniences and efficacious neurotropic activity for the progress of the precocious fibers. In this respect it could be compared to the early scar tissue of transected nerves. Naturally, the young connective tissue framework of the term fetus and newborn animal would lack these neurotropic influences. Also, in term and newborn animals, the enormity of the distances would constitute an insurmountable obstacle to the late arrival of sensory, special sense and motor fibers.*

---

*We must again repeat that our neurotropic concept is only a working hypothesis and that other hypotheses of equal merit could well be substituted for it. In the present state of science, and in view of the enormous complexity of the subject, it would be futile to consider any neurogenetic theory as definitive. (*Note for the French edition.*)

Chapter 5

CONTRIBUTION TO THE STUDY OF THE STRUCTURE OF MOTOR PLAQUES*[176]

IN OUR FIRST PAPER[174] on the reduced silver nitrate staining procedure we stated that under certain conditions one obtains a very expressive impregnation of neurofibrils of the terminal nervous arborization of muscle fibers. If the staining is perfect, we said, each wide portion of the arborization presents a network with clear spaces which narrow and finally disappear at the level of the strangulated portions of the terminal branches.

We have recently obtained good impregnations of the ocular muscles of the several day old rabbit, as well as the very young pigeon and other birds (4 to 6 days after hatching). We shall discuss these preparations.

As is seen in Figures 100 and 101, the axon of the efferent nerve fiber stains very intensely in young birds, and the transverse striations of the muscle are clearly distinguished. At the bifurcations, the neurofibrillar network condenses, appearing almost homogeneous, and the fiber presents a strangulated portion, such as is observed in preparations stained by methylene blue and gold chloride.

Ordinarily, the terminal arborization arises from a branch of bifurcation, the other branch pursuing its course to other motor plaques (Figs. 100 and 101). Once arrived at the granular substance of the plaque, this branch bifurcates (Fig. 100) or divides in a more complicated manner. The resultant twigs suddenly bulge out, as though a transparent liquid had dispersed the neurofibrils. The neurofibrils now appear sharply colored in a brown or red tone and are arranged in a loose and frequently anastomotic plexus. In some regions, the nerve branch again narrows, the filaments con-

---

*This short, extremely incomplete study is not comparable to the very extensive studies of Tello, Perroncito, or Boeke. Its only purpose is to describe, for the first time, the neurofibrillar framework of motor plaques in young animals. We consider these neurofibrillar arrangements, especially that reproduced in Figure 101, as early developmental phases. (*Note for the French edition.*)

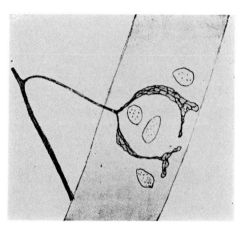

Fig. 100. A motor plaque of an ocular muscle of a several-day-old bird. Silver nitrate impregnation after ammoniacal alcohol fixation.

densing into a bundle in which it is impossible to distinguish any structure; they later present new dilatations. One can draw an interesting conclusion from this first observation: The moniliform or varicose appearance of the nervous arborization, attributed by some authors to the action of reagents (gold chloride, methylene blue, etc.), is actually a pre-existing arrangement, produced by the presence among the filaments of the nerve branches of a liquid or semiliquid substance which is refractory to silver impregnation. The unmistakable anastomoses of the varicose neurofibrils (which recalls the appearance of the nerve cell reticulum) proves, moreover, that the motor termination does not consist of a simple spreading out of neurofibrils, as has been believed, but rather of a continuous framework in which most of these filaments loose their individuality, giving rise to a system of interdependent conducting elements.

Finally, the branches in question divide again, giving birth to a new series of identical moniliform trunks which terminate, not in brush points, but in loops, i.e., in curvilinear trabeculae having a more or less complicated meshwork (Fig. 100).

The preceding description relates especially to the simplest arborizations of the avian motor plaque (Fig. 100). But more complicated arrangements also exist, as can be seen in Figure 101. In these motor plaques, some more or less thick branches terminate

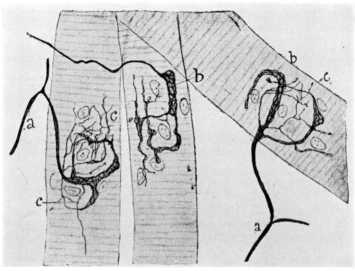

Fig. 101. Three motor plaques of the ocular muscles of a several-day-old bird. a) Efferent axon; b) thick reticular portions of the terminal arborization; c) free ramified neurofibrils.

in an obtuse point. Other detached, very slender, ramified fibrils also terminate freely in the territory of the plaque. These latter fibrils, which often arise from the points of bifurcation or the extremity of the large branches, can give rise to a complicated plexus (Fig. 101, c).

We do not know the significance of these subtle filaments; they could very well represent a developmental stage of the large branches, since we have not seen them again in birds more advanced in development nor in the 12 day old rabbit.

In mammals the results have been less elegant and more capricious than in birds. In Figure 102 we show segments of two motor arborizations of the ocular muscles of a 12 day old rabbit. In (a) is observed an efferent nerve fiber giving rise to an arborization, the form of which coincides with the well-known classical description. Several thick, loosely reticulated trunks and some strangulated parts without appreciable texture are seen. At the level of the terminal ends (b) one also observes a more or less complicated meshwork rather than free neurofibrillar points.

In Figure 102, d, e, we show some very simple arborizations connected by long nerve fibrils which may represent *ultraterminal branches,* since they are often noted in muscle fibers which possess a true typical motor plaque.

In summary (to avoid prolonging this brief note), from the preceding observations the following three conclusions may be drawn, of which one is technical, the second histological and the third physiological:

1. Formula 1 (fixation in 1.5% silver nitrate) and formula 2 (fixation in ammoniacal alcohol) of the reduced silver nitrate procedure can be applied to the study of the motor plaque, provided that newborn or very young animals are used.

2. The varicosities of the final arborization, like the terminal ends, do not arise from the spreading out of independent filaments, but from a reticulation of relatively large polygonal meshes.

3. Granting that only terminal nets exist (at least as the principal

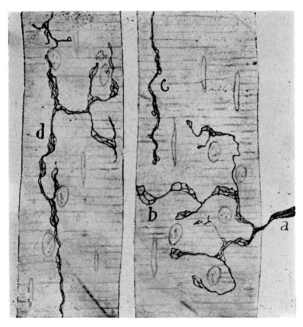

Fig. 102.   Nerve arborizations in muscle fibers of a young rabbit. a) Efferent axon; b) enlarged portion of the arborization; c, d) elongated terminal fibers.

arrangement), the theory of Bethe and Nissl concerning the functional and anatomical independence of neurofibrils becomes untenable.

One can also formulate similar doubts about the purely longitudinal conduction of these filaments. Granting the reticular arrangement, it is undeniable that the motor discharges must leave from the path of these filaments, that is to say, perpendicular to them; otherwise we will find ourselves forced to concede that the cytoplasm also participates in the conductive activity.

Chapter 6

REMARKS ON THE MOTOR PLAQUES OF THE MAMMALIAN TONQUE [195]

AS AN EXAMPLE of the results that can be obtained by applying the previously described formula [194] to the study of peripheral terminations, we present here some drawings of the motor plaques of the 3 month old rabbit.

In the rabbit's tongue the motor arborization usually lies near the ends of the muscle fibers, i.e., in the vicinity of the fibrous partitions into which the muscle fibers insert. This position has already been noted by many authors in certain muscles of fish and batrachians and by Tello in the ontogenetic development of the motor plaque. The neurofibrillar architecture of the terminal ramification coincides with that which we [176] and Tello [219,220] observed a long time ago. It was thoroughly studied later by Boeke and other authors who applied the Bielschowsky method to this subject.

Each branch encloses a fascicle of neurofibrils which, at the level of the varicosities and terminal swellings, presents a network of fibers separated by an abundant neuroplasm. The finest twigs terminate in rings or in free loops. No branch goes beyond the limits of the granular mass of the plaque (Fig. 103, A, B).

It is evident that the neurofibrils only represent the framework of the arborization. As is shown by the Ehrlich and gold chloride methods, one must acknowledge the existence of a thick sheath of neuroplasm around the rings and loops. In the adult rabbit (Figs. 103, 104 and 105) we have not found Ruffini's *ultraterminal fibers* nor Bremer's *accessory fibers,* structures which have been the subject of interesting studies by Perroncito, Regaud, Fabre, Cecherelli, Tello, and especially Boeke and his school. Only in the motor plaque, depicted in Figure 104, a, have we noted a fine fiber which arises from the very trunk of the efferent fiber and adds to the contingent of the projections of the arborization. It terminates by a bulb or spherule near the principal ramification.

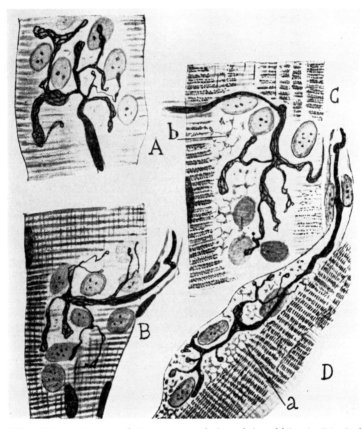

Fig. 103. Motor plaques of the tongue of the adult rabbit. A, B) Ordinary appearance of the terminal ramification; C, D) plaques in which Boeke's network (a, b) is seen.

But it is very possible that this fine fiber does not correspond at all to the one that Boeke described and considered as sympathetic in nature. It is important to recall that, according to many scholars, two types of accessory fibers are believed to exist: 1. Some would represent motor collaterals of fibers destined for other plaques. This type is the only one observed by Tello, who absolutely denies the existence of nerve branches of another type. As Perroncito has noted, the ultraterminal fiber of Ruffini could even be a variety of this type of axon. 2. The other fibers would be foreign to the hypo-

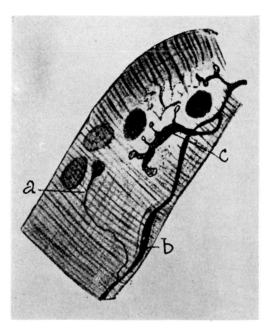

Fig. 104.   Muscle fiber of the tongue of the adult rabbit. a) Accessory fiber
terminating by means of a bulb.

glossal fibers and would belong to the sympathetic nervous system
(Boeke, Agduhr, Dusser de Barenne).

In our preparations of the tongue of the adult rabbit, cat and
young mouse, only fibers of the first category appear clearly. A glance
at Figures 106 and 107 (tongue of the 10 to 15 day old mouse) is
sufficient to reveal the arborization of two fibers in some plaques.
Generally one fiber is finer than the other. Thick sections clearly reveal that this accessory fiber is a collateral which emerges at right
angles from a neurite of a neighboring nerve fascicle (Fig. 106, a,
b).

To Tello's masterful study we can add nothing new concerning
the origin and varieties of these accessory branches. We therefore re-
commend the reader to Tello's tremendously important monograph
on the ontogeny of the motor plaque [223] and to his overly neglected
communication on the regeneration of motor plaques.[220] Allow us
to dwell on some already known details concerning the principal

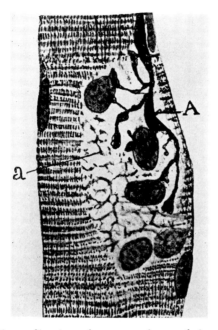

Fig. 105. A nearly profile view of a motor plaque of the tongue of a rabbit. A) Swelling of the efferent fiber; a) network of the granular substance of the plaque.

fiber, i.e., the one which usually exclusively forms the motor plaque. In preparations of the several day old cat and the 10 to 15 day old mouse where the motor ramification is still slightly embryonic, the attraction of the nuclei over the secondary and tertiary branches is plainly perceived. And when there is only one projection terminated in a falciform thickening, the latter almost always envelops one of the nuclei (Fig. 107, B). When two branches converge, each of their extremities sometimes envelops a nucleus, giving rise to shapes like a figure 8 or other even more complicated ones (Fig. 107, D). This attractive influence of the nuclei, and the relation between the number of nuclei and the richness of the ramification are among Tello's most interesting discoveries. The accessory or accidental motor fiber ordinarily terminates in a ring, a reticulated bulb or even a small rudimentary arborization. There are exceptions, however (Fig. 106, a, b, c, d).

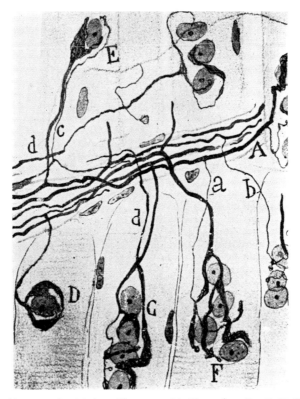

Fig. 106.   Tongue of a 15 day old mouse. A) Nerve bundle; C, E, F) accessory plaques (a, c, d); D) nucleus enveloped by a terminal nervous ramification.

Inasmuch as we have not observed the presence of accessory sympathetic fibers of the afore-mentioned second category in the adult cat or rabbit, we cannot say anything concrete about them. In any case, alongside the large fibers of nerve fascicles one sometimes finds other fine ramified fibers going to another bundle of nerves (Fig. 107, a).

Nevertheless, we do not deny existence of unmyelinated fibers as described by Boeke, Agduhr, Dusser de Barenne, and others. But we find ourselves very perplexed about this point, not only because the histological demonstration of such fibers is most difficult (it is almost impossible to distinguish a fine unmyelinated collateral located far from its parent myelinated fiber from a purely sympathetic fiber), but also because we have been greatly impressed by the opinions and criticisms of the great physiologist Langley,[90] who is an indisputable authority on the anatomy and physiology of the sympathetic nervous system. In any case, since this is a factual question which can only be resolved objectively, we reserve judgment until our observations are more extensive and complete.

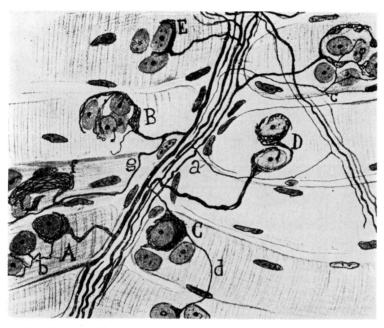

Fig. 107. Tongue of a 15 day old mouse. A) Terminal arborization from which a fine fiber (b) emanates; B) axon whose branches innervate 2 plaques; C, d) ultraterminal fiber of Ruffini; D) arborization shaped like a figure 8 in adaptation to some nuclei; E) ramification intimately applied to a nucleus; a) branch of an axon being incorporated into a neighboring fascicle; c) fine accessory fiber.

However, permit me to make a general commentary on this subject, which perhaps will bear some relation to the question of the two categories of accessory fibers. It seems to me that, except for Tello and a few others, scholars have not paid sufficient attention to the truly remarkable number of developmental errors found both in central as well as peripheral terminations. We have presented numerous examples of these in embryonic spinal ganglia, spinal cord, medulla oblongata, cerebellum, retina, and in the regeneration of nerves, ganglia, and spinal cord. In regard to this subject, recall the numerous strayed fibers which form balls in the spinal ganglia (Nageotte, Marinesco, Levi, Agduhr, de Castro, and ourselves).

In his numerous works on the development and regeneration of nerves, Tello himself has shown numerous examples of these developmental errors. De Castro has also described interesting unnatural or monstrous arrangements in the cerebellum and sensory ganglia, errors which persist in the adult state. Vadillo, extending one of our old observations on the chick embryo, commonly found a goodly number of wandered sensory cells undergoing degeneration around the meninges of the spinal cord.[228] Because of their physiological uselessness many of these anomalies undoubtedly disappear when the adult phase arrives. But there are others, which may remain (albeit somewhat altered) perhaps indefinitely, especially if the aberrant cell or fiber establishes a connection with some nerve fiber or neuron.

Two decisive questions now arise: Do the accessory fibers and other peculiar arrangements noted by these authors in fetal and young animals belong to the category of abnormal arrangements? And are they destined, at least in part, to disappear or be greatly transformed in the adult? Most certainly mechanical conditions capable of explaining unexpected developmental atrophies and metamorphoses are not lacking. As Tello has demonstrated, the later growth of muscle fibers, the stretching and ramification of the nerve fibers, etc., could also induce important changes in shape and composition of the nervous arborizations, even while supposing that their original principal formative factors might still persist.

Another of the arrangements which appears from time to time in our preparations is the reticulum of the plaque. This has been well described and drawn by Boeke and his disciples. In Figures 103, a, b, and 105, a, we show this framework which, in our preparations of the rabbit tongue, never leaves the boundary of the plaque. Its appearance is that of a pale net with thick irregular trabeculae which bound polygonal meshes of variable extent. In some regions they disappear or are represented by isolated clots, as though the staining were incomplete.

This reticulation is not at all perceptible in the immense majority of motor plaques, a fact which has already been mentioned by Boeke [15,16] and others,[2,18] who found them only in sections stained intensely with ammoniacal silver. The dark hue of the staining and the impossibility of staining this network by the other formulas which selectively and vigorously stain the branches of the nervous arborization (Ehrlich, Golgi, gold chloride methods) justify Tello's view that Boeke's findings can be considered the result of a coagulation artifact. Tello admits, however, that this interpretation is just a possibility.

In our opinion and without absolutely rejecting Tello's we are inclined to accept the existence of the afore-mentioned framework. The continuity of the trabeculae with certain lines of the striated matter (see Fig. 103, D, a) and several analogous arguments which we will come to later, lend some plausibility to this point of view.

On the other hand, we have not been able to convince ourselves of the continuity of this intraplacular reticulum with the neurofibrils of the nervous arborization. Apart from the fact that the trabeculae of this reticulum are paler than the neurofibrils (a very significant peculiarity even recognizable in several of Boeke's drawings), we have often noted that the former frequently pass beneath the branches of the nervous arborization without entering into any relationship with the latter other than that of proximity. Moreover, their appearance is somewhat granular and differs appreciably from the smoothness and homogeneity of the neurofibrils, at least as shown by our staining procedures (Figs. 103 and 104).

In summary, we provisionally view Boeke's network as being the skeleton or framework of the protoplasm of the plaque. It is in continuity with the striated matter, of which it constitutes a non-differentiated, seemingly embryonic portion. Such a hypothetical view acquires considerable plausibility when, to argue by analogy, we recall the following facts: a) During the embryonic period, in the myotubal phase of the muscle fiber, the axial granular substance sometimes shows (with Heidenhain's and other staining methods) an ill-formed reticular appearance in continuity with the lines of the striated matter. b) Certain interprotoplasmic frameworks, more or less similar to the neurofibrillar ones, have been described in numerous ectodermal and mesodermal cells by use of silver methods and even by formulas selective for the intraneuronal reticulum. In this regard let us recall the framework demonstrated by Tello in certain nonneural hypophysial cells (Achúcarro's method), are very fine intracellular net impregnated by Tello in embryonic connective elements (neurofibrillar method with pyridine fixation), the elegant nets discovered by Rio-Hortega in cancer cells and other tissues, the reticulum we noted in the soma of the ependymal cells of the cat (modified Levaditi procedure), the frameworks stainable by Heidenhain's method and its variants in many epithelial cells (Heidenhain, Prenant, and many others). Because of their diverse appearances, these frameworks have received different names (epitheliofibrils, tonofibrils, ergastoplasm, hinetoplasm, etc.).

We are therefore increasingly inclined to the view that every adult or embryonic meso-, ecto-, or endodermal cell contains a protoplasmic framework of delicate anastomotic fibers, homologous to the neurofibrillar framework. As Lenhossék states with regard to neurons, this reticulum would function in cellular growth and in the maintenance of cell shape. The architecture, chemical composition, and probably also the colloidal constitution of such sustentacular trabeculae could vary for each cellular type, on account of the division of labor and the adaptation to particular functions. Our observations on interrupted nerve fibers [198] lead us to believe that this framework plays an important role in growth and regeneration by the proliferation of its ultramicroscopic particles.

It goes without saying that this opinion, as it relates to the framework of the plaque, is subject to revision and requires new and more thorough research. For that reason we consider the preceding opinions merely as provisional views or as theoretical suggestions. Every histologist who proposes to study the problem posed by Boeke's interesting work must bear these considerations in mind. This subject will be treated at greater length in our laboratory as soon as we can gather adequate material.

Madrid, November, 1925

Part III

SPINAL CORD

Chapter 7

THE TIME OF APPEARANCE OF NERVE CELL PROCESSES IN THE CHICK SPINAL CORD[156]

H IS [69,70] DESCRIBED two zones in the spinal cord of the 4 week old human embryo: an internal epithelial ependymal layer, surrounding the medullary canal, and a peripheral mantle layer composed of primordial nerve cells or neuroblasts. The neuroblasts are pyriform and have a single process, the axis-cylinder, extended toward the white matter. This pyriform arrangement of the neuroblast has been confirmed recently by Lachi.[88]

Our research on the 3 and 4 day old chick embryo, employing routine techniques (celloidin or paraffin embedding, hematoxylin or carmine staining, etc.), has enabled us to verify His's interesting observations of neuroblasts and primordial epithelial cells. We have also found that the fascicle of white matter on the dorsolateral aspect of the cord of the 3 to 4 day embryo is formed exclusively by the central prolongations of the bipolar cells of the spinal ganglia.

Wishing to verify and extend His's findings with the Golgi technique and to learn in what order the nervous and protoplasmic processes appear in each region of the embryonic gray matter, we have made a series of attempts at impregnation (Golgi method) of spinal cords of 3, 4, 5, 6 and more days of incubation.

The data are very incomplete because, unfortunately, it is impossible to obtain a black reaction before the fourth day of incubation. Even at the fourth day the results are quite indistinct; only from the fifth day can all the medullary elements be stained with certainty.

We are going to describe briefly the development stages which we have been able to observe from the fourth day of incubation. Let us say in passing that these data pertain exclusively to the thoracic and cervical cord.

Fourth Day. At this time the neural elements of the ventral horn (i.e., the motor cells, the cells of the ventrolateral column, and some of the more ventrally placed commissural elements) are already well developed. However, in spite of their secondary protoplasmic outgrowths, the neuroblasts (e.g., the ventral horn cells) are still spindle-shaped, much like the pyriform neuroblasts of His (Fig. 108, A). This elongation is even more pronounced in certain elements (Fig. 108, C, B) whose axis-cylinder is continuous with the fibers of the lateral or ventral funiculi.

On the other hand, the cells of the ventral commissure, especially those located in the most dorsal part of the mantle layer, preserve their neuroblastic character perfectly and appear quite similar to the embryonic elements in the human spinal cord described by His (Fig. 108, D, E).

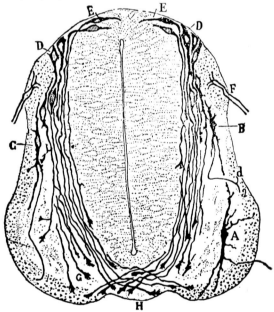

Fig. 108.   Section of the thoracic spinal cord of a 4 day chick embryo. Cells copied from 2 successive sections. Very rapid Golgi method. A) Ventral root cell; B) cell of the ventrolateral funiculus; C) cell of the ventral funiculus, D) pyriform neuroblasts whose axis-cylinder terminates at the level of the ventral commissure by a growth cone; E) primordial nerve cells which still retain the spongioblast form; F) dorsal root; G) growth cones; H) embryonic ventral commissure.

We will trace all the stages of growth and development of the neural and protoplasmic expansions of these elements. These cells are pyriform or pyramidal and possess facets which seem to touch those of neighboring cells. Those placed in the most dorsal region of the mantle layer in contact with the dorsal surface of the spinal cord are either devoid of protoplasmic processes or possess only a very short and thick one, which seems directed towards the ependyma (Fig. 108, E). But the cells located in the more ventral zone (D) are provided with irregular points, or rigid spines, which represent the early stage of future protoplasmic prolongations.

The ventral portion of these pyriform elements is stretched to form a very elongated cone and is continuous with a nerve fiber. This fiber is directed ventrad forming, with similar fibers, a ventro-dorsal fascicle which enters the ventral funiculus of the opposite side. Each fiber of this commissural fascicle terminates at a variable distance, proportional to its degree of development. The terminal structure is a conical swelling studded with very irregular spiny processes. This terminal swelling, which we call the growth cone, clearly demarcates the extremity of every developing nerve fiber. Moreover, one can recognize it very well, in silver chromate impregnations, by the brown or chestnut color of the small spiny processes which adorn its surface (Fig. 108, G, H). Sometimes the growth cone possesses long triangular, lamellated, occasionally branched prolongations which seem to wind among the neural elements while making their way through the interstitial substance.

The most embryonic of the commissural elements lie in the most dorsal zone of the mantle layer, in contact with the spinal cord surface, between the vertical fascicle of the dorsal root and the epithelial column (Fig. 108, D). Those commissural cells whose axis-cylinder is very short are scarcely distinguishable from epithelial elements. They are set among the latter, sharing their shape and their direction, sending forth two processes: one internal, ependymal, which terminates near the central canal; the other external, the primitive axis-cylinder, which describes a semicircle, becomes oriented dorsoventrally (Fig. 108, E), and terminates in a growth cone. Sometimes the very short axis-cylinder bifurcates, producing two terminal cones, of which one seems to go toward the ventral commissure, the other toward the nearby lateral funiculus.

These elements, whose epithelial appearance and location demonstrate their strict relationship with the spongioblasts, are also found in both the dorsal and the lateral part of the spinal epithelium of older embryos (up to 9 days' incubation). In Figure 111 we have pictured some of these elements taken from a section of spinal cord of an 8 day old chick embryo.

In our opinion, the production of neuroblasts is not only from round cells which multiply by mitosis and grow between the internal processes of the spongioblasts (*germinative cells* of His), but also takes place by differentiation and displacement of the epithelial elements. The external or radial filament constitutes the axis-cylinder and the ependymal or internal appendage perhaps becomes the first protoplasmic process. If we reject this direct epithelial origin, it is impossible to explain why the youngest neuroblasts have a more epithelioid shape than those more advanced in development and why certain embryonic nerve cells exhibit the location, orientation, and connections of the spongioblasts (see Figs. 108, E; 111, A, B, C; 114, a).*

It may be that atrophy of the ependymal process causes certain cells to become pyriform or polyhedral like those described by His. Nevertheless, not having succeeded in impregnating younger nerve elements (at the third day of incubation, for example), we do not presume to deny the existence of initially pyriform or spherical neuroblasts, especially in the region of the ventral horn where development is very precocious.

Fifth Day. The commissural cells which we have just described still retain their ventrodorsal elongation (Fig. 109, D, E) and their generally fusiform appearance. However, in some commissural cells, one can now observe lateral protoplasmic processes as well as a larger dorsally directed appendage (the ependymal process). Most of the axis-cylinders now reach the region of the contralateral

---

*We do not venture to affirm this interpretation now because the epithelial appearance of some neuroblasts could also be explained by a delay in their migration toward the periphery and by adaptation to the interstices of the epithelial columns. (*Note for the French edition.*)

funiculus after having traversed the commissure. However several growth cones are found at the level of the ventral commissure and adjacent regions.

The cells of the ventrolateral funiculus, those of the ventral root, and the more ventrally placed commissural elements are now completely formed. The elements of the dorsal funiculus have not yet appeared, or at least they are not as clearly distinguishable as the dorsal spongioblasts.

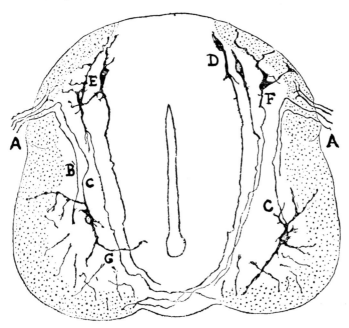

Fig. 109. Transverse section of the spinal cord of a 5 day chick embryo. Cells copied from 3 successive sections. A) Dorsal root; B) motor axis-cylinder forming part of the dorsal root; C) motor axis-cylinder arising from certain ventral horn cells and travelling to the dorsal root; D) cells of the ventral commissure which remain embryonic in appearance; E) further-developed cells; G) growing collateral fibrils of the white matter.

Well-stained motor fibers are sometimes found in the dorsal root of the 5 day embryo (Fig. 109, B, C). Lenhossék [94] claims that he has been able to impregnate these axis-cylinders at the fourth day. We have only suceeded in staining them at the beginning of the fifth day, but considering the degree of development of their cells of origin, it is certain that such fibers must appear at least at the third or fourth day of incubation.

Knowledge of these motor fibers of the dorsal root is very recent. They were discovered simultaneously by Lenhossék and ourselves. For almost a year we suspected their existence. We wrote in 1890:[154] "Sometimes in very young spinal cords (5 day old chick embryos) we have come across large dorsal root fibers which extend as far as the ventral horn cells without displaying the bifurcated and arborized appearance of the others (i.e., the sensory fibers of ganglionic origin); but the rarity of the observation prevents us from knowing whether it is a constant and peculiar feature of the large fibers." Afterwards, very recently, we sent a preparation to Lenhossék in which is seen a fiber that starts from the ventral horn, travels through the dorsal root and almost the entire spinal ganglion without terminating on the bipolar cells. In a letter that Lenhossék had the kindness to cite, we said, "It seems to us that they are dorsal motor roots emerging from cells of the ventrolateral horn." But we still retained doubts which were recently dissipated by the work of Lenhossék and especially by our new and more conclusive preparations.

The cells of origin of these motor fibers are copied very accurately in Figure 109, C. They are located in the dorsal part of the ventral horn and are slightly fusiform and quite large. The axis-cylinder emerges from a protoplasmic outgrowth, and at the level of the embryonic dorsal column (primordial posterior column of His) it describes an acute or right angle, travels obliquely ventrolaterally and penetrates the dorsal root. During its intra- and extramedullary path this axis-cylinder does not give off any collateral branches.

The number of these motor cells seems very restricted, for out of several hundred preparations of embryonic spinal cord, we have found 8 or 10 ventral horn elements whose axis-cylinder is directed towards the dorsal root. It is necessary to be aware of the difficulty of staining these fibers. The only effective staining of them has been obtained between the fifth and the sixth day. After this time, only the sensory root fibers are stained.

At the end of the fifth day the first collaterals of the white matter appear in the internal portion of the ventral column. These are very short, straight, nonbranched filaments terminating most often in conical swellings and provided at times with small divergent spines (Fig. 109, G). The other collaterals have not yet developed.

Sixth Day. The collaterals of the ventral funiculus elongate and are now provided with some terminal ramifications which penetrate deeply into the gray matter. Some newly forming collateral fibers also emerge from the lateral funiculus.

Seventh Day. The collaterals of the ventrolateral funiculus lengthen and ramify more and more (Fig.110, B). One now notes that some of these fibers, coming from the internal portion of the ventral funiculus, cross the ventral commissure and terminate by a large varicose arborization in the contralateral ventral horn (Fig. 110, A). At this time collateral fibers of the dorsal funiculus appear (Fig. 110, D), the youngest of which are those coming from the internal portion. They also terminate by swellings comparable to growth cones of axis-cylinders.

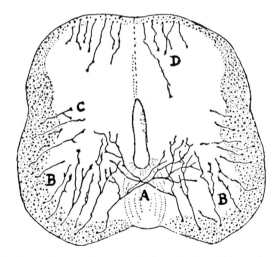

Fig. 110. Section of the spinal cord of a 7 day chick embryo. Very rapid Golgi method. A) Collateral fibers of the ventral funiculus forming a decussation in the ventral commissure; B) less developed collateral fibers which terminate by growth cones; C) the most embryonic collaterals which belong to the lateral funiculus; D) collaterals of the dorsal funiculus.

Eighth Day. The number of commissural and funicular cells is greatly increased as the result of differentiation and displacement of epithelial cells (Fig. 111). Several of the commissural cells clearly retain their elongated shape and their position among the epithelial elements. They can be differentiated from the epithelial elements principally by their external process, which bends and proceeds either to the ventral commissure or to the adjacent white matter. The axis-cylinder ultimately becomes continuous with one or more nerve fibers. One can see in these cells (Fig. 111, D, C) that the ependymal prolongation has become transformed into the

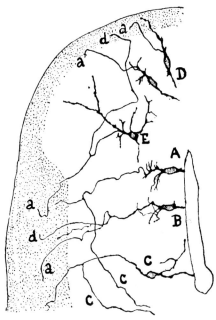

Fig. 111. Transverse section of the dorsal and lateral region of the spinal cord of an 8 day chick embryo. Cells having the appearance and location of epithelial cells are seen. A) Lateral nerve cell whose axis-cylinder travels towards the ventral commissure; B) another whose axis-cylinder divides in the lateral funiculus into ascending and descending twigs; C) cell whose ependymal prolongation is already ramified; D) embryonic nerve cells of the dorsal funiculus; E) a displaced cell whose axis-cylinder sends one fiber to the lateral funiculus and another to the dorsal funiculus.

Note: "a" signifies a fiber that ascends in the white matter and "d" signifies one that descends. Commissural fibers are designated by "c."

primary protoplasmic expansion. The secondary ramifications seem to emerge first from the sides of the primordial outgrowths (near the cell body) and then from the cell body, which remains free of processes for some time.

From the seventh to the eighth day the collateral fibers of the dorsal roots develop as straight short processes with terminal varicosities (growth cones). But the complete development of these twigs occurs only at the tenth to twelfth day on incubation.

During the eighth day of incubation, and perhaps during the following day as well, some new fibers of the ventral commissure develop. They derive from some dorsal horn cells whose axis-cylinder

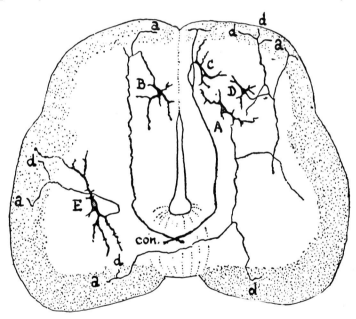

Fig. 112.   Section of the spinal cord of an 8 day chick embryo. Several cells possessing a complex axis-cylinder are collected in this figure. Cells copied from 3 nearby sections. A) Dorsal horn cell whose axis-cylinder gives rise to fibers of both left and right ventral funiculi, by means of a bifurcation in the form of a T; B,C) cells which send one fiber to the dorsal funiculus and another to the ventral commissure (the latter is still growing); D) dorsal horn cell continuous with 4 fibers of the dorsal funiculus; E) cell whose axis-cylinder bifurcates to give rise to 2 fibers of the ventrolateral funiculus which are located in different planes.

bifurcates, forming one fiber which enters the dorsal funiculus (becoming continuous with a vertical fiber, sometimes by bending at an angle, sometimes by division in T), and another which is directed ventrad and reaches the ventral commissure. In the ensuing days it arrives at the ventrolateral funiculus of the opposite side. The growth cone (Fig. 112, côn.) is very long and thick. In Figure 112, B, it has not yet completed crossing the commissural region.

Also during this time many cells having complex axis-cylinders are formed. The neural expansion of these peculiar elements furnishes two or more fibers to the white matter. In Figure 112 we have reproduced the elements of this category which are most often found in our preparations. According to the termination of the axis-cylinder one can classify them as: 1. cells of the two ventral funiculi (Fig. 112, A); 2. cells of the ipsilateral dorsal and lateral funiculi (Fig. 111, E); 3. cells of the ipsilateral dorsal funiculus and contralateral ventrolateral funiculus (Fig. 112, B, C); 4. cells of the ipsilateral lateral funiculus and contralateral ventral funiculus (Fig. 111, A, C); 5. cells whose axonal branches are continuous with diverse ipsilateral fibers of the ventral, lateral or dorsal funiculi (Fig. 112, D).

Ninth Day. By this day the collateral fibers of the white matter as well as those of the axis-cylinders which cross the gray matter are also fully formed. The latter present an inextricable plexus, one formed by the intersection of varicose arborizations of the collaterals of the columns and of the dorsal roots. The arborization of each fiber resembles that of the axis-cylinder in a plaque of Rouget, as Kölliker [81] has observed.

Tenth Day. At this day the gray commissure is formed by the intersection of several collateral fibers from the dorsal column (in the dorsal portion of the commissure) and from the ventrolateral column (ventral portion of the commissure).

The tardiest collaterals belonging to the lateral portion of the dorsal column also develop, growing and ramifying more and more during the ensuing days (Fig. 113).

CONCLUSIONS

Although our studies are not yet finished we can present the following conclusions as being very probable:

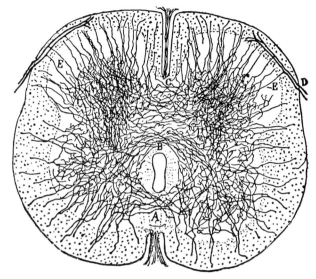

Fig. 113.   Transverse section of a 10 day chick embryo. A) Collaterals of the ventral commissure; B) collaterals of the dorsal commissure (ventral portion); C) collaterals of the dorsal portion of the dorsal commissure; D) dorsal roots; E) collaterals of the trunk of the sensory root.

1. Most of the primitive nerve cells or neuroblasts of His are displaced epithelial elements. This displacement and differentiation, by which the epithelial structures become nerve cells, continues from the third to the ninth or tenth day of incubation.*

2. The cells which develop first are those of the ventral root, those of the motor part of the dorsal root, and those of the ventral funiculus; then the elements of the lateral funiculus are differentiated and sometime later those of the ventral commissure. One may consider the cells of the dorsal funiculus as the slowest (seventh to twelfth day of incubation).

3. The neuroblasts present two outgrowths; an internal or ependymal one which represents the first protoplasmic branch and an external or radial one which constitutes the axis-cylinder. Sometimes the internal process is very short or atrophic, which makes

---

*My latest researches performed with the aid of neurofibrillar techniques do not confirm this interpretation. It could be, in agreement with His's opinion, that neuroblasts derive from a specific line of germinal cells. (*Note for the French edition.*)

the neuroblast pear-shaped as was described by His. Because of its origin the nerve cell has a bipolar form.

4. The secondary protoplasmic prolongations grow by means of spines which emerge from the cell body or from the two primordial processes. Their growth tip is varicose and very often rounded and swollen.

5. The nerve prolongation or axis-cylinder grows by means of a conical swelling at the peripheral tip. This swelling is often adorned with spiny excrescences that stain brownish yellow with silver chromate (growth cones). The cone or terminal protoplasmic bulb represents a rudimentary terminal arborization.

6. The collateral fibers of the white matter begin to develop in the region of the ventral funiculus at the fifth day of incubation. Those of the dorsal funiculus appear at the seventh day, then (from the seventh to the ninth day) the collateral branches of the dorsal roots and, finally (tenth day and following), the collateral filaments of the nerve fibers which cross the gray matter.

7. All the collateral branches also grow by means of cones or terminal protoplasmic bulbs. However, this cone is very small in comparison with that of the tips of the axis-cylinders.

ADDENDA

After having written this report we obtained impregnations of the chick spinal cord at the third day of incubation by slightly modifying the rapid method. We have had the pleasure of confirming our suppositions about the development of the nerve elements of the ventral roots and ventral commissure. The latter appear at the third day in a completely embryonic form as can be observed in Figure 114.

Most of the elements possess a growing axis-cylinder which has a very sturdy growth cone (Fig. 114). The youngest elements are very short and describe an arc with the concavity inwards. They are still located among the epithelial elements (Fig. 114, a) and, like the latter, have an ependymal process.* But as soon as the nerve

*This ependymal prolongation has been confirmed in recent years with neurofibrillar methods, first by Held and ourselves and later by Tello. (*Note for the French edition.*)

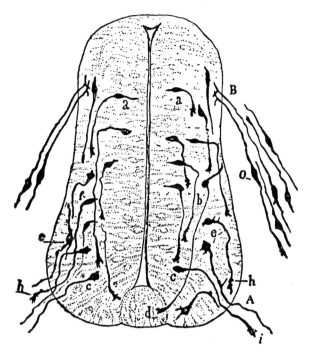

Fig. 114. Section of the spinal cord of a 3 day chick embryo. Cells copied from several successive sections of the same cord. A) Ventral root; B) dorsal root; a) very young nerve cells; b) more advanced cells which are probably commissural; c) pyriform cells of the ventral roots; d) growth cone of a commissural axis-cylinder; e) radicular cells which already show rudimentary protoplasmic branches; h, i) growth cones of the ventral roots; o) ganglion cells.

cells move laterally the ependymal process atrophies and protoplasmic outgrowths appear (b, e, f, c) in the form of barely perceptible rigid spines.

One can likewise see at this time that both dorsal (B) and ventral (A) roots are formed in great part. It is not rare to find developing axis-cylinders within these roots (Fig. 114, h, i).

In summary: Each nerve cell passes through three successive phases: 1. Epithelial or bipolar phase, during which the cell still preserves a convergent position among the spongioblasts and an ependymal or internal process (Fig. 114, a). 2. Unipolar phase (neuroblast of His) which occurs because of the more or less complete atrophy of the ependymal process (Fig. 114. f, c). Often this phase is missing, the ependymal process becoming the first protoplasmic appendage. 3. Multipolar phase, arising as a result of protoplasmic projections which emanate from the cell body and the most adjacent regions of the primordial processes.

Chapter 8

ON THE ORIGIN AND RAMIFICATIONS OF THE NERVE FIBERS OF THE EMBRYONIC SPINAL CORD [151,154]

THE OBSCURITY which exists concerning the connection of the nervous elements of the spinal cord derives from inadequacy of technique. Most authors have almost exclusively employed methods which stain the myelin sheath or the paths of the large axis-cylinders (Weigert-Pal stain, osmic acid method of Exner, gold chloride of Freud, carmine, etc.). We now know that these methods are absolutely ineffectual for demonstrating the path of fine unmyelinated nerve fibers or the delicate protoplasmic ramifications of nerve cells.

Only the Golgi method permits the fine nervous and protoplasmic processes to be traced, thanks to its singular property of staining only a few isolated elements of the many in the gray matter. But unfortunately this staining method, so efficacious for the cerebrum and cerebellum, only gives incomplete and very uncertain results when applied to the adult cord.

We think that the principal obstacle to the successful impregnation of the adult spinal cord is the sturdy layer of myelin which surrounds most of the nerve fibers. When this sheath is absent, as in embryonic nerve tissue, or when it is very fine, as in the gray matter of the cerebrum and cerebellum, the black coloration of the axis-cylinders occurs more constantly.

Our experiments with the Golgi technique have enabled us to recognize another peculiarity which we consider to be of major importance. The more embryonic the nerve tissue, the more rapid must be the preliminary hardening in the osmium-bichromate mixture. Our best preparations have been obtained by fixing small fragments of embryonic nerve tissue (3 to 4 millimeters on a side) for 21, 24 or 30 hours in 3 per cent potassium bichromate, 20 parts and 1 per cent osmic acid, 5 parts. The tissue is then immersed in silver nitrate for a short time. This rapid hardening yields many more successful impregnations, and in less than 3 days one may obtain a considerable number of illustrative sections of the various elements of the cord. When the induration is sufficient, an extraordinarily fine silver deposit precipitates exclusively on the nerve protoplasm;* but if the hardening is incomplete, the silver chromate precipitates more irregularly, coloring the background a granular red. Finally, excessive hardening is revealed by the absence of a reaction, or by deposition exclusively on some nerve fibers.

Our research has especially dealt with chick embryos from the sixth to the fourteenth day of incubation, at which time better impregnation of the axis-cylinders and their fine ramifications is obtained. Good results have been obtained in mammalian embryos and even in the terminal cord of newborn animals. Studies of calf, rabbit, and rat embryos completely substantiate data derived from avian spinal cords.

We shall now state briefly the most interesting facts concerning:

---

*We cannot accept the opinion of Rossbach and Sehrwald [209] concerning the localization of the silver precipitate in Golgi preparations. These authors state that the silver chromate is deposited in certain pericellular lymphatic spaces which communicate with those surrounding the vessels. We do not know if these lymphatic spaces exist for, as Fromann suggested, they might be artifacts. But no doubt is possible concerning the location where silver chromate is deposited; it deposits in the depths of the nerve protoplasm and its numerous processes. This is proved by the fact that the reaction is very fine and the volume of nerve elements is not appreciably increased, as can be judged by comparison with cells prepared by dissociation. This comparison is very easy for bipolar cells, the retinal rods and cones and the cerebellar granules. In these elements it is evident that the silver deposit impregnates the entire thickness of the protoplasm, sparing only the nucleus. The nucleus appears brown, because it is seen through a stained protoplasmic layer. Furthermore, one never obtains impregnations in the lymphatic spaces of the cornea, lymph vessels or connective tissue lacunae. This is not to say that the Golgi reaction is specific for nerve protoplasm, for we have succeeded in impregnating a great number of cells, such as connective tissue cells, epithelium, cartilage, striated muscle, young zoosperms and intercellular matter such as that within adult and embryonic biliary capillaries, salivary ducts, connective tissue fascicles, elastic fibers, fundamental bone substance, and epithelial and nerve cements.[152] That makes us suspect that silver chromate is attracted by some nearby element which occurs throughout the body but which is especially accumulated in the bile and in the protoplasm of the neural and neuroglial cells.

1. the fibers of the white matter; 2. the origin of the dorsal roots; 3. the arrangement of nerve cells; 4. the epithelial elements and the origin of the neuroglia.

FIBERS OF THE WHITE MATTER

The axis-cylinder of the spinal funiculi impregnate very well in chick embryos from the fifth day of incubation. They appear relatively thick, parallel, and quite varicose (Figs. 115, A, and 118). But their most important characteristic is the presence of a considerable number of fine collateral twigs which arise at a right angle, or almost at a right angle, from a slight triangular swelling. Sometimes the funicular fibers, at the level of the emergence of the collateral filaments, become bent into an S shape, approaching the gray matter (Fig. 115, F). The collateral twigs penetrate deeply into the

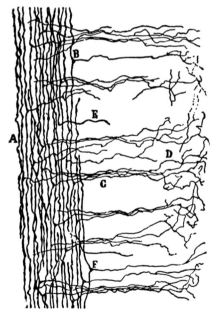

Fig. 115. Longitudinal ventrodorsal section of the dorsal funiculus of the spinal cord of a 15 day old cat. A) Fiber of the dorsal funiculus; B) collateral branch; C) group of collateral twigs which travel ventrad to reach the ventral part of the substance of Rolando; D) final arborization of these twigs at the level of the dorsal horn; E) axis-cylinder of a nerve cell.

cord, always converging on the ependyma. They terminate among the cells of the ventral and dorsal horns by a free and quite varicose arborization. The nerve plexus of which some writers speak, occurring among the nerve cells, is formed in great part by the gathering and intertwining of an infinite number of these terminal arborizations (Figs. 115, D, and 116, d, h, g).

We do not categorically deny the existence of anastomoses among the fibrils which constitute the afore-mentioned plexus. We only affirm that with the best Golgi preparations we have never observed a complete meshwork. It has seemed to us that each fiber always maintains its independence, as do the axis-cylinders coming from the nerve cells.

All the fibers of the funiculi give off collaterals but their arrangement varies a little in different regions of the cord, as can be seen in Figure 116. Those which derive from the ventral funiculus are thicker and ramify among the nerve cells of the ventral horn; a few reach the base of the dorsal horn. A small group of these collaterals arises from the more internal fibers of the ventral funiculus and arborize in the depths of the ventral white commissure where they decussate with the fibers of the other side (Fig. 116, h, i).

The collaterals which leave the dorsal funiculus are the finest and the most numerous. Almost all are gathered into small fascicles which cross the gelatinous substance of Rolando dorsoventrally, and they terminate at the summit of the dorsal horn (or in a more ventral location) by free and very tortuous arborizations. Some reach the intercellular plexus of the ventral horn. Finally, several of them which arise from the dorsal funiculus (Fig. 116, j) after their dispersal in Clarke's column, decussate in the midline, forming the dorsal gray commissure.

The collaterals which have just been described are a constant feature in all regions of the vertebrate spinal cord. We have verified them in the spinal cord of young or newborn mammals (cat, guinea pig, rat) as well as in embryos.

In reality these ramifications have been seen and described, by other authors, under various names, e.g., fibers from the dorsal roots, fibers from the funiculi. All these imply axis-cylinders arising from cells of the gray matter which, by having united to form the sub-

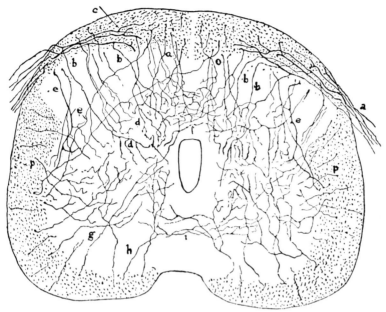

Fig. 116. Section of the spinal cord of a 9 day chick embryo. The fibers are copied from 3 successive sections. a) Dorsal root fibers; b) collaterals of the radicular trunks; d) terminal arborization of the radicular collaterals; g) collaterals of the ventral funiculus; h) collaterals which contribute to the ventral commissure; o) collaterals of the fasciculus gracilis forming the dorsal commissure in great part.

stance of the funiculi, bring into touch diverse levels of ganglion cells.

On comparing the preparations obtained by the Golgi method with those by Weigert-Pal, one notes that most of the collateral fibers, if not all of them, possess a myelin sheath which becomes thicker as the animal approaches the adult age. This myelin sheath is lacking in embryonic and newborn mammals, which makes possible the staining of the fibers with silver chromate.

The error committed by many authors results from the inadequacy of the methods employed. Myelin stains do allow these fibers to be followed during their transverse course. However such stains do not color the termination or the origin of the fibers because these regions lack a myelin sheath. We have been able to assure ourselves, by carefully examining longitudinal sections of the young cord impregnated by the Pal method, that the collateral fibers arise from fibers of the white matter at the level of myelin constrictions.

What do these collateral fibers represent? In our opinion, they are probably branches which all the fibers of the white matter send to the gray in order to link together nerve cells that are relatively great distances apart. The absence of myelin at the level of the contacts (cell bodies and arborizations of the collaterals) would facilitate the transmission of the nerve impulse.[148]

FIBERS OF THE SPINAL ROOTS

Ventral Roots. We concur with most authors concerning the origin of the axis-cylinders which compose these roots. These fibers (Fig. 117, c) emerge from the large cells of the ventrolateral group of the ventral horn and traverse the white matter in a rectilinear fashion, exhibiting large swellings along the way. Finally, they penetrate the ventral root, from where we have sometimes followed them to beyond the sensory ganglion. In the preparations of the embryonic chick or calf spinal cord we have never seen such fibers give off collateral branches.*

Dorsal Roots. The most interesting facts on this point have been obtained from spinal cords of 7 to 12 day chick embryos. Impregnation of dorsal root fibers is considerably more difficult in older bird embryos and in newborn mammals.

As is known, the dorsal roots arise from the cells of the corresponding sensory ganglion. These cells (Fig. 117, h, i, j) are bipolar in the spinal ganglia of the chick embryo, in contradistinction to those of mammals which are unipolar. This difference is secondary, since in birds as well as mammals the ganglion cell ultimately provides two fibers, a central one designed for the spinal cord and a peripheral one which goes to the sensory surfaces of the organism. As can be seen in Figure 117, in which an embryonic spinal ganglion impregnated with silver chromate has been reproduced exactly, the central and peripheral branches of the bipolar cells retain their independence, without ramifying, in their journey across the gang-

---

*This is an embryonic arrangement. Motor collaterals appear quite later. (*Note for the French edition.*)

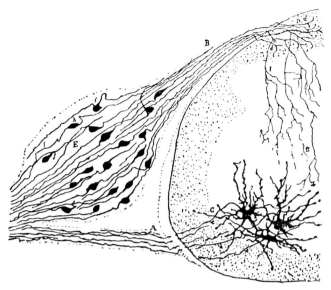

Fig. 117. Transverse section of the thoracic spinal cord, roots, and spinal ganglion of a 9 day chick embryo. A) Ventral root; B) dorsal root; C) an axis-cylinder of a motor cell; D) intraspinal portion of the dorsal roots; d) terminal bifurcations.

lionic web. We must note that the central branch is finer and more varicose than the peripheral. Some cells give rise to the two processes from the summit of a pedicle on one side of the cell body (Fig. 117, j). This arrangement is similar to that found in mammalian ganglion cells.

Once formed by the internal cellular processes, the dorsal root is directed dorsad, flattens transversely, and becomes applied to the lateral aspect of the white matter where it obliquely penetrates the dorsal funiculus. In the region of the column of Goll, and in separate places for each fiber, the axis-cylinders of the root divide into a Y, i.e., into two sturdy terminal branches — one ascending, the other descending. From their course, their thickness, and their connections these terminal branches cannot be distinguished from the longitudinal fibers of the dorsal funiculus. The bifurcation did not occur as a right angle, but rather as a Y, the branches tracing gentle curves, thereby shortly becoming longitudinal.

The principal trunk as well as the terminal branches emit fine collateral fibers. Those of the trunk (Figs. 116, b, and 117, e) are one to three in number; they arise at almost a right angle to the trunk, cross the substance of Rolando lateromediad, bifurcating, frequently along their way. They terminate in very fine and varicose free arborizations among the cells of the dorsal horn (Fig. 117, f. g). One frequently sees some of the longest of the collaterals reaching both ipsilateral and contralateral ventral horn cells. Those traveling contralaterally decussate in the dorsal commissure.*

The collaterals of the ascending and descending terminal branches behave similarly to those of the longitudinal fibers of the dorsal funiculus; i.e., they arise at a right angle at different levels and cross the substance of Rolando dorsoventrally to end in free arborizations among the cells of the dorsal horn (Fig. 118, C, D) and perhaps some end among cells of the ventral horn.

What becomes of the terminal dorsal root fibers? We do not know. We can only state that in the greatest extent over which we have been able to follow them (which in a few favorable preparations was not less than 2 millimeters), we never perceived their termination.

We do not dare to claim that all dorsal root fibers behave the same way. It could be that a few present the course and the complicated arrangement described by certain authors. However, in our best preparations all the dorsal root fibers that are clearly observed for great distances are as we have described (Fig. 118).

Furthermore, we consider most of the facts described by Lissauer,[102] Bechterew,[8] Kahler,[72] Obersteiner,[132] Edinger,[35] and Lenhossék[93] as possible. In agreement with these authors we have found two kinds of fibers in the dorsal roots: fine and coarse. And we must add that most of our observations deal with the fine axis-cylinders which (perhaps because of their lack of myelin at a relatively late stage) stain readily by the Golgi method. In very young cords (5 day chick embryo) we have sometimes encountered thick radicular fibers which reach the ventral

---

*These long collaterals, confirmed by Kölliker, who called them *Reflexcollateralen,* have been thoroughly studied by Lenhossék and other scholars. They may play an important role in the tendon reflexes. It goes without saying that they attain considerable development in young and adult animals. (*Note for the French edition.*)

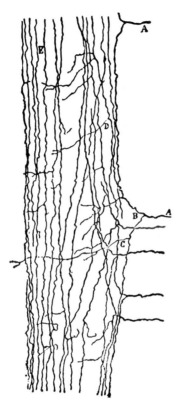

Fig. 118. Longitudinal and tangential section of the dorsal funiculus of the spinal cord of an 8 day chick embryo. This figure shows the path of 5 root fibers faithfully copied from one very successful preparation. A) Dorsal root fibers; B) bifurcation of a radicular trunk; C) collateral branch arising from a branch of bifurcation; E) longitudinal fibers of the fasciculus gracilis.

horn cells without showing the bifurcated and arborized arrangement of the others; but the rarity of the observation prevents us from knowing whether it constitutes a constant arrangement peculiar to the thick fibers.

The existence of arborizations and bifurcations is implicitly contained in the descriptions of many authors. The error committed by Edinger, Lissauer, and Lenhossék consists in having mistaken the numerous ramifications of a single radicular fiber for separate fibers of independent origin. Moreover some authors, including Edinger, have seen both the well-known ascending fibers (our ascending branches of the bifurcation), as well as descending radicular fibers which very probably correspond to our descending branches of the bifurcation. Edinger and others believed that other fibers enter the dorsal horn after having traversed the substance of Rolando in diverse directions. These fibers are identical either to our collateral twigs of the trunk or to our branches of the terminal bifurcation. Perhaps they have included among the former the innumerable collaterals arising from the fibers of the dorsal funiculus which traverse the substance of Rolando in small horizontal and curvilinear fascicles.

NERVE CELLS

These elements appear very well impregnated in the 5 to 12 day embryonic spinal cord. In very successful preparations one can follow the axis-cylinder up to the white matter and can very clearly verify its continuation with a longitudinal fiber. According to the behavior of their axis-cylinder the nerve cells can be classified as: 1. commissural cells; 2. funicular cells; 3. radicular cells; 4. cells of arborized axis-cylinders.

Commissural Cells (Fig 119, a, b, c, etc.). The fibers which are gathered in the ventral commissure derive, as Golgi and Edinger believed, from cells existing throughout the entire gray matter. It is therefore not possible to designate, as Lenhossék has done,[92] a special group of cells of the ventral horn as the commissural group. In Figure 119 we have exactly reproduced diverse commissural cells taken from various sections of the spinal cord of the 7 day chick embryo. The shape of these cells varies a little in different zones of the gray matter. Those which are in the medial part of the base of the dorsal horn (g, y, h) are fusiform, directed ventro-dorsally, and give rise to a small number of short lateral ramifications. The axis-cylinder ordinarily proceeds from the end of the ventral protoplasmic outgrowth (g, y). The other commissural cells are large, more or less stellate, and give rise to an axis-cylinder at the level of the protoplasmic body or after the origin of a large protoplasmic expansion.

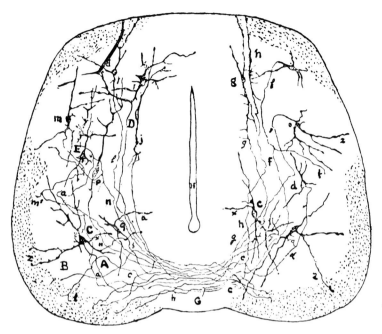

Fig. 119. Section of the spinal cord of a 7 day chick embryo. Commissural cells found in some very well impregnated sections in which the path of the nerve prolongations could be followed completely. Each cell was faithfully copied with the camera lucida from sections in which the cells stood out fully isolated. a) Ventral horn cell; d, p, o) cells of the central gray region; e, f, i, m, n) dorsal horn cells; f, m, n) cells whose axis-cylinders seem to give rise to fibers of the lateral funiculus; j, g, h) internal fusiform cells, d) cell whose axis-cylinder bifurcates giving rise to 2 cells of the ventral funiculus.

The ultimate arrangement of the axis-cylinder appears slightly variable. This could result from the fact that the impregnations are not always equally succesful and complete. Sometimes, after the axis-cylinder arrives at the contralateral ventral funiculus, it divides in the form of a T and becomes a longitudinal fiber of the white matter. Other times, it becomes one of the latter by a simple inflexion. Some axis-cylinders, usually derived from the most lateral dorsal horn cells (Fig. 119, f, i, m, n) give off some collateral twigs before forming the commissure. These collaterals seem to be continuous with some fibers of the lateral funiculus. Finally, some axis-cylinders, after having formed the commissure, are continuous with two longitudinal fibers of the ventral funiculus, placed some distance apart but traveling in the same direction (d).

Funicular Cells. These cells (Fig. 120) are scattered throughout the entire gray matter, and they are characterized by the fact that their axis-cylinders, after a very variable course, become fibers of one of the ipsilateral funiculi. The modes of continuation are as we have just described. Most of the nerve processes end by inserting into a longitudinal fiber (division into a T) of the corresponding funiculus (b, g, r). But some show only a simple terminal inflexion which appears continuous with the end of a funicular fiber. Finally, some axis-cylinders (f, h, o), before reaching the white matter, give rise in the gray matter to collateral ramifications whose

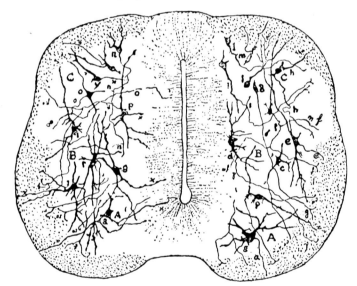

Fig. 120. Funicular cells of the spinal cord of a 7 day chick embryo. Cells from the same spinal region of different preparations have been gathered in this figure a) Ventral horn cell; b) cell whose axis-cylinder is incorporated into the ventral funiculus; c) cell whose axis-cylinder seems to be continuous with 2 fibers of the ventral funiculus; f) cell whose axis-cylinder ramifies and is continuous with a fiber of the lateral funiculus; m, f) cells of the dorsal horn whose axis-cylinder seems to be continuous with fibers of the dorsal funiculus; s, r, t) cells whose axons bifurcate after arriving at the white matter, producing ascending and descending twigs.

final disposition is unknown. Sometimes (c, s, t) we have been able to observe bifurcated axis-cylinders in the gray matter which are continuous with two or more funicular fibers located some distance apart and traveling in the same direction.*

Radicular Cells. The only ones which seem continuous with the nerve roots are those which are found in the lateral group of the ventral horn (Figs. 117, c, 118, and 120). The axis-cylinder does not ramify but penetrates the ventral root directly (Fig. 117, c). These axons are very sturdy and are especially distinguished by their rectilinear course and their frequent large swellings.

We have never observed dorsal horn cells continuous with the sensory roots.

Cells of Arborized Axis-Cylinders. The cells hitherto described are all provided with an axis-cylinder of obvious individuality which is continuous either with ventral root fibers or with fibers of the white matter. But, as Golgi has demonstrated in the dorsal horn, there are cells whose axis-cylinder loses its individuality by ramifying. We have recognized the existence of these cells in 16 day embryos and older ones (for these elements probably develop very late); but the rarity with which good impregnations are obtained in the chick spinal cord has caused us to study newborn mammals.

We have preferred to work on the spinal cord of the newborn cat. Among the elements contained in the substance of Rolando, many belong to the variety characterized by a ramified and plexiform axis-cylinder; but some of them unquestionably belong to other classes, especially to the group giving rise to funicular fibers. The inadequacy of our observations forces us at this point to abandon any attempt at classifying these elements. We will describe them beginning with the most dorsally placed cells.

The first cellular row is composed of large fusiform or stellate elements (30-40 μ), transversely oriented, which delimit the substance of Rolando dorsally. Their axis-cylinder is thick and is direct-

---

*This fact has already been casually mentioned by Golgi, in the Medical Journal of Reggio-Emila. We were unaware of this reference.[155] In this same journal he notes the existence of collateral branches in embryos, but without describing or drawing them. (*Note for the French edition.*)

ed horizontally either medially or laterally, without ramifying during its journey which ends in the white matter.

Further ventrad, and concentric to the preceding, is a layer of elongated, pyriform cells, oriented dorsoventrally. Their dorsally placed cell body is 7-8 μ in diameter. From their dorsal portion these elements give rise to only a very small number of protoplasmic twigs; ventrally the cell body is prolonged into a trunk terminating in a tuft of exceedingly varicose undulating threads. The axis-cylinder is very fine. It often emerges from the dorsal part of the cell body, travels obliquely dorsad, and terminates by a bifurcation in the vicinity of the white matter. Sometimes we have noted a vertical direction to these axis-cylinders, but we do not know their ultimate fate.

The cells of the substance of Rolando which form a concentric line ventrad to the preceding ones are fusiform, stellate and small (Fig. 121). The fusiform cells are the finest (6-8 μ in thickness);

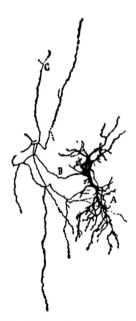

Fig. 121. Small nerve cell of the substance of Rolando of a 15 day old cat. A) Very granular and complicated protoplasmic expansions; B) axis-cylinder; C) granular twigs which seem to terminate freely.

they are directed ventrad and have two principal protoplasmic prolongations, ventral and dorsal. The axis-cylinder occasionally emerges from the cell body but more often from a protoplasmic branch. It seems to be directed ventrad, but soon it breaks up into a number of twigs (whose subsequent course is unknown to us) which form the very compact plexus surrounding the elements at the tip of the dorsal horn and the substance of Rolando. The stellate cells are distinguished from the preceding ones by their great number of varicose and tangled branches. The axis-cylinder breaks up into such a great number of flexuous branches that it becomes extremely difficult to make out the entire extent of the arborization and its true connections. A certain number of stellate cells possess a vertically elongated cell body, and the plexus formed by the branches of the axis-cylinder become, in great measure, longitudinal (Fig. 121).*

The cells at the tip of the dorsal horn are stellate with divergent expansions and are considerably larger than the cells of the substance of Rolando. Their axis-cylinder is usually directed ventrad and along its way emits some twigs that augment the plexus surrounding the cells of the dorsal horn. It appears that the axis-cylinder, after ramifying, is occasionally directed either towards the lateral funiculus, or to the ventral commissure. Unfortunately, the great extent of the field of observation ordinarily prevents the complete examination of the course of the nerve fibers in the mammalian spinal cord. On the other hand, in the spinal cord of bird embryos (9 to 11 days) we have very clearly observed some of these axis-cylinders to be continuous, after a recurrent course, with a longitudinal fiber of the corresponding lateral funiculus.

NEUROGLIA

Among the neuroglia it is necessary to distinguish two cell types: the ependymal epithelium or radial cells and the spider cells or neuroglial cells.

---

*After having studied hundreds of very successful preparations from birds and mammals that were several days old, we now think that these elements possess a very fine axon in continuation with a fiber of the white matter. Therefore the branches in the pictured cell (Fig. 121) which appear to be terminal may actually be collateral projections. (*Note for the French edition.*)

Epithelial Cells. Golgi [48] was the first author who, by means of this method, clearly demonstrated the arrangement of the ependymal cells. This author describes them as very elongated elements, thickened in their medial portion which surrounds the nucleus, and very fine in their peripheral portion. The latter part (radial fiber), after having traversed the entire thickness of the cord, terminates beneath the pia mater.

After Golgi, Magini [110] mentioned similar radial fibers in the embryonic brain. We had noted these cells in the optic lobe of the frog and in the brain of the chick embryo [153] long before we observed them in the spinal cord. Very recently Falzacapa [40] described an analogous arrangement in the spinal cord and brain of chick embryos. Like Magini, he employed the Golgi method.

In truth, the routine methods (dissociation, sections stained with carmine, etc.) prove the existence of long expansions in the epithelial cells. Some of these long cells have been well described by authors, notably Vignal, [231] who have not employed the black staining method. But only the Golgi method clearly shows the radiating arrangement and the extreme length of the epithelial cells in all embryonic nerve centers.

Our observations on the embryonic spinal cord of the chick clearly confirm the descriptions of Golgi and Magini. Nevertheless, we wish to add some details.

Setting aside the developmental question, and examining the fully formed ependymal cells, e.g., those of the spinal cord at the ninth day of incubation (Fig. 122), we note at once that not all are equal in shape or length. Each region of the transverse section of the cord possesses special cells. At the level of the dorsal commissure (a) they are straight, fine and gathered into a fascicle of parallel fibers which leave the central canal and finally terminate in large swellings in the depths of the barely visible dorsal sulcus, i.e., beneath the pia mater. Epithelial cells at the level of the ventral commissure are reproduced in Figure 122, b. The central ones are straight, but those that occupy a lateral position are arranged in an arc that is considerably more pronounced toward the periphery. Let us note one peculiarity: Each of these cells during its course through the deepest or purely epithelial zone of the commissure

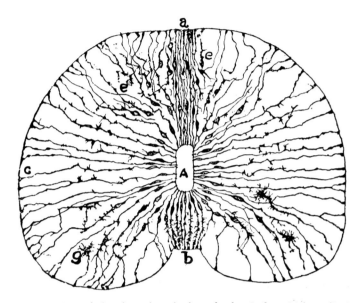

Fig. 122. Section of the thoracic spinal cord of a 9 day chick embryo. Golgi impregnation. A) Central canal; C) lateral funiculus; a) dorsal furrow and point of termination of the midline dorsal epithelial cells; b) ventral epithelial group; c) lateral cell; g) epithelial cells which already resemble neuroglial elements.

presents a smooth contour, but in the more ventral zone where they are crossed by the commissural nerve fibers they change in appearance, becoming granular and emitting small, varicose twigs which support the nerve fibers as the insulators of a telegraph pole support the wire (Fig. 122, b). The other radial epithelial cells of the spinal cord are very elongated and divergent (Fig. 122, c). The relatively thick internal end bounds the central canal and is prolonged at times in the interior of the latter in the form of a delicate, long cilium. The external part, after having shown numerous thickenings and small spiny branches along its course, terminates by a conical swelling beneath the pia mater. Sometimes the peripheral extremity is dichotomized or more or less ramified. In the afore-mentioned varicosities, which sometimes attain considerable size, as well as in the peripheral swelling, we have never succeeded in observing any nuclei. Thus we cannot accept the opinion of

Falzacapa who is inclined to interpret these nodosities as phenomena of cellular budding. In our opinion, it seems more reasonable to suppose that these swellings, like those of embryonic nerve fibers and cells, represent protoplasmic reserves destined to stretch out and disappear during the growth of the cells. By this we do not deny that epithelial cells proliferate, for we have seen radial fibers with two nuclei many times. However the nuclei are not located in the swellings but are in the internal segment of the cell very near the ependyma.

At the end of the eighth day of incubation one always observes that some of the ependymal elements are short and do not reach the central cavity (Fig. 122). They arise from the dislocation and perhaps also from the proliferation of the first epithelial elements and represent, as we shall soon see, the primordial forms of the spider cells.

It can be stated generally that the older the embryo the shorter and more ramified are the lateral ependymal fibers as well as the fibers which cross the ventral and dorsal funiculi. However, the commissural elements seem quite stable and we believe that their arrangement as shown in Figure 122 (which we have also observed in the spinal cord of newborn and several day old mammals) is preserved with but slight variations in the spinal cord of the adult animal.

Neuroglial or Spider Cells. These elements only become recognizable in the spinal cord of the 9 to 10 day chick embryo. They appear first in the region of the ventral horn. Soon they are found in the white matter of the funiculi, and they are last seen in the dorsal horns. We cannot state whether this order is constant, but it is what our preparations show.

What is the origin of these spider cells? The answer to this question seems very simple. The spider cells are merely dislocated and greatly transformed ependymal elements. It is proved indisputably in preparations of the 7 to 14 day embryonic chick spinal cord in which all the intermediary phases between the filamentous radial ependymal elements and the stellate spider cells can be seen. These gradations deal not only with shape but also with position. The more advanced the spinal cord in its development the less long, central, and convergent are the neuroglial cells. Even in the adult mammalian spinal cord (especially in the white matter) in some convergent neuroglial cells one often perceives a distinct central black filament traveling for some distance into the gray matter (ependymal prolongation) and one or more radial processes going towards the periphery (radial prolongations). Sometimes only one of these primitive prolongations remains, thus lending a neuronal appearance to these neuroglial elements, Moreover, oriented neuroglial cells are not rare in the cerebrum and the cerebellum. The radial cells of the cerebellar molecular layer are a good example of this.

In regard to the origin of the neuroglia, we share the opinion of Golgi,[48] Ranvier,[199] Renaut,[201] and Vignal.[231] Eichorst's [37] view of a leukocytic origin of the neuroglial cells does not seem tenable to us. However, we do not agree with Ranvier, Renaut, and Vignal concerning the arrangement of the spider cells. These authors consider them as anastomotic elements in whose meshwork the nerve cells are contained, an opinion which contradicts the results obtained from Golgi preparations. This method and even that of dissociation by means of isolating reagents, always shows that the neuroglial elements are perfectly independent. The same can be said of Müller's fibers of the retina,[146] the radial fibers of the optic lobe,[161] and the sustentacular cells of the olfactory mucosa.[152]

November, 1889

Part IV

CEREBELLUM

THE NERVE FIBERS OF THE CEREBELLAR GRANULAR LAYER AND THE DEVELOPMENT OF THE CEREBELLAR LAYERS [157]

THE NERVE FIBERS that the Golgi method reveals in the granular layer of the mammalian cerebellum include: 1. Some which come from the white matter and terminate freely in the gray. 2. Others which depart from cerebellar cells and go to the white matter. The following types of fibers belong to the first group: 1. those which terminate by arborizations throughout the granular layer and in the inferior third of the molecular layer; 2. those which terminate in nests of fibrils around the Purkinje cells; 3. those which end in the molecular layer by forming large divergent arborizations. All these fibers possess a myelin sheath except at their terminal arborizations.

First Type: Mossy Fibers. In discussing the structure of the avian cerebellum,[144] we showed that the majority of the large fibers coming from the white matter and ramifying in the granular zone present an interesting peculiarity. In an efflorescent manner they give rise at intervals to short, very varicose, freely terminating arborizations. We said that at the level of the arborizations the fiber appears thickened and that the arborizations often constitute the terminal structure of these fibers (Fig. 123, e). Work recently begun on the mammalian cerebellum has confirmed this fact and permits us to add some details.

At first we recognized that this arrangement is especially prominent in the cerebellum of young mammals. Here the branches (which we call mossy because of their resemblance to the moss which adorns trees) are the very finest and longest; their rosettelike arrangement is more striking, and it is readily seen that such efflorescences are not only found along the course of the fibers, but at most of their bifurcations and invariably at their termination. The area of distribution and ramification of each fiber is very extensive,

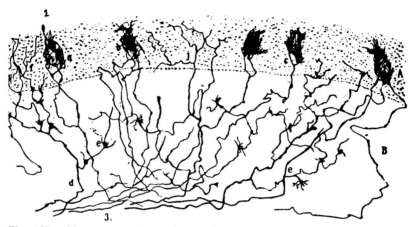

Fig. 123.   Transverse section of a cerebellar convolution of a newborn dog. Rapid Golgi method. A) Inferior portion of the molecular zone; B) granular zone; a) cerebellar nest formed by the ramifications of an ascending fiber originating in the white matter (a clear space, occupied by the Purkinje cell, is seen in the center of the arborization); b) another cerebellar nest formed by the arborization of several fibers; d) a richly-ramified mossy fiber; e) mossy efflorescences; f) more superficial branches of the mossy fibers; j) some mossy fiber ramifications which terminate in the inferior margin of the molecular zone.

so that at times up to 20 or 30 secondary ramifications can be counted. These ramifications fill half of the cerebellar lamella (Fig. 123, d). The shortest branches terminate in efflorescent arborizations located throughout the granular layer and especially in the zone of Purkinje cells. In adult mammals the Golgi method does not enable us to ascertain whether these arborizations reach the molecular layer. In spite of patient study and a great number of preparations, we have never been able to demonstrate any anastomosis among the ramifications of these filaments, nor any type of connection with the cerebellar cells. Consequently we are unaware of the true nature of these nerve fibers.*

If, judging by analogy, we were permitted to ascribe a physiological character to these fibers, we would say that they may be sensory

---

*Subsequent research [105,185] demonstrated that the mossy fibers terminate freely in the cerebellar glomeruli, i.e., among the terminal digitations of the protoplasmic expansions of the granules. This connection has been confirmed by Held and others. (*Note for the French edition*).

terminations of peripheral or ganglion cells. To appreciate the merit of this hypothesis it is well to recall that sensory and special sense nerves terminate in free central arborizations, just as motor nerves end in free peripheral arborizations. Thus, for example, we have demonstrated that the optic nerve in birds [161] terminates not in the cells of the optic lobe, but by very extensive and complicated arborizations located among the cells of the superficial layers of this organ. On the other hand, the sensory roots of the embryonic chick spinal cord [149] bifurcate into an ascending and a descending branch which travel vertically in the dorsal funiculus and finally decompose into a number of collateral branches which terminate in a free arborization among the dorsal horn cells. If cellular terminations exist, as certain authors have suggested, the Golgi method and (to our best knowledge) the other analytical methods do not reveal them. One could say the same for mammalian olfactory nerves. These nerves terminate (in the glomeruli of the olfactory bulb) not in networks or cells, but by extremely undulating, freely-terminating varicose ramifications. These terminal twigs are in intimate contact with the rich, very varicose, protoplasmic arborizations that are furnished by the nerve elements of the lower cellular layers (the large pyramidal cells and those located in the inferior part of the molecular zone). I believe that if we some day succeed in observing the other special sensory terminations we will find that they behave similarly. There is nothing astonishing in these facts. It is quite natural to suppose that all axis-cylinders of peripheral origin have true central terminations. This is very well established for fibers from retinal and spinal ganglion cells. Recently, we have also succeeded, by a slight modification of the Golgi method,* in seeing the cellular origins of the nerve fibers of the mammalian (rat, guinea pig, rabbit) olfactory epithelium. This peculiarity had already been suspected by Schultze, but as far as we know, no observer has furnished rigorous proof.

But setting aside these considerations which we intend to develop in another work, let us return to the cerebellar fibers.

Second Type: Fibers Terminating in Pericellular Nests. In a

---

*We are presently preparing a report on the origin and termination of the olfactory nerve.

previous work [147] we demonstrated the existence of a complete system of filaments arranged in a compact plexus and surrounding the lateral and inferior part of the Purkinje cells (descending brushes). Let us add that subsequent research on the cerebellum of newborn or several day old mammals have shown a quite similar arrangement, although different in some fibers of origin (Fig. 123, a, b).

Some thick, ramified fibers reach the granular layer from the white matter. These fibers are less numerous than the mossy fibers and lack their efflorescences. Following a variable course they ascend to the molecular zone arriving at the superior and lateral part of the Purkinje cells. They terminate by a fine, varicose tuft of fibers which forms an inextricable web around the Purkinje cell body (Fig. 123, a, b, c). The resemblance of these tufts to the nest of birds has suggested the name cerebellar nests to us. A nest is occasionally formed by the arborizations of a single terminal fiber, but more often each nest is formed by two or more fibers from different points in the white matter. If, as we presume, a similar arrangement occurs in the adult cerebellum (our impregnations have only been successful in the cerebellum of the newborn or several day old dog, cat, and rabbit and only occasionally in the chick embryo), two nests or fibrillar tufts would be found around the Purkinje cells: one formed beneath them by the descending brushes; the other formed above by the special fibers that we have just described.*

Third Type: Fibers Terminating in the Molecular Layer by Stellate Ramifications. Among the fibers that cross the granular layer are some which pursue a tortuous path above the Purkinje cells and terminate by divergent and very extensive arborizations in the molecular layer. We have already described these arborizations [145,147] but will now add some details. In the mammalian cerebellum the terminal arborization of these fibers is not as stellate as in birds. After a short ascending journey across the molecular zone, the fiber ordinarily emits arciform, divergent, descending branches which divide into various secondary branches. The majority of these

---

*Subsequent research demonstrated that the nests formed by the fibers under discussion are nothing more than the embryonic phases of fibers of the third category or climbing fibers. (*Note for the French edition.*)

secondary branches join the principal branches, following their path and ramifying with them. The almost parallel advance of this great number of branches produces the impression of the existence of two or more similar, superimposed arborizations.

The doubts that we previously felt regarding these double ramifications are dissipated; we have succeeded in seeing that all the branches of the stellate arborization proceed from the same trunk or from one of its principal branches.

On the other hand, we consider our previous hypothesis less probable, viz.: that these fibers or arborizing trunks are identical with those in the inferior part of the molecular zone demonstrable by the Exner or Weigert methods. These methods demonstrate myelinated fibers that are longitudinally directed (parallel to the cerebellar lamellae) and appear to arise from the white matter. We based this opinion on the analogous path of the two types of fibers in the molecular zone and on the fact that the Golgi method did not permit us to follow any fibers from the white matter to the interior of the molecular zone other than those which terminate by a divergent arborization. But having lately obtained some very complete preparations, we have noted that the number of divergent arborizations whose trunk travels longitudinally with respect to the circumvolutions is very limited; the majority, after having described a variably directed arc among the Purkinje cells, mount vertically in the molecular zone (Fig. 124, a).

The trunk of the divergent arborizations can be followed up to the white matter. It does not present thickenings or mossy efflorescences during its tortuous course across the granular zone. Moreover, we have observed that the terminal arborization in the molecular zone seems flattened and that this flattening is in the same direction as that of the protoplasmic arborization of the Purkinje cells.*

The nerve fibers of cerebellar origin that cross the granular layer

---

*Subsequent observations made with the Golgi method and with neurofibrillar procedures have enabled us to demonstrate that the arborizations of the fibers of the third type are intimately applied, in the adult, to the trunk and branches of the Purkinje cells, becoming that which we have designated climbing arborizations.[185] (*Note for the French edition.*)

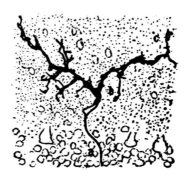

Fig. 124.   Portion of a transverse section of the molecular layer of the cerebellum of a 15 day old cat. Golgi method. a) Branch of an ascending fiber;
b) division of the latter into a complicated arborization; varicose terminal rami.*

are: 1. the ramified axis-cylinders of the large stellate cells; 2.
those of the Purkinje cells; 3. those ascending from the granules.

**First Type: Axis-cylinders of the Large Stellate Cells of the
Granular Layer.** In birds, the innumerable ramifications of these
fibers terminate by short, varicose, frequently arciform, granular
arborizations (Fig. 125, g). We have found an identical arrangement in the cerebellum of the cat, dog, rabbit, and rat.

In our opinion, all the ramifications of these axons terminate
freely among the granule cells, to the surface of which cells they
apply their varicose arborizations. There are no prolongations continuous with fibers coming from the white matter nor any anastomoses with the nerve expansions of diverse origin that cross the
granular layer. The form of the total ramification of all these axis-
cylinders is rounded or cuboidal, and by the wandering of its innumerable ramifications it comprises the entire thickness of the
granular zone. When one of these axis-cylinders appears completely impregnated in a preparation, it is almost impossible to follow
the entire arborization, so abundant, flexuous, and entangled are
its ramifications. The path and divisions of the axon can be studied

*These rami constitute the terminal arborization of a climbing fiber. The rela-
tionship of these elements with the nests of Figure 123 had not yet been discovered by us at the time of publication of this memoir. (*Note for the French
edition.*)

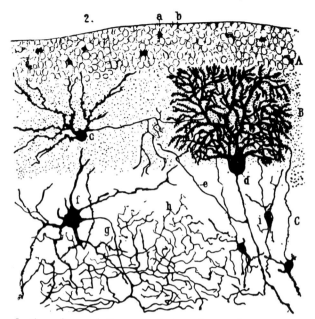

Fig. 125. Section of a cerebellar convolution of a 15 day old cat. Rapid Golgi method. In this figure we have grouped the most characteristic neural elements of several good preparations. A) Superficial granular zone; B) molecular zone; C) true granular zone; a) stellate superficial granule cell (neuroglial); b) spheroidal granule; c) stellate cell of the molecular layer with its axis-cylinder; d) Purkinje cell; e) ascending branch of the axis-cylinder of the Purkinje cell; f) large stellate cell of the molecular layer; g) very highly ramified nerve prolongation of cell "f"; h) final varicose ramifications of prolongation "g"; i) an elongated granule cell with its ascending axis-cylinder.

only in incomplete impregnations of adult animals, and particularly in those of young mammals where the fibers are less sturdy and less numerous (Fig. 125, g, h).

It is hardly necessary to add that the individuality of the axis-cylinder becomes completely lost as the result of its ramifying, a condition already described by Golgi. Sometimes one axonal branch that is a little larger than the others can be followed to the boundary of the white matter; but after that it bends back along the granular layer and becomes dissipated in infinite ramifications.

Second Type: Axis-cylinders of the Purkinje Cells. We have nothing to add to Golgi's descriptions and to those we have published on the avian cerebellum. It will suffice merely to indicate that some of the collateral branches of these nerve expansions reach the molecular layer where they bend and often become longitudinal. We have not been able to specify the point of termination of these fibers, whose ascending path was demonstrated by Golgi (Fig. 125, e).

We will say nothing about the axis-cylinders of the granule cells, which have been completely described in our previous publications.

Myelinated Fibers. The gray matter of the cerebellum possesses a great number of myelinated fibers, recognizable by many methods including those of Exner, Freud, and Weigert. Those fibers form a very dense plexus among the granules, a plexus which seems to be continuous with the fibers radiating from the white matter. A small number of them, passing among the Purkinje cells, reach the inferior fourth of the molecular zone where they become longitudinally arranged, i.e., in the same direction as the longitudinal fibers. This arrangement has been very well described and drawn by Henle.[63] There also are fibers oriented in other ways but they are few in number, just as are those which ascend to the region of the cerebellar surface.

But, whatever method is employed, the infinite number of fibers which cross the granular layer and the superposed Purkinje elements makes it very difficult to observe the path of each of them and to determine their point of departure. Fortunately the Golgi method greatly clarifies the obscurities of Weigert preparations.

Of the diverse fibers revealed by the Golgi method in the granular layer, which ones are myelinated? In the first place, there is no doubt that the Purkinje cell prolongations are myelinated, as Boll, Denissenko, and others have recognized, divining rather than demonstrating this peculiarity. We say divining even though Denissenko[27] claims to have followed these expansions up the white matter (rat, cat); for it seems impossible to us to make such a determination from osmium impregnated sections of adult mammalian cerebellum. Only since we have studied the cerebellum of small birds (e.g., greenfinch, sparrow) with osmic acid or Pal methods, have we been able to distinguish which ones truly belong to the Purkinje cells. In these animals the Purkinje cell prolongations travel almost directly to the white matter and their myelin sheath is considerably thicker than that of other fibers. Moreover, osmic acid stains the myelin sheaths of these elements a little more intensely, thus facilitating observation of the Purkinje axons.

The myelin sheath does not reach the cell body, as Denissenko believed, but only the summit of a descending brush; i.e., there is a certain distance between the termination of the myelin and the origin of the axis-cylinder, an arrangement already indicated by Koschewnikoff.[87] The naked axis-cylinder then traverses the axis of the brush (becoming almost invisible because of the fibrils which surround it) and reaches the inferior pole of the cell.

A similar arrangement can be demonstrated in the cerebellum of the cat or dog 10 to 30 days after birth. At this time the myelinated fibers are already quite advanced but the thickness and direction of those of the Purkinje elements permits them to be easily distinguished from the other myelinated fibers. In these animals the myelin also stops beneath a small mass of granular matter located beneath the cell body. This granular matter represents, according to Weigert or Exner preparations, the descending rudimentary brush that is observed in Golgi preparations of young mammals (Fig. 126, i).

Let us call attention in passing to some peculiarities of the myelinated fibers of the Purkinje cells. All, or almost all, present constrictions (Fig. 126, g) and some possess two very characteristic ones. At the level of the constrictions the myelin, but not the axis-cylinder, is lacking as can be observed with a good oil immersion objective. At the point where the myelin sheath stops, the fiber becomes thinner (Fig. 126, e), penetrates the granular matter of the brush as a naked axis-cylinder and ceases to be visible in Weigert or Exner preparations. This place where the fiber lacks myelin is precisely that which stains best by the Golgi method, for in general, the Golgi method only very rarely impregnates the myelinated portions of nerve prolongations.

In spite of Hadlich,[50] who described dichotomies in these myelinated fibers, we have not been able to discover, either by Weigert or by osmic acid procedures, any collateral ramifications; in our opinion, this is because the fine ramifications demonstrable by the Golgi

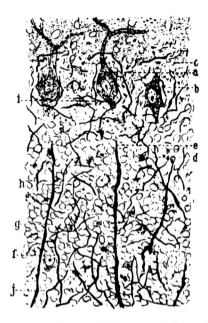

Fig. 126. Vertical section of a cerebellar convolution of a month old dog. Pal-Weigert method. a) Purkinje cell; b) large stellate cell in same row as Purkinje cells; c) cross-section of a longitudinal myelinated fiber; d) brown-stained neuroglial cell; e) termination of the myelin sheath of a Purkinje cell nerve prolongation; f) very robust stellate cell of the granular layer; g) constriction of a myelinated fiber; h) globular nucleus; i) descending mass or brush beneath a Purkinje element: j) finer myelinated fibers.

method lack myelin, or rather that they perhaps arise at the level of a constriction. The latter hypothesis could explain the impossibility of tracing the collateral twigs because of the lack of continuity of myelin at the level of the constrictions. It is furthermore in accord with the fact that in the cerebellum of young mammals (dog, cat) we have found a correlation between the number and origin of the collateral twigs revealed by Golgi preparations and the number and position of the constrictions seen in Weigert preparations.

The other myelinated fibers are ordinarily thinner and do not show a very consistent orientation. One cannot state what these fibers correspond to in Golgi preparations. It is impossible to follow them because of their tortuous course and very frequent interruptions in the myelin. Sometimes, nevertheless, one succeeds in observing the continuation of some of these fibers with the axiscylinders of the large stellate elements located in the same plane as the Purkinje axons (Fig. 126, b). As for the remainder of the myelinated fibers of the granular layer, they probably correspond in great part to the mossy fibers stainable by the Golgi procedure, for they show the same tortuous path and the same radial arrangement upon leaving the white matter as do the latter.

Many of the cerebellar nerve fibers lack a myelin sheath. These include the axis-cylinders of the stellate cells, the axis-cylinders of the granule cells with their parallel terminal branches, and all the collateral branches of the nerve expansions of the large stellate or Golgi cells of the granular zone.

DEVELOPMENT OF THE CEREBELLAR LAYERS

Since some of our investigations have been on newborn mammals, we have frequently had the opportunity to observe certain developmental peculiarities which we will describe briefly.

When a thin section of the cerebellum of the newborn cat or dog is stained with carmine or hematoxylin, one perceives that the molecular layer is divided into three very distinct zones: 1. zone of superficial granules; 2. molecular zone proper; 3. zone of the Purkinje cells.

Superficial Granular Zone. The superficial granular cells of the cerebellum have been seen and described by several authors, particularly by Schultze, Obersteiner,[131] Schwalbe[213] and Vignal.[233]

These granule cells (*cellules migratrices* of Vignal) are small, polyhedrical cells, intimately bound together by a kind of semiliquid cement analogous to that of the epithelium. Their relatively voluminous nucleus fills the cell body almost entirely. They are never seen undergoing mitotic division.

The protoplasm of these cells is not stained by the Golgi method, at least not in the correct fashion; in this regard they behave like ordinary epithelial elements. Exceptionally, we have seen them stained in the cerebellum of the 15 day chick embryo where they appear slightly elongated and frequently provided with two appendages, ascending and descending. However the impregnation was disorderly and unequal.

Among the polyhedrical granular cells of this zone, there are other more refringent cells. The latter are stellate in form, placed at intervals, and possessing every appearance of neuroglial cells, for they also emit divergent expansions. We have not succeeded in staining them with silver chromate; their true form and connections also remain unknown to us.

The superficial granular layer is crossed by a multitude of ascending fibers which terminate superficially on the pia mater by a conical enlargement (Fig. 127, b). These fibers are merely the terminal expansions of the elongated neuroglial elements which are found at the level of or inferior to the Purkinje cells. Furthermore, these fibers correspond quite exactly to the *radial fibers* of Bergmann [10] and Obersteiner.[130] The Golgi method, which allows the histologist to find their cell body of origin, stains them perfectly in the 11 day chick embryo. In their passage through the molecular zone these fibers never show the nucleus described by Henle.[63]

As is well known, the zone of superficial granules is transitory. As the animal advances in age the zone diminishes in thickness until it disappears entirely. In 11 to 14 day chick embryos this zone is very thick (from 0.08 to 0.09 millimeter in the 14 day embryo). The molecular layer proper is very fine (from 0.026 to 0.03 millimeter) and consists of a finely granular zone located above the Purkinje elements. In the newborn dog the thickness of the superficial granular zone is from 0.04 to 0.05 millimeter, whereas in a one month old dog it is scarcely 0.024 to 0.028 millimeter. By two months it has disappeared almost entirely. It is very difficult to understand the significance of the cells of this superficial granular zone. They appear to belong neither to neural nor to neuroglial elements.

Vignal [233] states that they are migrated cells from the vessels of the pia mater which have infiltrated the molecular layer; but the presence of a globular nucleus, without those gibbosities or fragmentations that are the characteristic of most leucocytes, seems to contradict such an hypothesis somewhat and, furthermore, if it were true, it would constitute a unique scientific fact.

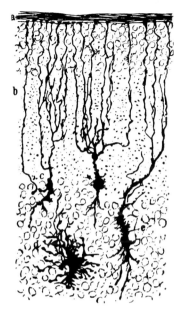

Fig. 127. Section of a cerebellar lamella of a 15 day old cat. Rapid Golgi method. Several neuroglial elements are illustrated in this figure. a) Pia mater; b) ascending neuroglial fiber (radial fiber) terminating superficially in a cone; c) elongated neuroglial element near the molecular layer; d) stellate neuroglial element.

Schwalbe's opinion [213] does not seem tenable either. This author believes that the afore-mentioned small cells seen on the surface of the cerebellum of young animals have the property of forming radial fibers or even the reticular matter (molecular layer of the adult cerebellum). This opinion, as well as that of Obersteiner,[132] who believes that the afore-mentioned elements secrete the basal membrane covering the surface of the cerebellum, is based on the erroneous doctrine that neuroglial cells form amorphous or reticular substances. We feel that the recent research on the nervous system by Golgi, Fusari, and Mondino as well as Tartuferi's, Dogiel's, and our own on the retina have sufficiently demonstrated that the apparently reticular or granular matter of the nervous system (molecular *neurospongium* of the retina) is merely a nerve plexus formed by the intertwining of an infinite number of neuronal protoplasmic and axonal ramifications.

In our previous work on this subject [150] we had not made any suggestion regarding the significance of the superficial granule cells. We now think that these elements are very probably the small stellate cells of the molecular layer of the adult cerebellum. These cells retain their epithelial appearance until the longitudinal fibers of the inferior granule cells and the protoplasmic arborization of the Purkinje cells are successively incorporated into the subjacent molecular layer. This opinion is in accord with the fact, already noted by other authors, that as the superficial granule cells disappear in growing animals the molecular substance thickens, considerably augmenting its content of cellular elements (the small stellate cells). In the 12 to 13 day chick embryo the molecular layer consists only of a fine, granular, narrow band placed above the bodies of the Purkinje elements and it does not contain any stellate elements, although it does appear fully formed in regard to its fundamental components (protoplasmic arborization of the Purkinje elements, longitudinal fibers of the granular cells, and radial or neuroglial fibers). From the fifteenth to the seventeenth day one begins to see some cells incorporated into it, and this coalescence increases until there is a complete disappearance of the superficial granule cells, which in birds occurs some months after hatching. Sometimes, in sections of the embryonic cerebellum the stages of this coalescence may be noted, i.e., some granules, separated by fibrils, are half submerged in the molecular layer and are gradually invading the latter zone.

If this interpretation is true, one can easily explain why the granules are never found undergoing division and why their number, at first extraordinarily large, instead of increasing, diminishes and even ends up by being reduced to zero. We must merely acknowledge that as the molecular layer increases in thickness and in length, the granule cells successively sink into it, being disseminated and scattered over a considerable extent by the very growth of the molecular substance. It is not necessary, consequently, to suggest the later destruction of the superficial granular cells, nor their resorption, but merely a simple change of position followed by a development which transforms them into true nerve cells.

We are inclined to admit that even in the adult cerebellum the most superficial stellate cells of the molecular layer, which are naturally the last granular elements annexed, retain a certain embryonic character, recognizable by the varicose appearance of the axis-cylinder and by the shortness of their descending filaments, which do not succeed in forming terminal brushes of the Purkinje elements.*

Molecular Zone Proper. This zone is situated between the Purkinje elements and the superficial granules. From the outset it possesses all the characteristics of the adult cerebellum. The Golgi procedure (which is even successful in the 12 or 13 day chick embryo) shows that it is composed of: 1. protoplasmic expansions of the Purkinje cells which form a short rigid arborization (Fig. 125, d) terminating on the inferior aspect of the zone of superficial granules; 2. longitudinal fibers or terminal ramifications of the axis-cylinders of the granules; 3. transverse fibers or nerve prolongations of the small stellate cells; 4. protoplasmic arborizations of these stellate cells; 5. radial fibers or ascending prolongations of the neuroglial cells. The mixing and interweaving of all these elements gives to the molecular zone, when examined in routine preparations stained with carmine, that mixed-up and indecipherable aspect that authors have often taken for a reticular formation or a granular cement.

The descending brushes appear considerably later after all the cerebellar elements are completely formed and when the molecular layer is thicker than the superficial granular layer. For example, in the cat, they are present, although rudimentary, fifteen days after birth. The longitudinal fibers appear at the very moment when the formation of the molecular layer is initiated. We have found them very well stained by silver chromate in the 12 day chick embryo; they appear considerably thicker, but with the same direction and the same properties as those of the adult cerebellum.

Zone of the Purkinje Elements. In chick embryos this zone is fully demarcated at the end of the tenth day of incubation. Its con-

---

*As the superficial granules disappear there is an increase in the number of deep granule cells. In a future work we will discuss the curious transformation and migration that accounts for this phenomenon. (*Note for the French edition.*)

stituent cells are characterized at the outset by a noteworthy size, by a less elongated form than in the adult and by a transversely flattened protoplasmic arborization whose short, thick and ascending branches are very poor in secondary and tertiary ramifications. Furthermore, almost all the branches are provided with slender spines inserted perpendicularly into their contour (Fig. 125, B). These spines are of clear coffee-color and are larger than those of the terminal protoplasmic branches of the adult cells. The younger the embryo the shorter, fewer and more irregular are the protoplasmic prolongations.

The axis-cylinder of these cells is thicker and more easily stainable with silver chromate than in the adult. Its collateral branches, two or three in number, present a notable thickness also, being directed upwards to terminate in the molecular layer (Fig. 125, e).

Granular Zone. We have succeeded in impregnating granule cells in the 12 day chick embryo. In the cat, we have stained them 15 days after birth. At these times the granules exhibit all the adult peculiarities. One notes, however, certain slight differences. The shape is elongated instead of spheroidal, especially when they are retarded in development; their elongation is perpendicular to the surface of the cerebellar lamella. Their diameter appears slightly greater in young animals than in adult animals. Thus, in the newborn cat measurements have given a mean of 0.008 to 0.009 millimeter and at 1 to 6 months of age, 0.005 to 0.008 millimeter. At birth they already possess all their expansions, both nervous as well as protoplasmic; however, the small varicose terminal arborization of each protoplasmic branch is barely indicated, often being found represented by a simple terminal thickening or by a bifurcation with very short branches.

As for the large stellate cells of the granular layer (Fig. 125, f), they seem to be a trifle larger in newborn mammals than in the adult. The nervous expansion, ordinarily directed downwards, is thicker than usual and its very rich arborization terminates in free, varicose and slightly enlarged extremities (Fig. 125, h). In Figure 125, copied from the cerebellum of a 15 day old cat, the short arborizations terminating in the form of an arc are still not developed.

Neuroglial Elements. These can be impregnated in the 12 day chick embryo. Both in the bird embryos as well as in newborn mammals these elements are generally distinguished by two characteristics: the relatively considerable volume of the cell body and the rough, varicose and, so to speak, thick appearance of the divergent expansions.

Let us examine, for example, the cerebellar cells of a 15 day old cat (Fig. 127). All the neuroglial cells revealed by silver chromate are found in the white matter or in the granular zone. None is found in the molecular layer and, as for the superficial granular zone, when present, the black staining procedure is powerless to reveal them.

Those of the granular zone can be classified into two types: 1. short, stellate elements with rigid, notably varicose expansions which diverge in every direction (Fig. 127, d); 2. elongated elements located throughout the thickness of the granular zone but, most especially near, and even in the same row as, the Purkinje cells. The latter neuroglial cells are characterized, above all, by their long ascending prolongations (Fig. 127, c, e). These expansions, which correspond to Bergmann's radial fibers, often form an arc at their origin. They then mount, so to speak, in parallel fashion, presenting a varicose aspect. Once arrived at the superficial granular layer, they become tortuous, being bent to the curves of these cells, and they finally terminate on the inferior surface of the pia mater by a conical thickening like Müller's fibers of the retina (Fig. 127, a, b). The amorphous membrane, which authorities have described on the free surface of the cerebellum, seems to us to derive very simply from the gathering of all the terminal cones of the radial fibers. Moreover, the internal limiting layer of the retina is formed in this way, and so is the basal membrane which externally limits the optic lobes of birds. The descending expansions of the elongated neuroglial elements are short, thick and varicose. In the cerebellum of mammalian and avian embryos, they descend considerably, traveling across the white matter; but in the cerebellum of one month old animals they are often rudimentary or even lacking and, in fact, they do not exist in the adult. In our opinion, the inferior expansion as well as the superior one or ones of such elements undoubtedly have an ependymal character suggestive of an epithelial origin, the same as the internal and external appendages of the neuroglial cells of the embryonic spinal cord.[149]

Radial fibers also emerge from the inferiorly placed stellate cells near the white matter, but most of them proceed from the neuroglial elements situated just beneath the bodies of the Purkinje cells. These neuroglial elements undoubtedly represent the forked elements described by Golgi in the adult cerebellum.

The developmental facts which we have just described are few and incomplete. This results from the rarity with which one can obtain Golgi impregnations of the cerebellum of the early fetus. To observe the origin of the cerebellar elements, it would be necessary to make a great number of trials at impregnation, varying the conditions according to the subjects of study. The Weigert method is hardly applicable, since the myelin of the cerebellar folia appears very late, when the structure of the cerebellar gray matter is probably completed.

As for the methods of osmic acid fixation, carmine staining, dissociation by alcohol in thirds, and all the staining methods applied to thin sections, these give inconclusive results because they are incapable of showing an element in its entirety including the long protoplasmic and axis-cylinder prolongations. To arrive at an understanding of the morphological development and true connections of the nerve elements, it is necessary to employ procedures which selectively visualize the processes of the nerve cells without fear of error and which permit them to be traced in sections that are very thick yet absolutely transparent. Until now, the Golgi method, properly and patiently utilized, is the only method which fulfills these conditions in great part.

Chapter 10

SOME BIPOLAR CEREBELLAR ELEMENTS AND NEW DETAILS CONCERNING THE DEVELOPMENT OF CEREBELLAR FIBERS [158]

 F OLLOWING OUR WORK on the structure of the cerebellar granular layer and the development of its elements [157] we discovered some additional details which we will describe briefly.

METHODS

As we have already indicated in our previous works, we preferentially employ the rapid Golgi method in our research. Experience has proved that this method, properly and patiently employed, is the only one capable of staining all the nerve cells and fibers of the nervous system. We have stated that the method gives better results for the nervous system of embryos and newborn animals than for the adult, provided that the time of induration in the osmic bichromate mixture is appropriately diminished (instead of 3 to 5 days or more as Golgi advises, 20, 24, 36, or 48 hours suffice).

Thirty to 36 hours of induration is required for staining cerebellar axis-cylinders in the newborn dog or cat. A greater duration hinders the reaction, or limits it to the most deeply located fibers. Fragments of the cerebellum of the 15 to 20 day old mammal require a hardening of 2 to 3 days, i.e., proportionately more time as the animal is older because the rapidity of the diffusion of the osmium-bichromate mixture is inversely proportional to the degree of development of the nervous system.

Before immersing the pieces in silver nitrate we wash them in distilled water for 1 or 2 minutes in order to diminish the superficial precipitate.[115] They are removed from the silver bath and cut in thick sections 30 or 36 hours later. The subsequent treatment follows Golgi's recommendations, except that we employ alcohol at 40° for the washes, which preserves fineness of detail better than at 36°. We also clear the sections for some minutes in essence of cloves in order to prevent them from becoming brittle and curled.

When the procedure is well performed, the neuroglial cells, the nerve cells, and even the vessels and axis-cylinders appear very finely stained black. The only preparations suitable for study are those in which silver chromate is deposited exclusively in the depths of the protoplasm (not on the surface of the elements as Rossbach and Sehrwald [209] claim and as Edinger [36] seemed to believe).

In the central nervous system something is present between the cells. This intercellular material is not a lymphatic space but a uniting cement which must be present since this is a tissue of epithelial origin. This cement is sometimes impregnated by means of the rapid Golgi method, but then the cells, instead of appearing black and solid, stand out clearly against a black or brown background. This black background is arranged in continuous partitions which gives a honeycomb appearance to the nervous tissue, very much like stratified epithelium stained with silver nitrate.

SUPERFICIAL GRANULAR LAYER

The cerebellar cortex of embryonic and young mammals and birds contains a third layer in addition to the molecular and granular layers of the adult cerebellum. This special layer is situated outside the molecular zone beneath the pia mater, and is composed of diverse rows of fine, compact, polyhedrical cells of epithelial appearance. This zone has been mentioned by several authors, notably by Schwalbe,[213] Vignal [233] and Obersteiner.[132]

We have termed it the *superficial granular zone,* to differentiate it from the true granular zone (red layer) which it resembles in carmine preparations.

The true form and significance of these cells is still unknown. Vignal believes that they represent migrated leucocytes, whereas Schwalbe and Obersteiner are inclined to consider them as elements which produce interstitial substances (reticular matter, radial fibers, etc). None of these theories is sufficiently grounded in facts, however. What is perfectly demonstrated is that this granular layer is transitory; it gradually thins and disappears as the subjacent molecular zone thickens and terminates its development.

Our attempts in the past year to stain these elements by the

Golgi method and to discern their form and their connections did not give us a satisfactory result. But having persisted recently both in the cerebellum of newborn animals (dog, rat, and cat) as well as in older fetuses of cow and rat, we have succeeded in impregnating some of these elements (Figs. 128, 129). These figures reveal that the zone of superficial granules is, in reality, composed of two distinct layers: 1. superficial layer of epithelioid cells; 2. deep layer of bipolar horizontal elements.

Superficial Layer. This zone is impregnated very rarely and then usually irregularly and inconsistently. Nevertheless, occasionally these cells are clearly stained. They are spheroidal, lack an axonal expansion, and possess a short robust prolongation which sometimes reaches the superficial part of the cerebellum.

Figure 128, a, copied from a preparation from the cerebellum of a 16 day old dog, shows the principal forms which are seen in successful impregnations.

The preceding characteristics plus the absence of a nervous expansion give rise to the thought that the cells of this first zone still belong completely to the class of germinative ectodermal elements. The later phases by which they come to form some of the adult cerebellar elements are completely unknown to us because of the virtual impossibility of obtaining clear impregnations of these cells in young animals (from 20 to 40 days after birth).

Deep Zone of Horizontal Bipolar Cells (Fig. 129, C). Even in thin sections of the young cerebellum stained with carmine or hematoxylin this zone is distinguished from the preceding by an obvious longitudinal striation and by longitudinal elongation of its nuclei. But only the Golgi method reveals the form of these cells very clearly. The latter are bipolar with an elongated oval body and two expansions leaving from the protoplasmic poles and extending a great distance parallel to the directions of the convolutions.

These two expansions do not seem identical to us: one is larger and shorter than the other and possesses the appearance of a protoplasmic branch; the other, fine and delicate, retains its thickness for a long distance and terminates in an undetermined fashion, perhaps in a free extremity (Figs. 129, e). Let us add that it is not

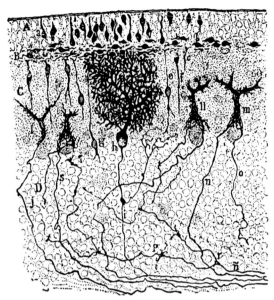

Fig. 128. Transverse section of the cerebellum of a 16 day old dog. A) Superficial granular layer; B) horizontal bipolar cells; C) molecular layer; D) deep granular layer; a) epithelioid cell; b) horizontal bipolar cell; c) triangular element; e, f, g) vertical bipolar cells; h) Purkinje cell whose axis-cylinder (i) emits a collateral; j) fiber from the white matter which terminates in the molecular layer by a ramified plexus; o, n, s) similar fibers terminating in a climbing plexus around Purkinje cells; r) mossy fiber.

rare to see secondary ramifications in the protoplasmic expansion. The most deeply situated elements (Fig. 129, d) sometimes emit a descending protoplasmic appendage which penetrates and terminates in the depths of the molecular zone.

The two zones of the superficial granular layer that we have just described do not vary and are never lacking in either avian or mammalian embryos; nevertheless the division of the two layers seems to be considerably more apparent in the cerebellum of mammals that are several days old (8 to 20 day old rat, cat, and dog). The younger the animal the thicker the zone of epithelioid cells, as compared with the zone of bipolar cells. In the cerebellum of the 12 day old rat (Fig. 129) the two layers are nearly equal in thickness.

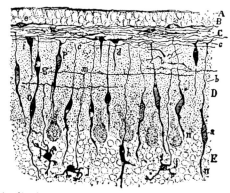

Fig. 129. Longitudinal section of a cerebellar convolution of a 12 day old rat. A) Cuticle; B) layer of epithelioid cells; C) zone of bipolar horizontal cells; D) molecular layer; E) granular layer; a) vertical bipolar cell; b) ascending nerve prolongation terminating at "c" by a bifurcation; d) transition cell between the vertical and horizontal bipolar forms; e) horizontal bipolar cell; j) deep granule cell with its axis-cylinder (m); o) vertical bipolar cell with some nuclei.

MOLECULAR ZONE

All the elements composing this layer seem fully developed in the cerebellum of the dog, cat, and rat from the fifteenth day of birth on. In newborn animals the longitudinal fibers are already as completely formed as the transverse ones. On the other hand, the descending twigs are rudimentary and lack the brushes or tufts that are characteristic of the adult cerebellum.

But let us not dwell on these and other characteristics that we have examined elsewhere;[157] let us only mention the existence of a new element which is clearly revealed in our sections of the cerebellum of young mammals. (Fig. 129, a, n, h, o.) This is a vertical bipolar cell placed at various heights both in the depths of the molecular layer as well as (though more rarely) in the most external portion of the deep granular zone (h). These elements possess an elongated, fusiform body enclosing a vertically elongated ovoid nucleus, comparable to that of muscle fiber cells. Thanks to the extreme thinness of the surrounding protoplasmic layer, the aforementioned nucleus is observed clearly, possessing a chestnut color against a black background (Fig. 129, a).

The descending cellular expansion is vigorous and has all the appearances of a protoplasmic branch. In the uppermost cells this expansion terminates by thinning in the molecular layer, but in the inferior cells it descends to the granular zone where it terminates in a point which is occasionally ramified.

The ascending expansion (b) is fine; for a long while it retains its fineness and gives every appearance of a neural or Deiters prolongation. Once arrived at the zone of superficial granules and at the level of the bipolar cells which form the inferior layer, it ends by being inserted at almost a right angle into the course of a longitudinal fiber. These longitudinal fibers, which seem to be an expansion of the ascending filament, travel parallel to the cerebellar convolutions, following a slightly flexuous course and extending for a considerable distance. In transverse sections they appear obliquely cut, whereas in longitudinal ones they are seen to be arranged in small parallel fascicles which occupy the thickness of the horizontal bipolar layer (c).

Within the bipolar component of the superficial granular layer there is a strata of longitudinal fibers from the deep granular zone which is placed above the fibers of the same name and direction originating from the molecular zone. In addition to the difference in origin and position, they are further distinguished from the latter by their greater thickness and roughness.

As can be seen from the preceding description, the arrangement of the molecular bipolar cells is similar to that of the deep granular cells. But their location, their marked elongation and the absence of transition forms uniting them with the granular cells, are the reasons which prevent them from being considered as a variety of the latter. Furthermore, at the time the bipolar cells appear, the granule cells are perfectly and definitively formed (Fig. 129, j).

Perhaps these cells are able to multiply by fission. The cell labeled "o" (Fig. 129) presents two nuclei with an intermediary thinning of the uniting protoplasm.

Sometimes it has seemed possible for us to recognize transitions between the bipolar elements that we have just described and the horizontal ones of the superficial cerebellar zone. Thus in Figure 129, f, we have drawn a cell which shows two expansions above its body, directed longitudinally between the bipolar horizontal cells. But these transition forms are too rare in our preparations for us to dare to relate these two species of cells genetically.

The bipolar cells that we have just described can be recognized, although less clearly, in sections of the embryonic cerebellum stained with routine methods. Staining by lithiocarmine followed by counterstaining with indigo carmine is especially suitable for this control study. Let us say in passing that the indigo carmine employed in this manner is fixed especially to the Purkinje cells and their expansions in the molecular layer, coloring virtually no other protoplasm, and thus facilitating the study of the growth and development of these elements.

Do these bipolar cells exist in the adult cerebellum? Are they purely embryonic arrangements, destined to undergo other transformations when the development of this organ is concluded? It is impossible to answer these questions definitively. Up to now we have not been able to successfully impregnate these cells in the adult mammalian and avian cerebellum, in spite of the great number of trials essayed by us during the course of three years. We have found them only in the cerebellum of young mammals (8 to 20 day old dog, cat, and rat) and in a 4 month old cow embryo.

PURKINJE CELLS

We believe it necessary to add some details regarding the growth of these cells and the arrangement of their nerve prolongations. The Purkinje elements are extremely embryonic in the newborn cat and dog. Everyone can be convinced of this fact by the examination of Figures 130 and 131. The cell body attracts immediate attention because of its stoutness and its very irregular form which in no way resembles its future appearance. Extremely intermixed varicose expansions of unequal length and thickness emerge in every direction from the protoplasmic periphery. Those which proceed from the inferior part of the protoplasmic body are the shortest, being directed downwards and sideways; some leave from the cone of origin of the axis-cylinder (Fig. 130).

The neural expansion of the Purkinje cells is developed very early. In the newborn dog and cat it can be followed very easily up

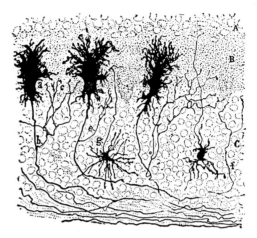

Fig. 130.   Transverse section of a cerebellar convolution of a newborn dog. A) Superficial granular layer; B) molecular layer; C) deep granular layer; D) white matter; a) embryonic Purkinje cell; b, c, e) collaterals of the Purkinje cell axis-cylinders; f) collateral arising far-off, almost at the white matter; g) granule cell with its ascending fiber.

to the white matter. Its collateral twigs, much better impregnated than in the adult, are clearly shown from their origin to their termination(Figs. 130, e, and 131, d).

These collateral twigs, one, two, or three in number, emerge from the parent nerve fiber at a right or obtuse angle and ascend to the molecular layer where they give off a great number of small, varicose, and divergent branches. Frequently this terminal ramification has the form of a plume and some of the terminal branches seem to wish to change direction and become longitudinal.

In the cat we have very often seen terminal arborizations so rich that they fill the molecular zone in great part, and thus lend considerable support to our opinion that these twigs represent a good portion of the myelinated fibers that the Weigert method reveals in the most inferior portions of this zone.

When the axis-cylinder of the Purkinje cell possesses two collaterals, one often notes that they emerge from opposite sides and that they may terminate in very distant parts of the molecular zone. It is not rare to see the second collateral emerge from the axis-cyl-

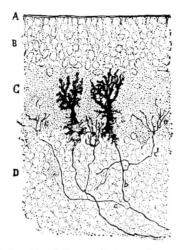

Fig. 131. Two Purkinje cells of the cerebellum of a newborn dog. These cells are from the top of a convolution, i.e., from a region that is relatively advanced developmentally. A) Cuticle with the insertion of the radial fibers; B) superficial granular layer; D) true or deep granular layer; a) Purkinje cell terminating above by a tuft of large spiny branches; b) nerve prolongation; d) collateral terminating by an arborization (e); c) another collateral directed in an opposite direction.

inder in the white matter itself (Fig. 130, f); then the point of termination is even farther away.

In summary, the collaterals of the axis-cylinders of the Purkinje cells go, for the most part, to the molecular layer, as Golgi and Kölliker have already noted, where they form terminal arborizations of great dimensions. What connections do these fibers establish? In the light of present knowledge it is impossible to establish a satisfactory hypothesis. The terminal plumes themselves might only be embryonic arrangements, destined to be modified profoundly in the adult, where, unfortunately, good impregnations are almost never obtained.*

In the cerebellum of the newborn dog and cat the most embryonic

---

*Subsequent research with neurofibrillar methods has convinced us that, after a variable longitudinal journey in the inferior third of the molecular layer, these branches terminate by *boutons* on the soma and thick branches of the Purkinje cells. (*Note for the French edition.*)

Purkinje elements (Fig. 130) are found in the deepest anfractuosities or in the concavity of the superficial lamellae. Those which adorn the external portion of the lamellae show a more advanced development (Fig. 131). They are already provided with a thick ascending trunk which emits several protoplasmic branches that are similar in form to the adult structure. A transverse flattening of the protoplasmic arborization is often noted. Let us further note a transverse thinning of the cell body and the shortening of some inferior expansions. Superficially the protoplasmic plume barely attains the inferior limit of the superficial granules.*

In the cerebellum of the 16 day old dog, development is almost complete. The protoplasmic arborization, very rich in secondary branches with spiny contours, occupies a great extent and struggles upwards to forge a path across the superficial granules (Fig. 128, h). The radial diameter of the cell body has diminished and the short descending and lateral expansions no longer exist. The cone of emergence of the axon has become smooth and lacks spiny ramifications. Furthermore, the axis-cylinder retains its form and its other characteristics, except that it is more voluminous and longer and ordinarily shows a large varicosity at the point of emergence of the collaterals (Fig. 128, i). The latter have grown sizably and, as in the embryonic phases, they are also seen to terminate in the depths of the molecular layer and among the neighboring Purkinje cell bodies by an extensive arborization of varicose, frequently longitudinal, branches. However an occasional twig is found which winds among the granules or seems to be lost after having a more or less descending direction.

In summary, in the growth of the Purkinje cells two phenomena toplasmic expansions; 2. resorption or retraction of the original are observed: 1. formation, elongation and ramification of the protoplasmic expansions. These two processes are slightly analogous to the double work, creative and destructive, to which bones are subject during the embryonic period.

---

*This development of the Purkinje cells has been confirmed by many scholars, especially by Tello employing neurofibrillar methods. (*Note for the French edition.*)

INFERIOR GRANULAR LAYER

All of the elements composing this layer appear differentiated in the newborn dog. It is only remarkable in that the large stellate cells are enormous, their protoplasmic arborizations reaching to the superficial granular layer. On the other hand, the collateral ramifications of the axis-cylinder are reduced in extent as compared with adult cells. The granules also appear fully formed at the same time, and it is very easy to follow their axis-cylinder up to the molecular layer and their continuation with a longitudinal fiber (Fig. 130, g). It is noteworthy that the protoplasmic expansions are more numerous than in the adult and that they terminate by a simple varicosity instead of a digitiform arborization. One must also observe that new ramifications emerge during development as the originally formed ones are partially absorbed.*

FIBERS OF THE WHITE MATTER

In our preceding works, we have demonstrated that silver chromate stains four kinds of nerve fibers that are continuous with the fibers of the white matter: 1. fibers which we have named *mossy,* meaning thereby to describe one of their most special characteristics, viz., the presence at intervals of short and small collateral arborizations resembling the moss which covers trees (Fig. 128, r, p); 2. fibers continuous with the Purkinje cells (the axis-cylinders of the latter); 3. fibers terminated in the molecular layer by transversely flattened plexiform arborizations; 4. fibers which become lost around Purkinje cells forming varicose periprotoplasmic nests or tufts.

Mossy Fibers. This first type is already developed in the brain of the newborn dog. The number of its ramifications and the extent of the granular layer that it embraces are remarkable. But these fibers do not yet exhibit their small mossy efflorescences. Only after the tenth or twelfth day do these fibers exhibit all their characteristics (Fig. 128, p).

Axis-Cylinders of the Purkinje Cells. We have already spoken of these fibers in this paper; it will suffice to add that they must develop

---

*As we will see further on, there are a great number of embryonic granules, in newborn mammals, which have not descended from the superficial layers. (*Note for the French edition.*)

very precociously since we have never been able to observe them during growth. In our numerous preparations of fetal and newborn animals they always present the same appearance as in the adult. To uncover the secret of their genesis it would be necessary to impregnate them at very early stages, but we have not as yet been able to obtain such preparations.

Fibers Terminated by Nerve Plexuses in the Molecular Layer. Under the above heading we combine the third and fourth types of fibers coming from the white matter. Our recent work has revealed that these two classes of fibers are identical. We can now add some new facts relating to the growth and mode of termination of these fibers.

In the work cited above,[157] we said that the fibers terminating by nests around the Purkinje cells had not yet been observed by us in the adult cerebellum but that their existence seemed probable, since their very special form of terminal arborization did not allow them to be considered as embryonic forms of other nerve ramifications. But more successful impregnations in the cerebellum of the 10 to 16 day old dog and cat, has revealed every transition of position and form among these two types of terminal arborizations, enabling us to state that the fibers terminated by nests around the cell bodies of the Purkinje elements are nothing more than the embryonic phase of the fibers terminating in the molecular layer by bifurcated or ramified plexuses. That is why we have never observed these plexuses in newborn animals and why the terminal nests, absolutely constant in embryos, are never present in adult animals (Figs. 132, D, C, and 133, a, e, t).

The study of the afore-mentioned transition forms and comparison with the adult arrangement has permitted us to discover a very singular fact. The ramified plexiform arborization, formed by the fibers of the fourth type in the midst of the molecular layer, twines around and twists in some way along the ascending protoplasmic trunk of the Purkinje cell as well as around the principal branches of the latter, the way creepers of ivy climb up alongside the trunk and the large branches of a tree. That is why we name these terminal plexuses *climbing arborizations* or *plexuses*.

As singular as this fact appears, the observations on which it

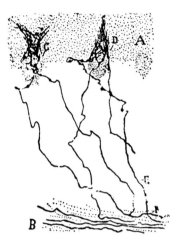

Fig. 132. Two climbing arborizations of the cerebellum of an 8 day old dog. A) molecular layer; B) white matter; C, D) nerve plexuses around Purkinje cells; E) one of the fibers forming this arborization (D); F) fiber whose two branches form arborization "C."

rests are too conclusive for doubt. Here are some of the observations:

1. Carefully examining some of these terminal plexuses in 15 to 20 day old mammals (Fig. 128, 1, 11, m), one notes that they begin even above a Purkinje cell and that they cover the ascending trunk and the principal branches of the latter, reproducing the shape, direction, and the thickness of the parts surrounded. To facilitate this observation it is necessary to examine sections very simply cleared in spirits of turpentine; mounted and dried preparations are too transparent for the cell body and the principal trunk of the Purkinje cells to be clearly recognized.

2. Transverse sections of these terminal plexuses present the appearance of a circle having a center free of branches, the center obviously corresponding to the ascending trunk of Purkinje cells.

3. When these terminal ramifications are observed in adult animals (Fig. 133) their form and direction in every respect mimic the shape, position and direction of the branches of the protoplasmic trunk of the Purkinje cells. The very orientation of the climbing plexuses is similar to that of the arborization of these cells, i.e., flattened perpendicularly to the convolutions. Before mounting into

the molecular layer, the nerve fiber of origin of the climbing plexus always passes just beside the body of a Purkinje element (Fig. 133, a, e, g, t).

4. In birds, in which the arborization of the Purkinje cells is simpler, the climbing plexus also appears more simplified and with the same form.

The development of these terminal plexuses is very curious. In newborn animals such as the dog and the cat their shape and location are completely different from that which they later acquire. One or more extremely thick fibers are seen coming from the white matter and forming a compact, varicose, extremely complex and entangled arborization around the body and especially the upper part of the Purkinje cells (Fig. 132, D). These are the cerebellar nests of our previous descriptions.

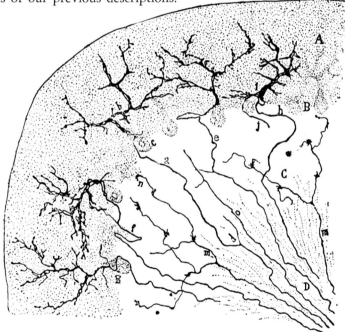

Fig. 133. Transverse section of a cerebellar convolution of an adult rat. Only fibers coming from the white matter are represented here. Each of these fibers and its arborizations has been faithfully copied from perfectly conclusive preparations, with no artifice other than the collection in one figure of fibers observed in various regions of the same sections. A) Molecular layer; B) Purkinje

A few days after birth the branches of the climbing plexus multiply considerably and increase in thickness and it becomes extremely difficult to make out their individuality. The latticework that these filaments form becomes thinner towards the top like a brush point; it glides along the trunk of the Purkinje cells, attains the depth of the molecular layer and is slightly extended there onto the principal protoplasmic branches (Fig. 128, 11, m).

Finally, following the fifteenth day, the plexus climbs on the principal branches of the protoplasmic arborization of the Purkinje cells, abandoning the Purkinje cell body. Only the nerve fiber of origin ultimately retains contact with the Purkinje cell body (Fig. 133.) During this last period of growth, which could be compared with that of embryonic peripheral nerves, the plexus elongates and ramifies considerably while diminishing in thickness. The larger and more varicose fibers which compose it present a more clear cut individuality and terminate by a globular swelling after having traversed the length of the protoplasmic branches of the Purkinje cells (Fig. 133, b).

As regards the fibers contributing to each climbing arborization, they vary in their arrangement. The small plexuses, both in the adult as well as in the young animal, seem to have arisen from the terminal ramification of a single nerve fiber which maintains its individuality without furnishing any branches during its passage across the granular layer and the white matter. This property of not ramifying and of not providing any mossy efflorescences in its path distinguishes these from other fibers (axis-cylinders of Purkinje cells and mossy fibers). When a collateral twig exists, it takes part in the same arborization, as is clearly seen in one of the climbing plexuses of Figure 132, C.

The most extensive climbing plexuses are always formed by two or more fibers coming from the white matter (Figs. 128, 132). Figure 133, f, i, also shows some climbing plexuses in which at least two fibers arrive at the arborization. The collateral twigs (Fig. 133, c, d) are identical to those which, in young animals, after a more

←―――――――

cell layer; C) granular layer; D) white matter; a, e, f, g) fibers from the white matter terminating in the molecular layer by climbing plexuses; b, i) climbing plexuses; c) Purkinje cell; m) mossy fibers; o) Purkinje cell axis-cylinder.

or less extensive and irregular course, enter into the same arborization as the principal trunk.

All the Purkinje cells seem to possess climbing plexuses, although the rarity of good impregnations of these arborizations in the adult does not allow for categorical statements in this regard. Ordinarily, when the terminal arborization is impregnated the nerve fibers which support it are not colored. In only a small number of cases have we succeeded in obtaining complete impregnations both of the trunk as well as the terminal plexus in the adult. That is why young mammals, even newborn ones, are much preferable for the study of these interesting arrangements; in such specimens it is not rare to see several series of climbing arborizations with their fibers of origin all stained in their entirety.

As for the significance of these curious pericellular nerve terminations, one cannot say anything which would not be a pure physiological hypothesis. What can be affirmed with some plausibility, is that they are myelinated fibers arising from cells in other parts of the nervous system and terminating on the Purkinje cells just as motor nerves terminate on muscle cells. It is evident that the intimate and exclusive connection that the climbing plexuses establish with the protoplasmic arborization of the Purkinje cells serves to transmit the nerve impulse to the Purkinje cells. But nothing can be stated concerning the nature of the dynamic connection established. In the present state of knowledge we do not possess any certain anatomical criterion to decide whether a cell (e. g., the Purkinje cell) is sensory or motor or whether such a fiber, terminating in the gray matter, receives peripheral or central stimuli.

CONCLUSIONS

The observations that we have just described confirm the suppositions of Forel [41] and His [66,67] regarding the absolute independence of nerve cells. As is known, His first discovered that the neuroblasts of the embryonic human spinal cord lack anastomoses. They possess a single expansion, the axis-cylinder, which retains its individuality indefinitely.

The doctrine of independence of cells and of nerve fibers of the central nervous system has also received the adherence of Kölliker

[80] and there is reason to hope that it will soon be accepted generally. In reality, Golgi has proved that anastomoses between the dendritic expansions of nerve cells do not exist. But no one, so far as we know, has furnished similar proof concerning the axis-cylinder of central neurons or the termination of sensory and special sense fibers which originate in peripheral ganglia (retina, olfactory mucosa, spinal ganglia). We believe we have demonstrated such freely arborizing pericellular, supracellular, or intracellular terminations in our research on the embryonic nervous system. Because of the brevity of the distances traversed by embryonic nerve fibers and the greater facility with which these fibers can be stained, the embryo constitutes the only subject offering a favorable opportunity for the solution of such a difficult problem.

We can cite as examples of free terminations: those of the optic nerve of birds in the peripheral layer of the optic lobe; those of the olfactory nerve of mammals in the glomeruli of the olfactory bulb; those of the dorsal roots of the spinal cord (at least for many of their collaterals.) One can also accept as very probable the existence of free arborizations in the terminations of certain axis-cylinders of central origin, such as those of the stellate cells of the molecular layer of the cerebellum; those of the ganglionic cells of the granular layer; those of the bipolar elements of the retina; those of the nerve cells of the spinal cord, etc.

Only in the peripheral ganglia of the sympathetic nervous system are true anastomoses found.[152] They are also noted in the nervous system of insects [160] which, perhaps, correspond to the ganglionic bundles of the vertebrate sympathetic system*. But in the cerebrospinal centers, we repeat, one can never demonstrate the slightest trace of anastomoses.

We think that connections are established by multiple contacts, often rendered more intimate by interlacings which produce a veritable meshwork. The climbing arborizations of the cerebellum support this point of view especially. Perhaps, as His is inclined to admit,

---

*At present we consider these sympathetic anastomoses very doubtful. As regards the nervous system of insects, our researches and those of Sanchez have shown that the connections between neurons take place exclusively by contact between dendrons and axonal ramifications. (*Note for the French edition.*)

a conductive matter comparable to the granular substance of motor plaques also exists between the nervous parts in contact. We believe we have seen some such thing around the body and ascending trunk of the Purkinje cells. It is a granular layer which is colored brown or yellow by silver chromate and remains independent of the cells and the fibers. In the other parts of the nervous system, we have seen nothing similar save the intercellular cement, whose nature seems to us slightly different, for it is homogeneously colored back or deep brown and it is continuous in all parts of the gray matter.

The intercellular contacts show some variations in arrangement. The reality of the following arrangements seems almost completely demonstrated.

1. When the cells must establish connections with neighboring elements of either different or the same nature, the relationship is effected by contacts between the protoplasmic expansions (dendrons).*

2. Furthermore, when the nerve cells must maintain a relationship with one or more distant elements, either nervous or of other nature (muscular, epithelial), it is the axis-cylinder which is charged with this connection, which invariably takes place by a free arborization closely applied to the elements which it must influence. Example: motor plaques of muscles; cells of the gray matter of the spinal cord whose axis-cylinder is united by numerous collaterals with the cells of diverse levels of the central nervous system [81,149, 154,159] perhaps even up to the brain; cells of the spinal ganglia whose axis-cylinder also furnishes an infinite number of collateral twigs, penetrating into the gray matter and terminating among the dorsal and ventral horn cells; stellate cells of the molecular layer of the cerebellum whose axons arborize around diverse Purkinje cells.† Perhaps the majority of axis-cylinders belong to this variety.

3. When several cells must establish a connection with a single one, the ramifications of their nervous expansions intermix and

---

*We no longer admit the propagation of the nerve impulse by contact between the protoplasmic prolongations or dendrons. We consider the theory of *axipetal polarization* [185] to be valid only for the normal, weakened nervous system. (*Note for the French edition.*)

establish contact either with the cell body or the protoplasmic arborizations of the latter.

The Purkinje elements are an example of multiple contacts. Their cell body is united with the stellate cells of the molecular zone by means of the descending brushes of the stellate cell axon, their principal protoplasmic trunk makes contact with the *climbing arborizations* (fibers of unknown origin deriving from the white matter), and the secondary and tertiary branches of their protoplasmic arborization is united with the granular cells via the longitudinal fibers of the latter. In general, the relations are established between cell body and protoplasmic expansions, on the one hand, and arborization of axis-cylinders on the other. Up to now, we have not been able to observe any connection by arborizations of axis-cylinders alone.

By virtue of the innumerable ramifications of many axis-cylinders, e.g., those of the cerebral and spinal neurons, it is possible for a single cell to be in mediate relation with a great number of elements of the central nervous system (Golgi). The problem of microscopic anatomy consists in the determination of these coordinated systems for each category of cells or, perhaps, for each cell in particular.

At the present we cannot go further forward in so complicated a field. What we have described enables one to imagine the extreme structural complexity of the central nervous system and to recognize the new direction which we believe anatomical analysis must follow in order to shed some light on the obscure problem of cellular relationships in the central nervous system.

←———

† The facts we have described about the molecular layer of the cerebellum [147] have been confirmed in great part by Kölliker.[80,82] We wish to express our sincere gratitude to the eminent professor for having had the kindness to verify certain facts which, because of their strangeness, seemed somewhat unbelievable to him. Furthermore, all the authorities who have seen our preparations have been obliged to acknowledge that the greater part of our descriptions are correct.

Chapter 11

DEVELOPMENT OF VARIOUS CEREBELLAR ELEMENTS

DEVELOPMENT OF THE GRANULE CELLS

IN OUR PREVIOUS works on this subject we had left one very important question unanswered: the significance of certain fusiform radial cells dispersed throughout the molecular layer. Our later research fills this gap and allows us to call attention to the phases by which the superficial granule cells become the deep granule cells. The superficial granules undergo some extremely curious metamorphoses which recall in part those of the unipolar spinal ganglion cells.

The cerebellum of newborn mammals (mouse, rabbit, dog, and man) possesses a special zone above the molecular layer, formed by small cells crowded one against the other, that has been named the *superficial granular zone.* The cells of this zone diminish in number proportionately as the cerebellum develops, and they disappear completely sometime in the adult period (Fig. 135, A). Furthermore, concomitant with the decrease in number of superficial granule cells there is an increase in the number of deep granule cells.

In our initial studies on the cerebellum, we noted that the deeper layers of the superficial granules are composed of bipolar, fusiform, tangentially elongated cells provided with long expansions parallel to the longitudinal axis of the cerebellar lamella. One could have believed that they were parallel fibers, analogous to those which arise from the axis-cylinder of the deep granules. In reality these bipolar cells are none other than the primitive forms of the deep granules. Thanks to a migration across the subjacent molecular layer these cells (contrary to the bipolar cells of the spinal ganglia which travel peripherally from the central nervous system) attain the depths of the cerebellar lamellae where they adopt all the characteristics of adult granule cells. Before arriving there these

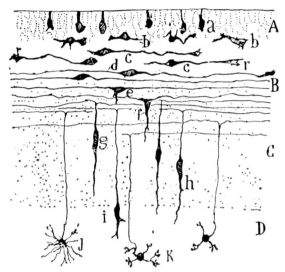

Fig. 134. Schematic figure to show all the forms and locations adopted by the granule cells during their development. A) Indifferent cell layer; B) layer of granule cells in the horizontal bipolar stage; C) plexiform layer; D) granular layer; g, h) stage of vertical bipolarity; i, j) embryonic granule cells; k) almost fully-developed granule cell.

cells pass through the following phases: 1. From the body of the horizontal bipolar cell a protoplasmic appendage descends. Little by little it drags the cell body including the nucleus with it towards the depths. 2. This appendage travels perpendicularly through the molecular zone. It is an elongated structure provided with two expansions: one ascending, being continuous with the superior part of the molecular layer by a parallel fibril, the other descending, freely terminating near the zone of the deep granules (Fig. 134, h). 3. When the cell, dragged by and within the descending appendage, arrives at the layer of deep granules, the ascending expansion becomes thinner and adopts the appearance of an axis-cylinder continuous with a parallel fiber; the cell body then gives birth to three or more short appendages which immediately become the protoplasmic expansions characteristic of the deep granules (Fig. 134, i, j).

This developmental history therefore teaches us two interesting facts. First, we see that the parallel fiber remains permanently and definitively in the region that it occupied initially when it was represented by the two extremities of the bipolar horizontal cell. Secondly, the ascending axis-cylinder and the digitiform expansions of the granule cell are the result of protoplasmic stretching.*

Figure 135 illustrates a Nissl preparation of the cerebellum at the time of migration of the superficial granules. This figure reveals that in the newborn rabbit there is a very active mitotic process in the depths of the superficial granular layer (Fig. 135, A).

DEVELOPMENT OF THE LARGE STELLATE CELLS[172]

In Figures 136 and 137 we have reproduced the principal developmental phases of the short-axon stellate cells. These neurons have already gone beyond the neuroblastic stage at the time silver chromate can impregnate them. Therefore they are seen in the bipolar form from the outset. Terrazas[226] has shown that the fusiform appearance predominates. They possess two appendages: one dendritic or external; the other axonal or internal which is varicose, of variable length, and terminates, after having given rise to some rudimentary collaterals, in the middle of the granular layer (Figs. 136 and 137). A descending protoplasmic expansion generally emerges from the cell body, especially in the region where the axis-cylinder is born. This expansion is often the root of the axon.

Later the cell body increases in volume, the basilar expansions multiply, elongating and emitting numerous ramifications; the polar dendron, formerly undivided, blossoms out into a bouquet of spiny branches which invade an increasingly vast territory in the plexiform zone. The small terminal branches ordinarily stop at the limit of the superficial granules; sometimes, however, they cross it, becoming considerably thinner, and end against the basal mem-

---

*We have borrowed this description from a work by my brother.[143] In this memoir, while describing the neurogenesis of the cerebellum, he expressed my opinion on the curious development of the granules. For our present text, we have benefited from the French translation made by Dr. Azoulay of our conferences in Barcelona.[166]

Without knowledge of our discovery, Lugaro arrived at the same conclusions.[108] Calleja, Schaper, Athias, Terrazas, Waterville and others have presented, *mutatis mutandis,* similar descriptions.

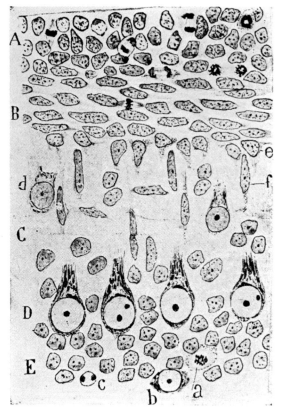

Fig. 135. Section of a cerebellar convolution of a newborn rabbit. Nissl method. A) Zone of indifferent cells, some cells of which are undergoing mitosis; B) zone of fusiform horizontal cells; C) plexiform zone, D) zone of Purkinje cells; E) granular zone; a) dividing cell in the midst of the granules; b) Golgi cell; f) fusiform granule cell migrating towards the granular zone (E).

brane. It is noteworthy that these dendrons, which are spiny and unequal in the molecular layer, become smooth during their passage across Obersteiner's layer (Fig. 137, B).

As for the axis-cylinder, it grows little by little, takes a more or less oblique or horizontal direction, and is very sinuous. Its collaterals increase in number at the same time, so that its terminal arborization is already very complicated in the 15 day old cat, almost as much so as in the adult. However, the varicose and flexuous term-

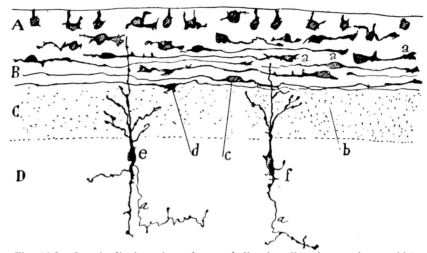

Fig. 136. Longitudinal section of a cerebellar lamella of a newborn rabbit. Golgi method. A) layer of indifferent cells; B) layer of bipolar cells, i.e., granule cells in the bipolar horizontal stage; a) growth cones; e, f) very embryonic Golgi cells.

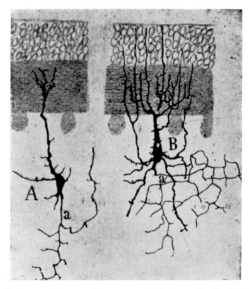

Fig. 137. Cerebellum of a newborn cat. Golgi method. A) Very embryonic Golgi cell; B) more advanced Golgi cell; a) the short axis-cylinder of these cells.

inal axonal rami, which are the very ones which penetrate into the cerebellar islets, only appear completely developed at one month of age. The same is true of the rabbit. Popoff [140,141] notes with surprise some stellate cells in the middle of the plexiform layer in a 14 centimeter sheep embryo. This position would indicate, according to him, that these cells derive from Obersteiner's layer. Athias [3] shares this opinion. The displaced Golgi cells that we have discovered and that he has also observed in the cerebellum of the cat would be, according to this author, one more argument in favor of this point of view.

DEVELOPMENT OF THE NEUROFIBRILLAR FRAMEWORK IN THE ROSACEAE OF THE MOSSY FIBERS

It is already an old observation that some diffusely ramified fibers originate in the white matter and arrive at the granular layer. It was noted in fetal, newborn, or young animals by Golgi, Retzius, Calleja, Terrazas, Athias, and ourselves. As we have noted,[172] the silver chromate method ordinarily reveals such fibers in newborn or several day old animals; they lack visible excrescences or rosaceae. However, in the 16 day old dog this reagent does outline some collateral and terminal appendages. They appear even sooner in the cat, the pigeon, and especially in the guinea pig.

But these rudimentary rosaceae which are undergoing development, transformation, and even reabsorption, lack a neurofibrillar framework or, if present, it does not attract the colloidal silver precipitate at all. The neurofibrillar methods impregnate only the trunks and large branches of bifurcation (several day old rabbit, cat, and dog).

A careful examination of the development of the rosaceae in mammals reveals that the path and termination begins to enlarge only towards the eighteenth or twentieth day (cat, rabbit, and dog). This enlargement would seem to represent the rudimentary framework of the digitiform ramifications. Even in the 25 day old dog these ramifications are far from being formed. As we show in Figure 138, some thickenings (b) and even an actual fusiform unraveling (c) can be distinguished along the course of several fibers.

Some rudimentary terminal ramifications (a) in the form of an ansiform swelling show a tendency to emit terminal twigs.

During the successive days, i.e., from the twenty-fifth to the fortieth day, the mossy efflorescences are formed and enriched, although they do not as yet attain the complexity and the abundance of the adult. As we have suggested above, it is possible in old animals that certain terminal ramifications, after having attained excessive development, undergo a partial process of degeneration.

To avoid prolonging this description we will note in summary: 1. The rosaceae are created many days before their interior framework is differentiated or, at the very least before this framework can be stained by means of silver methods. 2. The full neurofibrillar development of the mossy fibers is attained only when all the granule cells and their dendrons are perfectly formed. 3. Ordinarily, the first framework to appear corresponds to the terminal end of the mossy fiber (rudiment of the terminal ramification). 4. Consequently, the force which gathers together the two elements of

Fig. 138.   Development of the mossy fibers in a 25 day old dog. A) Brushes; B) cell of the granular layer surrounded by brushes; a) termination of young mossy fibers by ansiform swellings; b) a beginning mossy rosacea; c) an unravelling along the path of a mossy fiber.

the articulation (granule cell dendrons and mossy efflorenscences), whatever hypothesis be adopted regarding its mechanism (neurotropism, difference in electrical potential between the associated neurons, etc.), seems conditioned by the neuroplasm and not by the arising neurofibrils, unless we attribute to the latter a developmental precocity not demonstrable by present methods.

We cannot make any concrete and definite statements regarding the cells of origin of the mossy fibers. The purely anatomical methods, in particular the neurofibrillar procedure, that we have employed almost exclusively during these recent years, do not permit us to resolve this problem. It would be necessary to apply physiological experiments in combination with the anatomicopathological procedures (e.g., lesions of the pathways which are supposedly associated with the cerebellum). This would be far from easy, considering the deep position of the pons, the central vestibular ganglia, restiform body, olive, etc. The reader who is desirous of learning about the status of this difficult question should consult the works of Bárány, Villaverde, Estable, and Lorente de Nó,* to cite only some modern authors.

DEVELOPMENT OF THE BASKET CELL[172]

In our first work on cerebellar histogenesis,[157] before the discovery of the development of the granule cells, we had expressed the opinion that the superficial granules might very well give rise to the stellate cells of the plexiform layer by migration towards the depths and gradual transformation. Later, Schaper[210] noted that the superficial granular layer is an indifferent germinal formation, capable of forming nerve cells such as the stellate neurons and even neuroglial cells.

Several authors, especially Popoff,[140,141] Athias,[3] and Terrazas[226] independently and almost concurrently gave thorough and complete confirmation to the suppositions that we and Schaper had expressed regarding the origin of the stellate basket cells. They established, and the fact was verified by us in the newborn rab-

---

*Lorente de Nó[104] has presented a very interesting schema concerning the connections of the Purkinje axons and the mossy fibers.

bit, cat, and mouse, that the basket cells originate, like the granules, from the region of the external granules or superficial germinal elements, by passing through the following phases:

Phase of Horizontal Bipolarity. According to Athias, differentiation begins in the most external rows of the superficial granules. The future stellate cells are distinguished by their spindle shape and by two polar expansions, one short, thick, and protoplasmic in nature, the other finer and often terminated by a growth cone. These cells supposedly sink little by little into the plexiform layer and by degrees are transformed into young stellate cells which have an axis-cylinder almost entirely lacking in collaterals. These are the same cells that we and later Kölliker, Retzius, Lui, and Calleja, had encountered at different levels in the first zone of the cerebellar cortex in mammals of several days' age.

Thanks to its orientation, it is easy to recognize the rudimentary stellate cell from its very first phases, as Popoff, Athias, and Terrazas have noted. In fact, the bipolar cell which will become the basket cell is oriented perpendicularly to the longitudinal fibers of the granules and parallel to the Purkinje cells, whereas the bipolar cell which will form a granule is directed in the same sense as the longitudinal fibers (Fig. 139, a, b).

Phase of the Young Stellate Cell. Once arrived at the molecular zone, the cell only briefly retains the shortness of its polar

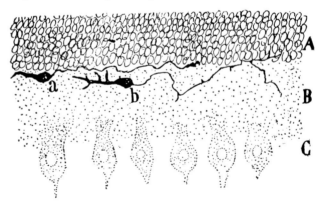

Fig. 139. A) Superficial granular or Obersteiner's layer; B) molecular zone; C) Purkinje cells; a) stellate cell in the bipolar phase; b) another stellate cell in the same phase but possessing short dendrites.

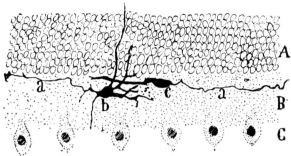

Fig. 140. Section parallel to the Purkinje cells of the cerebellum of a newborn cat. Golgi method. A) Granular or Obersteiner's layer; B) molecular zone; C) Purkinje cells; a) axis-cylinders of the stellate or embryonic basket cells; b) another basket cell having polar and somatic prolongations; c) bipolar basket cell.

expansions and the nudity of its axis-cylinder; it presents neither collaterals nor terminal axonal arborization as yet (Fig. 140, b, c). But soon the cell attains deeper and deeper layers and its protoplasmic polar appendage emits secondary branches which gradually elongate; the axis-cylinder, which now terminates in a growth cone or a large varicosity, bifurcates and emits some short collaterals whose course is still irregular, as though undecided. The descent of these cells is not spontaneous. Terrazas noted that it took place, in reality, under the centripetal force of the newly formed elements of the zone of bipolar cells. These elements include the recently formed parallel fibers and the last contingent of stellate cells disengaged from the germinal layer. The stellate neurons near the Purkinje cells are the oldest. Consequently, those which are found in the adult state in the superficial zones are the youngest. Some stellate cells cannot send descending collaterals around the Purkinje cell bodies because the latter are already occupied by more precocious stellate cells. These cells are then restricted to making connection only with the protoplasmic branches of the Purkinje cells.

Phase of Basket Formation. When the young stellate cell approaches the Purkinje neuron its body is covered by a great number of divergent and spiny dendrons. This is clearly visible in Figure 141, E. At the same time the axis-cylinder, already very elongated, projects large, tortuous and very irregular branches. These latter, by

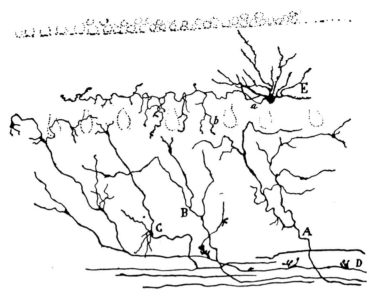

Fig. 141. Transverse section of the cerebellum of a several-day-old rabbit. Golgi method. A, B) Primordial mossy fibers in the stage of smooth arborizations; C) fibers provided with fibrillar appendages arising from certain nuclei; D) nearly adult mossy fibers; E) very advanced basket cell.

applying themselves to the body of the Purkinje cells, form a rudimentary basket around it. Little by little their length grows, their complexity increases, bifurcations and ramifications replace their free varicose, thickened extremities; the basket is then adult, or almost adult.

The initial course of the axis-cylinder is very complicated in some stellate cells. Instead of being transverse and nearly rectilinear, it describes, as Calleja had already noted, great curves and even entire circles. The axon seems disoriented and groping for its route among the Purkinje cells. The disorientation ceases when the baskets have nearly attained their definitive appearance, but the initial detour or curve often persists. For the reasons we have just described, not all of the developmental phenomena of the stellate cells have been explained. One of them, the primitive transverse orientation of these neuroblastic neurons, seems not to be subject to the chemicomechanical conditions invoked by us. The initial curve or detour of the axis-cylinder of a great many stellate cells is not very easy to understand. One could explain it by supposing that, at the moment when the axis-cylinder begins to grow, the Purkinje cells which it will contact are still embryonic, i.e., they still lack multiple and irregular dendritic prolongations and have not yet begun to secrete attractive substances. The axis-cylinder is unguided; it wanders and turns upon itself like a ship which tacks while awaiting the proper moment to enter the port.*

---

*Our more modern research with neurofibrillar methods clearly confirms this description of the development of the stellate cells. However the first phases, before the ramification of the axon, cannot be revealed by colloidal silver. (*Note for the French edition.*)

Chapter 12

DEVELOPMENT OF THE NEUROFIBRILLAR FRAMEWORK OF THE PURKINJE CELL [174,197]

THE TRANSFORMATION of the Purkinje cells are also very clearly revealed in preparations made by the reduced silver nitrate neurofibrillar method. The phases of growth and the metamorphoses of the dendritic branches can be followed (Fig. 142); one notes likewise that the axis-cylinder is very thick from the start, that the dendrons arise from the base of the cell body and that the nucleus occupies a lateral position.

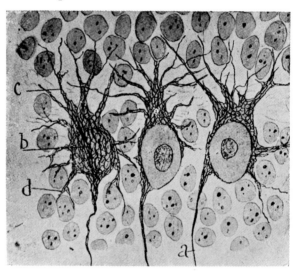

Fig. 142. Purkinje cells of a 3 or 4 day old dog. Silver nitrate impregnation without fixation. a) Axis-cylinder; b) stream of neurofibrils converging on the axis-cylinder; d) neurofibrils of the basilar dendrites.

But this kind of preparation is especially intended to demonstrate the neurofibrillar network in the various parts of the developing cell. As is seen in Figure 142, a, the axis-cylinder is formed by a fascicle of neurofibrils. The cell body encloses a very evident network whose thick, longitudinal fibers extend from the axis-cylinder to the thick ascending dendrons. The latter are also filled with a reticulum having an elongated meshwork. Their terminal small rami, which disappear in the molecular layer, seem to be formed by a single fiber only, freely ending and sometimes redoubled. A thick layer of neuroplasm undoubtedly exists around the dendrons, judging by their relatively large diameter in Golgi preparations. Figures 142 and 143 show two phases of the development of the neurofibrillar apparatus of the Purkinje cell of the dog.

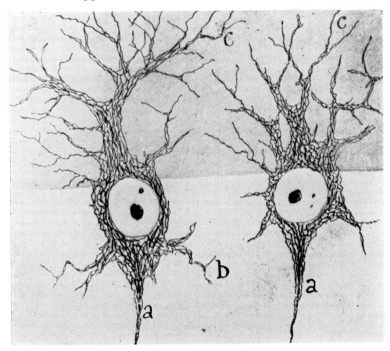

Fig. 143. Two Purkinje cells from the cerebellum of a 10 day old dog. Silver nitrate impregnation without fixation (formula I). a) Axis-cylinder; b) basilar dendrites; c) fine dendrites composed of a single neurofibril.

We have already said that the embryonic neurofibrillar reticulum of the Purkinje cells has been confirmed by Tello [217] in birds, in which the aforesaid neurons are discontinuously arranged in the form of linear agglomerations.

In a recent work [197] we explored this reticulum anew, both in avian embryos as well as in newborn or very young mammals. The following paragraphs are borrowed from this memoir. This description extends and completes our very concise earlier report.[174]

We distinguish three phases in the development of the Purkinje cells, namely, the phase of the *fusiform cell,* that of the *stellate cell with disoriented dendrons, and the phase of orientation and of flattening of the dendritic branched pattern or plume.*

Phase of the Fusiform Cell. In spite of the now old works of Popoff, Calleja, Athias, and ourselves, no one has yet been able to observe the neuroblastic stage of the Purkinje neurons precisely and with certainty. When one stains 10 and even 11 day chick embryos with ordinary methods (Nissl, hematoxylin,) the cerebellar cortex appears formed by a multitude of compact cells without well-defined stratification. However, at a certain depth in the cellular mass (10 to 11 day chick embryo), one perceives a band of more voluminous nuclei arranged in several irregular strata and surrounded by a relatively abundant protoplasm, especially towards the superficial pole. These are the young Purkinje cells whose expansions do not yet attract colloidal silver nor fix silver chromate. At least, in our trials with the Golgi method we have not succeeded in obtaining a positive result.

By the twelfth or thirteenth day of incubation one can obtain an acceptable staining of the dendrons and axon by the neurofibrillar methods. Variations in intensity according to the regions explored occur even at this stage, for it is well known that not all the cerebellar territories exhibit the same degree of development. On the other hand, impregnations are more general and more constant in 14 day embryos, making possible a useful analysis.

As is shown in Figure 144, D, the radially elongated Purkinje cell bodies range in several strata. The axons emerge toward the base and become lost in the depths of the cerebellum. The dendrons emerge from the sides and superior pole of the cell body and are arranged in the form of occasionally dichotomized neurofibrillar fascicles. It is fitting to note that the dendrons of the most inferior cells clear a passage among the cell bodies of those situated in more tangential planes, reaching the deep layers of the superficial granular or Obersteiner layer. The ovoidal nucleus ordinarily occupies the inferior pole of the cell and is more or less eccentric, which is the reason why the expansions seem to be continuous with a tangential protoplasmic mass (Figs. 144 and 145). Since some Purkinje cells are situated very deeply beneath other ones, it is evident that their ascending dendrons attain a great length while crossing the interstices of the superposed congeneral elements. At this time the molecular layer is not yet differentiated, from which it follows that one could not as yet truly speak of *superficial granules* and *deep granules* since the differentiation of these diminutive neuronal types has not yet begun.

Fig. 144. Cerebellum of a 12 day old chick embryo. A) Layer of superficial or germinal granule cells; B) layer of differentiating cells; D, fusiform Purkinje cells; E) deep granular layer.

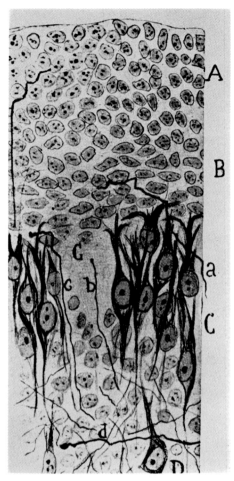

Fig. 145.   Section of the cerebellum of a 14 day chick embryo. A) Superficial granule cells; B) developing granule cells; C) Purkinje cell layer; D) a deeply placed neuron; a) fiber wandering among the granule cells; b) fibers terminating in a bouton which is located in a space devoid of Purkinje cells.

At this stage the Purkinje cell is in a phase prior to that which we have named [174] the *phase of initial disorientation*, which Tello [217] confirmed in heron embryos.

In mammals and especially in the white mouse, the phase of the fusiform cell is only seen in the latter days of fetal life in the cerebellar *vermis*. However, if our observations are made on the flocculus (of the newborn mouse), where the cerebellar development appears retarded, the said phase is also seen with its typical characteristics, as we note in Figure 146, C. In such preparations the Purkinje cells appear arranged in several compact layers, with the axon directed towards the depths and the dendrons, variable in number, directed towards the mass of superposed granules. These dendrons bud from all sides of the soma, but one or two especially robust radially oriented ones always stand out.

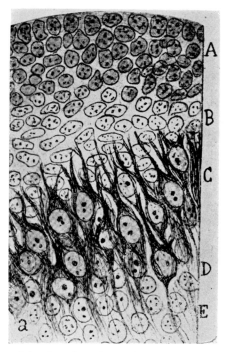

Fig. 146.   Section of the flocculus of a newborn mouse. C) Embryonic Purkinje
cells arranged ni 3 or 4 layers; E) deep granular layer.

It follows from what we have just stated that the monostratified arrangement of the adult Purkinje cell bodies arises from the tangential spreading or sliding of these cells which takes place as the superficial cerebellar surface and lamellae develop. It therefore seems probable that the consignment of Purkinje cells is already complete at this time, since no signs of multiplication are perceived. The last process would therefore consist of a series of tangential dislocations and migrations, with successive differentiation of neuro-fibrils. One must not lose sight of the fact that in the previously described band of embryonic Purkinje cells, some are less differentiated than others and, therefore, younger. Actually, some cells are noted in which the neurofibrils can hardly be made out and whose expansions are apparently finer and simpler. As a general rule, these less differentiated elements lie beneath the larger, more differentiated ones.

Finally, some solitary large fusiform or triangular cells are also found at a considerable distance beneath the Purkinje neurons (Fig. 145, D). Do these represent young forms of the Golgi cells which will reside, in time, in the granular layer? Or are they retarded or strayed Purkinje elements?

Phase of the Stellate Cell with Disoriented Dendrons. This phase, contemporaneous in appearance with the rudiment of the molecular layer and which we have described several years ago, is characterized by the formation of a great number of lateral and ascending dendrons which dichotomize several times and terminate at diverse levels by means of conical points. The longest of them just reaches to the zone of bipolar horizontal cells which are now differentiated. Sections tangential to the lamellae prove that the dendritic branched pattern has not yet undergone the flattening characteristic of later phases (Figs. 147, 148, A). The cells are stellate and their expansions intertwine and form a complicated plexus. The latter is proportionately simplified, however, at more superficial levels; this occurrence bespeaks a beginning regularization of the terminal tuft.

We will not dwell here on the characteristics of this phase, for we described it a long time ago; we will be content with adding some details. Let us first note that in newborn birds (swallow, sparrow) the Purkinje elements are not continuous but, as Tello noted in the heron, they are arranged in groups separated by pale anteroposterior zones or bands. In the newborn swallow each lamella has eight or even more clusters of this kind, the cellular quantity varying for each of them. This division into nuclei is already visible in the 14 day chick embryo.

Another interesting peculiarity consists in the appearance of efferent nerve fibers, ordinarily situated below the level of the Purkinje cells, among the differentiating deep granules.

The fibers to which we allude are of four varieties:

(a) The largest, most abundant and most convergent are the Purkinje axons. Without doubt, at this stage, these neurites are already provided with one or more collaterals, as the Golgi method reveals; but the neurofibrillar methods do not demonstrate them clearly.

(b) Other equally robust fibers cross the mass of Purkinje cells

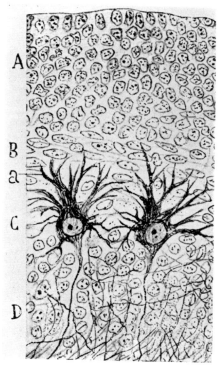

Fig. 147. Two Purkinje neurons of the cerebellum of a newborn dog (lateral lobe). Note the presence of lateral prolongations and the lack of flattening of the ascending dendritic arborization.

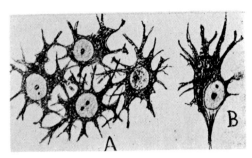

Fig. 148.   Tangential section of a cerebellar lamella of a swallow about to hatch.

and invade the zone of superficial granules where they frequently terminate in balls. These axis-cylinders probably belong to the category of misplaced ones and, perhaps, are "ansiform fibers" of Cajal-Smirnow. Some of these ascending axons are so precocious that they are already present in the 13 to 14 day chick embryo.

(c) Do the numerous fine and pale fibers which form a smooth plexus among the deep granules belong to collaterals of the Purkinje axons? We cannot state precisely.

(d) Finally, there are robust horizontal or oblique axis-cylinders which cross the zone of deep granules and ordinarily terminate by ovoid enlargements.

In preparations of the 14 day chick embryo, in the deepest portion of the superficial granular zone above the region where the molecular layer will be organized, we have noted some longitudinal fibers provided with thickenings. These may be in continuity with certain fusiform elements (bipolar horizontal phase of the granules). We will refer to these inconsistently staining fibers later on (Fig. 150, a).

Phase of Orientation and of Flattening of the Dendritic Branched Pattern or Plume. We have treated this interesting transformation at length in our memoirs on the cerebellum and we refer the reader to the descriptions and the drawings that they contain. Let us recall that this phase is characterized by the following features: (a) appearance of a granular or plexiform zone at the level of the dendritic tufts; (b) successive anteroposterior flattening of the dendritic tufts (*vermis*), associated with the enrichment of the secondary and, especially, of the terminal branches of the tuft; (c) disappearance of the lateral and of the descending branches of the cell body which now acquires an elongated pyriform configuration; (d) gradually increasing differentiation of the following layers in the superficial granular zone: one inferior, formed by longitudinal fusiform elements, that is to say parallel to the cerebellar lamellae; the other *superior,* composed of polyhedrical cells, some of which show signs of mitosis. This zone represents the reserve of germinative or undifferentiated cells from which will later derive the granules and all the neurons of the plexiform layer of the adult. The reader desirous of refreshing his memory about these curious migrations and about the metamorphosis of the granules will find some old facts in our previous cerebellar research and in the valuable memoir by Lugaro.

For the moment, in order to avoid repetition we will restrict ourselves to calling attention to some developmental peculiarities of the neurofibrillar network of the Purkinje cell dendritic tuft in the phase with which we are concerned. Let us first note that the cell body is almost completely furnished with neurofibrils and that the nucleus occupies an axial position instead of an eccentric one

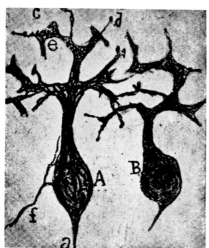

Fig. 149.   Details of the structure of the Purkinje cells of a 4-5 day old swallow. a) Axon; d) neurofibrillar filament terminating in a bouton; e) chiasmatic swellings; f) climbing fiber.

as in the earlier phases. For this reason the axon arises from the inferior pole of the cell. It gathers the fibers which surround the nucleus into a pale conical fascicle of filaments which are concentrated and welded into a compact and intensely stained fiber (Figs. 150 and 151). In avian embryos (Fig. 150), only a single large radial expansion, which dichotomizes several times, emerges from the superficial pole. Certain triangular thickenings appear at the level of the divisions, like neurofibrillar chiasms. The oblique or ascending branches terminate either by varicose thickenings which appear to be made up of several filaments or be isolated filaments crowned by a very small *bouton* (Fig. 149, d). The collateral projections terminate in the midst of the rudimentary molecular layer; whereas the terminal projections travel right into the zone of horizontal fusiform cells.

It is evident that the degree of development of the terminal tuft

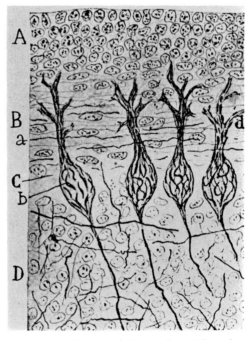

Fig. 150. Sagittal section of the cerebellum of a chick embryo near term. A) Undifferentiated granular layer; B) primitive molecular zone; C) Purkinje cells; D) deep granular zone; a) parallel fibers; b, d) neurofibrillar nuclei.

and the number of its secondary collateral branches varies with the age of the animal. Thus, in 6 to 17 day chick embryos, secondary branches are rare and the tuft is poor in expansions, whereas in the newborn swallow and sparrow the branches take on a greater complexity and abundance.

It appears even richer in the 2 to 4 day old dog where, instead of only a single ascending trunk emerging from the cell body, often two or more arise, giving rise to a flattened and relatively bushy ramification. In Figure 151, C, corresponding to the 8 day old dog, one perceives a quite thickened molecular zone and a great quantity of collateral protoplasmic expansions terminated throughout the afore-mentioned zone. Observe that the highest branches, often pointed, seem to perforate the zone of *fusiform horizontal cells,* a zone which progressively diminishes in thickness. In this phase the flattening of the tuft is already complete, a perfection which has arisen by degrees. In 17 to 18 day chick embryos and in newborn or in 2 to 3 day old birds (horizontal sections of the *vermis*), the intervals between these tufts are usually unequal, the lateral expansions almost touching adjacent ones.

In these preparations, besides the preceding constant facts, the following details have been observed which are unusual and difficult to interpret:

In addition to the intergranular nerve plexus (Fig. 151), numerous strayed fibers terminated in a ball are frequently found (Fig. 151, a). The fine ones plough obliquely through the molecular layer and the large ones are confined within the granular zone. It is not rare, furthermore, to observe some abruptly dilated fibers, from the tumefaction of which spring one or two ascending branches (Fig. 151, b). One can only specify the nature of these fibers with difficulty, but it seems reasonable that they are detained mossy fibers. In this same figure some fine, perfectly delineated axons arise from the granular layer, cross the entire molecular layer and bifurcate in the depths of the zone of horizontal cells, or, i.e., between the inferior subzone of superficial granules and the superficial subzone of the undifferentiated elements. Since this condition is unusual and since the dichotomized fibers appear continuous with a parallel fiber, we believe that we are dealing with a precocious de-

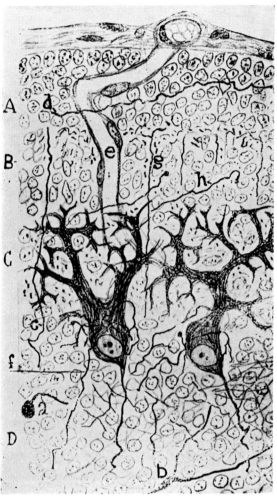

Fig. 151.   Section of the cerebellum of an 8 day old dog. A) Layer of germinal cells or granules; B) layer of fusiform cells (developing granules); C) molecular layer; D) deep or migrated granules; a) fiber terminating in a ball; b) swelling along the path of a fiber (probably a mossy fiber); c) wandering fiber of Cajal-Smirnow; d) another tangential wandering fiber; e) capillary; g) granule cell axon; h) another wandering fiber terminating by a ball.

velopment of the expansions of the fusiform horizontal cells and an abnormally precocious dislocation of the soma towards the region of the deep granules (Fig. 151, g). Whatever the case may be, it seems to us to constitute one of many such aberrations of migration and development of embryonic neurons, anomalies which are more common in the cerebellum than in the other centers. Moreover, aberrations of distribution and path of the young climbing fibers are not rare. De Castro [25] has made a fine study of these developmental anomalies, especially of the hypertrophic forms of the terminal arborization.

Another peculiarity of the Purkinje cells of young animals was noted by Tello in newborn birds (heron or magpie) a long time ago: The reticulum of the Purkinje cells appears rarified, revealing fusiform thickenings and arched anastomotic forms which constitute a robust framework that is apparent even at low magnifications. Such fusiform tumefactions are so similar to those which occur in young mammals subject to the action of cold (newborn or several day old rabbit, dog, and cat), that it is impossible not to attribute them to the same cause. In fact, according to our notes this phenomenon occurs constantly in newborn or several day old birds (sparrow, swallow, magpie) that have been subjected to a temperature of 20° or 22°. The fusiform swellings are present also in the chick, provided that the eggs were chilled several hours before removing the embryo. Such is the case with the cells of the 19 to 20 day old chick embryo reproduced in Figure 150, b. Let us remark that the fusiform enlargements stand out clearly even in the finest dendrons in which, because of the coalescence of the argentophilic matter, a great quantity of neuroplasm, often peripherally located, is observed.

The preceding observation demonstrates that the transformation of the reticulum by the action of cold (a transformation which has many features in common with the metamorphosis of the neurofibrils in rabies) can be demonstrated in very early embryos and fetuses. This fact must necessarily be taken into consideration to avoid considering some frankly pathological arrangements as normal.

We ourselves fell into this error in our first work on the neurofibrils*[174] of the newborn and young rabbit, an error excusable at that time, for the singular effects of cold on the neurofibrillar apparatus were not yet known. Only much later did we, Tello, Donaggio, and others clarify this surprising phenomenon, one which is far too much overlooked today by neurologists, even though it is demonstrable by three methods: that of reduced silver nitrate (with a variety of fixatives), that of Donaggio, and that of Bielschowsky.

To conclude this brief study of the embryonic cerebellum as stained by neurofibrillar procedures, we show in Figure 151 (8 day old dog) a very advanced phase of the Purkinje branched pattern. Note the presence of climbing fibers at the level of the Purkinje cell bodies (Fig. 151 f), some of which terminate by rings or by small *boutons*. The fine interstitial plexuses of the deep granular zone and a capillary vessel which traverses the molecular layer do not seem to exert any attraction over the dendrons (Fig. 151, e).

What hypothetical agents induce the formation of the dendritic branched pattern of the Purkinje cells? In some of our former communications we related the growth and complexity of the pattern to the appearance of the *parallel fibers* of the molecular layer and, consequently, to the migration of the granules. But this opinion, which is in good agreement with the doctrine of Ariëns Kappers relative to the stimulopetal progression of dendrons (the stimuli probably arrive at the Purkinje cells from the parallel and basket fibers), is no more than a conjecture which must be confirmed. Until the true mechanism of such a curious metamorphosis is discovered, we can accept this supposition as a tentative hypothesis.

In any case, our recent observations oblige us to slightly modify our former opinion regarding the time at which the parallel fibers begin to act. In the subzone of fusiform cells of the 16 or 17 day chick embryo, before the molecular layer is clearly differentiated, we have occasionally noted a considerable number of longitudinal interrupted fibers which seem to arise from the poles of the fusiform cells. The cell bodies of the latter do not yet attract colloidal silver.

---

*Almost all the figures dealing with the spinal cord in this paper show the effects of cold on the neurofibrils.

We therefore suspect without prejudice to the stimulating action of adult or ordinary parallel fibers, that the prolongations of the fusiform elements also exert their influence at an earlier period of development. Thus they may orient the Purkinje dendrons at the outset and consequently initiate the stretching and modeling of the terminal branched pattern. Only later do the nerve nets and the transverse fibers exert their influence.

Chapter 13

SOME DEVELOPMENTAL ERRORS IN THE CEREBELLAR CORTEX

I N ALL NEURAL organs one occasionally sees atypical and accidental arrangements with regard to the locations and relationships among neurons, as well as with regard to the path and orientation of axons. As for the neurons, anomalous location of Golgi cells and especially of Purkinje cells are not unusual; because of retarded migration, these cells may lie in the plexiform layer. Occasionally the inferior pole of these elements is perforated by a capillary, and sometimes the axon is seen to arise, not from this pole, but from a dendron. Estable [38] has recently shown a good example of this curious arrangement. This peculiarity involves the dislocation of the descending brushes or apical tips of the basket cells.

All these aberrations are produced during fetal development and can be explained by the obstacles which the neurons must surmount during migration. If these curious anomalies seem more frequent in the cerebellum than in other organs (except the retina), it is because cerebellar cytoarchitecture and the journey and orientation of cerebellar nerve fibers is better understood. Concerning the abnormal deviations of the axons, we wish to recall two arrangements that we noted a long time ago in the cerebellum of the mouse and other mammals: parallel fibers bent back in form of an ansa and the misplaced axons coming from the white matter.

Dislocated Parallel Fibers. [185] These are fine longitudinal fibers which often traverse the plexiform and superficial granular layers in zig-zag fashion. They are found in newborn animals or animals several days old. They ultimately descend to deeper planes of the aforementioned layers and there become longitudinal fibers, completely similar to those arising from the axon of the deep or normal granule cells. Perhaps the cause of the deviation of some parallel fibers must be ascribed to the thrust of the sturdy dendrons of the Golgi cells towards the periphery. By running against some parallel fibers, these dendrons would force them to bend at one or several points during their journey, to form ansas or rings and to penetrate more or less deeply into adjoining layers. It must be admitted that these fine young fibers are quite accidental, for it has never been possible to perceive them in adult mammals or even after 20 days of age. Perhaps they are ultimately resorbed.

Ansiform Fibers from the White Matter. There are other ansal fibers which obviously come from the white matter (Fig. 152, B, D). These fibers, we noted several years ago,* cross the granular and molecular layers and reach the external basal membrane. After having traveled beneath the latter for a certain time in various directions, they redescend obliquely or perpendicularly to re-enter the cerebellar white matter. These fibers, which are impregnated very well by reduced silver nitrate, are found in a great number of young and adult animals, cat, dog, mouse, rabbit, sparrow, as well as in chick embryos. They are also encountered in man, though very rarely. These fibers, often very thick and covered by a myelin sheath, sometimes show ramifications (Fig. 152, e) which do not seem to terminate in the cerebellum but form new erratic fibers instead. Other fibers, as we have seen in the young dog, after having pierced the basal membrane, terminate in the midst of the pia mater by a growth mass (Fig. 152, C).

These thick or fine fibers which are a continuation of certain fibers of the white matter can no longer be considered as constant elements of the cerebellar cortex; they are often lacking. Furthermore, their existence is so capricious that only one may be observed in one animal and a relatively considerable number in another

---

*The work which we have mentioned bears the date 1895.[167] We reproduce the text, because some authors erroneously attribute this small discovery to Smirnow:

"Neural ansas: In the rat fetus as well as in the newborn and several day old rat, we have occasionally stained some fine fibers which arise from the white matter and ascend to the superficial granular zone. After tracing an arc of variable length in this zone they redescend to the white matter and leave. These peripheral arcs do not have any consistent orientation nor do they give off any collaterals. We are ignorant of the nature of these fibers, although from their appearance they may be considered as axis-cylinders of passage, whose origin and termination are problematical. In any event, we must note that the said fibers can never be impregnated in the adult cerebellum."

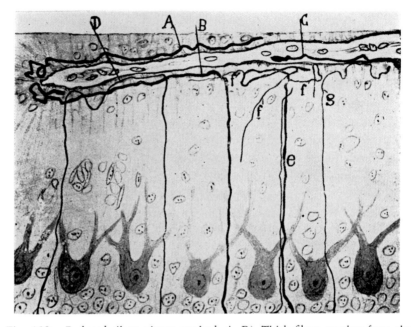

Fig. 152.   Reduced silver nitrate method. A, B) Thick fibers coming from the white matter and straying beneath the basal membrane where they twist into hooks; C) fiber possessing a terminal mass which has accidentally fallen outside of the basal membrane; D anasiform fiber; e, f) trunk and branch of another strayed fiber which arose in the white matter.

animal of the same species and age. Perhaps they are Purkinje cell axons, which despite their deviation, are preserved in excellent condition because they have succeeded in attaining their terminal station in the olive or in the emboliform nucleus of the cerebellum.

From what we have said above, we do not doubt that the myelinated fibers, called *fibers of Smirnow* by certain authors, correspond to this species of ansiform fibers derived from the white matter. Smirnow, who did not know of our work on this point, discovered these fibers in the adult dog by means of Weigert and Golgi methods. He considered them as a peculiarity quite exclusive to the *vermis* of this animal. According to him, they are sensory or normal centripetal fibers which emanate from other centers and which, after having traversed the cerebellar cortex and after having wandered for a certain time parallel and near to its basement membrane, disintegrate into an infinite number of collateral branches.[216]

The first two assertions are evidently inexact, since these fibers are encountered in many species and both cerebellar hemispheres. As to their nature as terminal sensory fibers, this seems too questionable an assertion. In our opinion, Smirnow has allowed himself to be misled by the observation of a few collateral branches and especially by the considerable extent that their fibers of origin embrace in the adult during their tangential course. For, in more than 500 of these fibers observed in several animal species we have only twice encountered some collaterals showing a tendency to terminate. In Figure 152, f, we show these branches stained by silver nitrate in the cat. Furthermore, when one observes serial sections from embryonic or newborn mammals, one always notes that the descending branch of the ansiform fiber is continuous with a fiber of the white matter.

However poorly founded may be some of Smirnow's opinions, it is nonetheless true that this scholar has contributed to our understanding of the ansal fibers by finding them in an adult animal and by describing their ramifications and myelin sheath.

Part V

CEREBRAL CORTEX

Chapter 14

DEVELOPMENT OF THE CELLS OF THE CEREBRAL CORTEX [162,164,172]

W E DO NOT INTEND to study the first histogenetic phases of the cerebral cortex. This has been the subject of numerous works, among which must be cited those of Boll,[19] Eichorst,[37] Besser,[11] Kölliker,[79] Löwe,[106] Vignal,[232,233] the more recent ones of His,[70] and Lenhossék.[95,96] We have devoted some pages to the study of this interesting question.[156] Here we are concerned with some observations on the growth and transformations of the cortical elements after their differentiation into nerve and epithelial cells.

Epithelial Cells. Our research confirms that of Golgi, Magini, and Falzacappa. The epithelial cells of newborn mammals (mouse, rat, rabbit) are very elongated elements, extending from the ventricular cavity to the cerebral surface. Initially they possess a short thick body provided with several granular expansions and an ovoid nucleus. They are later drawn out in length by an extremely varicose and nearly rectilinear fiber which crosses the corpus callosum, the layers of the cortex, and finally terminates beneath the pia mater. The termination is composed of a tuft of ascending filaments which end in conical thickenings in the cerebral surface (Fig. 153, B, d).

The varicosities along the course of the radial fibers have attracted the attention of Magini[110] who considers them to be superposed nuclei. We are inclined to regard them as protoplasmic thickenings, for were they nuclei they would be more regular in size and silver chromate would not stain them, since silver chromate does not stain the nuclei of embryonic epithelial cells. In any event, the presence of these varicosities as well as the absence of ramifications are important characteristics of radial fibers. Those characteristics allow a distinction to be made between these epithelial prolongations and the axis-cylinders of the pyramidal cells.

Towards the eighth day after birth the epithelial fibers become appreciably thinner and the varicosities are partially effaced. After

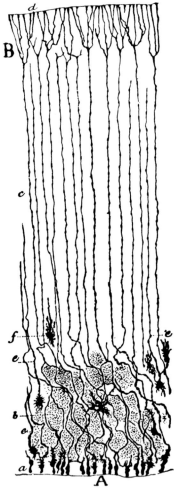

Fig. 153. Epithelial and neuroglial cells of the cerebral cortex of a several-day-old rabbit. Golgi method. A) Bodies of the epithelial cells; B) peripheral plumes of these cells; b) fascicles of white matter; c) perpendicular or radial fibers; e) displaced epithelial cells.

the twentieth day only a meager, practically agranular filament represents the remainder of the radial fiber. We therefore believe that the external expansion of the epithelial cells disappears by atrophy; in fact, only a short and ramified appendage remains, not extending beyond the inferior layers of the corpus callosum. We have ob-

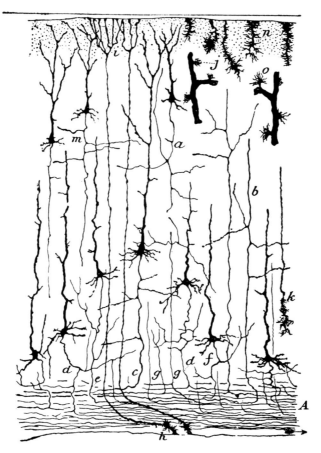

Fig. 154. Frontal section of the supraventricular region of the cortex of a 15 day old mouse. The layer of white matter shows all the callosal and association fibers (transverse fascicle). The arrow indicates the direction of the corpus callosum or midline. a) Axis-cylinder of a small pyramidal cell; b) another which is continuous with an association fiber; c) neural prolongation of a giant pyramidal cell directed outwards to probably become an association fiber; d) globose cells of the fourth layer terminating in a in the white matter; the finest branches are directed inwards, like the fibers of the corps callosum; e) association or callosal fibers travelling inwards; f) another directed outwards; g) collaterals of the white matter; h) epithelial cells; i) external tuft of the epithelial elements; j) perivascular neuroglial cells; k) displaced epithelial cell; n) neuroglial cells of the molecular layer.

served an analogous atrophy in epithelial cells of the spinal cord.

The course and the arrangement of the epithelial cells varies in different cortical areas. In the corpus callosum of newborn animals they are gathered into small flexuous fascicles (Fig. 153, b, c); the latter bend slightly leaving transverse cylindrical spaces between adjacent fibers. In these spaces the large fascicles of callosal fibers are lodged. The inferior part of the fibers is covered with irregular, varicose, and extremely complicated spines.

The epithelial cells belonging to the lateral regions of the hemispheres travel outwards at first while crossing the corpus callosum; they then adopt a radial direction and terminate at the cerebral surface (Fig. 154, h, i). These changes in course are also very evident in the cells which return to the internal surface (interhemispherical fissure) of the hemispheres. They go outwards at first, crossing the corpus callosum obliquely and later return inwards to terminate as tufts on the free aspect of the median fissure.

It is not easy to determine the role of the embryonic epithelial cells. We cannot agree with Magini who considers them the predecessors of nerve cells. In fact, according to His's important works on the histogenesis of the spinal cord, it is very probable that all nerve cells derive from *neuroblasts* (pyriform cells which arise from the division of certain primitive spheroidal cells).*

The hypothesis that the radial cells represent a temporary support or scaffolding, designed to maintain the shape of the central nervous system during the development of the nerve cells, seems quite reasonable. His's view that the epithelial cells serve the direct and to orient the development of the axis-cylinders, is scarcely applicable to the brain, for in this organ the radial fibers are finer than in the spinal cord and they leave large spaces between them, across which the embryonic nerve fibers can course without obstacle and in all directions. Furthermore, why growing axis-cylin-

---

*After having observed neurons which in shape and location were similar to epithelial cells (embryonic chick spinal cord), we did believe that in certain cases the ependymal epithelium could give rise to true nerve elements. But we now recognize that these cells are neuroblasts which remained in place among the epithelial cells at the time of their transformation into neurons and consequently retained a certain radial orientation and an elongated cell body bounding the medullary canal.

ders adopt one direction rather than another, is one of the most difficult and obscure histogenetic questions.

Neuroglia. Most of the authors who have recently studied the
origin of neuroglia, such as Duval,[33,34] Unger,[227] Löwe,[106] Ranvier,
[199] Kölliker,[80,84] Gierke,[47] Merk,[118] Golgi,[48] Rauber,[200] Bourckhardt,
[20] Vignal,[233] Lahousse,[89] Magini,[110] Falzacappa,[40] Lachi,[88] and
Lenhossék[97] unanimously regard the spiderlike elements as an
ectodermal derivative. Some of them, including Vignal, Lachi, and
ourselves, are inclined to think that some neuroglial elements are
simply ependymal epithelial cells which have migrated towards
the periphery.

The phases of this migration can be observed in the cortex of
the mouse or rat fetus. Before birth all the epithelial cells reach the
ventricular cavity. But some days after birth some of them have
moved away from the epithelial row and appear at various levels
of the callosal commissure and even in the midst of the cortex (Fig.
153, e). One could say that they go towards the periphery by means
of ameboid contractions. We believe that the displaced elements
are transformed into Deiters cells by a mechanism identical to that
occurring in epithelial elements of the embryonic spinal cord. In
fact, their cell body shortens, and varicose appendages emerge
from the periphery of the cell body and from the sides of the radial
expansions. These appendages emerge at a right angle and travel
in every direction. Little by little the radial trunk atrophies; it
becomes transformed into a delicate filament, more robust than
the others, and retains its initial orientation. Sometimes an internal
convergent prolongation representing the former epithelial cell
body is observed. These convergent appendages testify to the
origin and primitive orientation of the epithelial elements.

As regards those spiderlike cells lacking a radial orientation
(which in the adult brain are found in rapport with the vessels),
we think that they do not arise from the epithelium but rather
from the endothelial cells or else from flattened connective tissue
which have been able to penetrate into the cerebral cortex along
with the capillaries.

In Figure 154, j, we represent the first phase of the spider cells.
One sees simple perivascular hillocks blackened by silver chromate

and apparently continuous with the endothelial walls. The following phase (o) consists of the successive stretching of the aforementioned swelling which thus becomes pyriform and acquires a certain independence. This independence, however, is never complete, for one always sees a more or less fine elongated bridge uniting the spider cell to the vascular wall. The neuroglial filaments, at first thick and varicose, become progressively thinner and more elongated until they achieve the adult form that Golgi and Petrone have described.

In the first phases of the process it is impossible to perceive a well-demarcated limit between the vascular endothelium and the neuroglial mounds. The use of other staining methods has not provided us with clear enough results to determine the nature of these swellings. We therefore do not venture to advance a hypothesis on this subject. Nor do we know whether, besides the two mentioned species of neuroglial cells, certain spiderlike elements exist which arise from the connective tissue of the pia mater and are disseminated preferentially throughout the white matter, as Lachi claims. Perhaps, as Kölliker indicated,[83] they are indifferent ectodermal cells which begin their development after the differentiation of the neuroblasts and the epithelial elements.

In summary: In the depths of the gray and white matter of the cerebral cortex there are two species of neuroglial or sustentacular cells: one of epithelial origin, disposed more or less radially and independent of the vessels; the other of uncertain origin, appearing around the vessels into which they often insert a thick filament, as described by Golgi.*

Nerve Cells. Figure 155 represents a vertical transverse section through the cortex of a mouse embryo two or three days before birth. The nerve cells are already completely formed in almost all the cortical layers and they show a very characteristic radial orientation.

---

*We are no longer convinced that this second species of glia (perivascular glia) are of mesodermal origin. These elements, intimately applied to the vessels, could result from a very precocious migration of cells of ependymal origin which are attracted by the capillary endothelium. Furthermore they do not seem to correspond to the perivascular neuroglial cells previously described by Andriezen.[1] (*Note for the French edition.*)

Fig. 155.   Portion of the cerebral cortex of a term fetus. Golgi method. A)
White matter; a) large pyramidal cells; b, c) small and medium pyramidal
cells; d) initial collaterals of the axis-cylinder; e) axis-cylinder; f) horizontal
cell of the plexiform layer.

Note that basal protoplasmic expansions are either lacking or
are represented by thick spines in most of the cells, whereas the
radial or external expansion is now very robust, flexuous, and bears
indentations in which the neighboring elements are lodged. It terminates in the molecular layer by a tuft of thick, short, and extremely
varicose branches. The cell body is ovoid, similar to the small cells
of Ammon's horn, as Magini has noted. In some cells, often the
most superficial pyramidal ones, the perikaryon is fusiform and
provided with two thick protoplasmic expansions, the descending
one serving as point of departure of the axis-cylinder (Fig. 155, e).
The nervous expansions are relatively thick, nearly rectilinear,

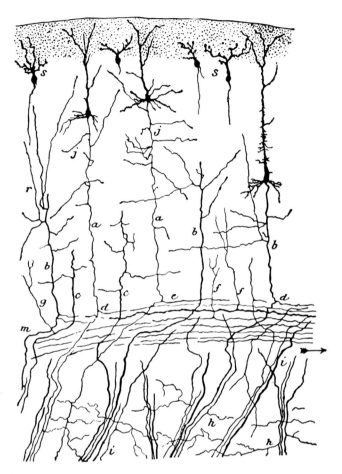

Fig. 156. Frontal section of the cortex of an 8 day old mouse. Projection fibers which, after having crossed the corpus callosum, go to the corpus striatum. The collaterals of the pyramidal cell axis-cylinders are seen throughout their entire extent. a) Fine projection fibers coming from the medium pyramidal cells; b) other thicker fibers leaving the giant pyramidal cells; c) short projection fibers coming from the polymorphic elements of the fourth layer; d) callosal collateral emerging emerging from the thick projection fibers; e) branch of bifurcation of a fine projection fiber going to the corpus callosum; f, g) collaterals of projection and callosal fibers; h) collaterals to the corpus striatum emerging from fine projection fibers; i) fascicles traversing the corpus striatum; s) more externally-placed small pyramidal cells.

and possess certain varicosities noted by Magini. Those of the medium and large pyramids can be easily followed to the white matter. But what is most interesting is that the axis-cylinders lack collaterals or, if some are present, they are reduced to simple short spines arising at a right angle and terminating by a varicosity (Fig. 155, d).

The giant pyramidal cells of the newborn mouse are considerably larger (Fig. 157) and begin to exhibit sizable but rarely ramified basilar expansions (a). The axis-cylinder bears some slightly longer collaterals terminating in a protoplasmic thickening. Each collateral arises from a swelling of the nervous expansion (Fig. 157, b, c).

Fig. 157. A pyramidal cell of the cortex of a newborn mouse. a) growing basilar protoplasmic branches; b) embryonic collaterals of the axis-cylinder; c) terminal nodosity of the collaterals.

Finally, the 8 to 10 day old mouse shows quite well-developed collaterals whose course and mode of termination can be readily studied (Figs. 156, j, and 155). By this period the protoplasmic arborizations of the pyramids are well-developed. Only those of

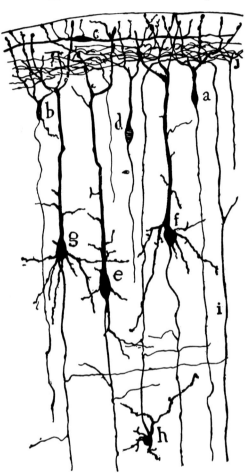

Fig. 158.   Portion of a frontal section of the brain of a 4 day old mouse. Golgi method. (This figure has been borrowed from volume 2 of our *Histologie du Système Nerveux.*[184] a) Small pyramidal cell in the bipolar stage; b) same type of cell which now possesses an ascending dendrite; c) horizontal cell of the plexiform layer; d) small pyramidal cell in the bipolar stage; e, f, g) pyramidal cells; h) cell of Martinotti; i) fiber coming from the white matter; j) terminal arborization of the ascending axis-cylinder.

the higher small pyramids retain a certain fusiform and, so to speak, embryonic appearance; moreover they possess very varicose and thickly arborized ascending branches.

Appearance of the Basilar Dendrons and of the Branches of the Protoplasmic Trunk. Shortly after the secondary bipolar phase and several days before birth in the mouse and the rabbit, a descending dendron is seen to leave the cell body of the large pyramidal cells in the neighborhood of the axis-cylinder. It sometimes forms a short common trunk with the latter. Other basilar protoplasmic branches also appear. The lateral dendritic expansions of the perikaryon appear virtually at the same moment, initially in the form of short spines. The branches of the protoplasmic trunk then develop successively from the bottom to the top (Fig. 158, e, g), according to Stephanowska's observation. However the terminal protoplasmic bouquet differentiates before the blossoming of all these dendrons; it is thick at first and formed by two or three short and very varicose divisions which almost reach the pia mater (Figs. 155 and 156). Even several days after birth, in the mouse, a great number of small pyramidal cells do not yet exhibit dendrons or only present a small number of incompletely formed basilar expansions (Figs. 156, s, and 158, a, d). The spines or pyriform appendages of the protoplasmic trunk and of its terminal bouquet are the last morphological details to appear in the nerve cell, as Stephanowska has recognized. Their appearance indicates functional maturity of the neuron.

Chapter 15

SPECIAL CELLS OF THE MOLECULAR LAYER
OF THE CEREBRAL CORTEX

IN WEIGERT PREPARATIONS of the cerebral cortex one sees that the molecular layer is traversed by many varicose myelinated fibers. These are variable in thickness and are directed horizontally or almost parallel to the cerebral surface. These fibers were discovered a long time ago by Kölliker[78] by means of the potash procedure, and later Exner,[39] using the osmic acid method, described them very well. Recently Obersteiner,[132] Edinger,[36] and Martinotti[116] have studied and drawn these fibers, employing the Weigert-Pal hematoxylin stain. But these methods stain only a very minimal number of the nerve fibers of the first layer, for even in adult animals the majority lack myelin. To make the unmyelinated nerve fibers stand out, it is necessary to use the rapid Golgi method, applying it especially to young mammals.

In good preparations an extraordinary multitude of very fine fibers are seen. They are often varicose and flexuous, lying especially in the most superficial portion of the molecular layer and oriented in all directions but principally horizontally. Furthermore, in small animals such as the mouse, rat, and rabbit, most of the fibers follow an anteroposterior direction.

Several of these fibers are obviously ramified, as Martinotti recognized. He also observed that some of these fibers descend into the subjacent layers to become continuous with certain ascending axis-cylinders. We will return to this fact which our observations confirm precisely.

The ascending axis-cylinders which we have just mentioned furnish only a part of those nervous ramifications demonstrable in the first layer by the Weigert and Golgi methods. Some of these fibers originate from special nerve cells lying in the midst of the superficial nerve plexus of the first layer (Fig. 159).

These cells have been mentioned by all the anatomists of the

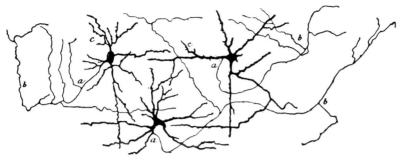

Fig. 159. Part of an anteroposterior section of the cerebral cortex of an 8 day old rabbit. Young polygonal cells of the molecular layer are represented. a) Axis-cylinders; b) collaterals; c) protoplasmic branches.

last 20 years, including Meynert, Henle, Schwalbe, Krause, Ranvier, Toldt and Kahler, and Obersteiner. They have been considered as stellate or triangular cells, scattered some distance apart throughout the first layer which has therefore been designated the *zone poor in cells* (*zellenarme Schicht*). But, because of the ineffectiveness of the Golgi method in staining these elements, the scholars who used this technique in the study of the cortex (Golgi, Mondino, Edinger, and Martinotti) have ended by excluding these cells. They considered them as probably being neuroglial cells. It is necessary to distinguish two classes of cells: *small elements with short axon and special large and very elongated elements.*

Small Cells with Short Axon.* These elements, not numerous, are scattered without order throughout the molecular layer. They are polygonal or stellate in form and provided with 4, 5, or more varicose divergent and ramified protoplasmic expansions. These expansions travel in every direction, reaching the free cerebral surface above and penetrating to the layer of small pyramids below.

The axis-cylinder ordinarily leaves from a lateral part of the cell, more rarely from the superior and inferior parts. It takes either a horizontal or ascending direction and then ramifies, giving birth

---

*We change the name from *polygonal cells,* by which term we originally described them, to *cells with short axon.* This designation leads to less confusion. (*Note for the French edition.*)

to a great number of fine varicose fibers whose path is variable but frequently parallel to the free surface. These twigs never exhibit any tendency to descend to the subjacent layers; they always remain within the confines of the molecular layer and terminate freely there.

Elongated or Special Cells (Fig. 160). These elements are slender, smooth and enormously elongated. In the 8 day old rabbit, where they stain very well, they appear perfectly fusiform, horizontal, and extend anteroposteriorly; they must therefore be studied in similarly oriented sections.

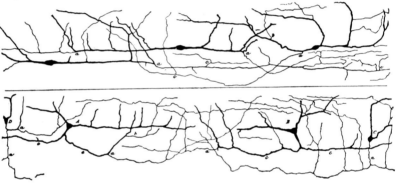

Fig. 160. Longitudinal section of the molecular layer of the cerebral cortex of an 8 day old rabbit. Rapid Golgi impregnation. In the upper figure are drawn 3 anteroposterior, pluripolar, fusiform cells. a) Initially polar axis-cylinders going off in an opposite direction; b) supernumary axis-cylinders emerging from various protoplasmic branches; c) ramifications of the axis-cylinders. In the lower part of the figure we have drawn some similar cells which are triangular in shape (A, B, C). a) Processes having the appearance of axons.

The protoplasmic expansions, two in number, emerge from opposite poles of the cell and extend horizontally for a considerable distance. Because of this extreme length the entire cell is rarely found in one section. Finally, after a variable and nearly rectilinear course, they bend obtusely and approach the cerebral surface where they seem to end freely. During their horizontal course these expansions emit collateral protoplasmic twigs which also seem to terminate in the highest part of the molecular zone. However, this termination does not always appear very clearly because of irregular silver chromate deposits which frequently contaminate the external limiting membrane of this layer.

The axis-cylinder prolongation does not emerge from the cell body or from the thickest part of the protoplasmic expansions. That is why we were unable to visualize it in our first somewhat incompletely stained preparations. After further observation of more successfully impregnated material we were surprised to see that the axis-cylinder was double, sometimes triple, and that it arose from the protoplasmic branches at great distance from the cell body.*

The fusiform cells of the molecular layer are not very numerous. We found only 6 or 7 of them in an anteroposterior section 5 millimeters long (8 day old rabbit). However, we believe that they are more abundant, for it is necessary to take into account the rarity and difficulty of impregnating them. Very often the molecular layer does not stain because of excessive hardening in the osmium-bichromate mixture, or else it is contaminated by irregular precipitates; other times, only the neurofibrils are stained and it is impossible to determine their origin.

As could be expected, preparations simply stained with carmine or nigrosine reveal these elements with some clarity. They are, in truth, less abundant although in certain regions of the cortex they seem quite numerous. Their fusiform body is very pale and does not bind carmine nor osmic acid; it stands out clearly against the obscure granular background. The nucleus is elongated in the same direction as the cell.

Triangular Cells. These elements are thicker and more numerous than the preceding ones. Most of them possess a triangular body and three thick and very long protoplasmic expansions which are nearly rectilinear and barely ramified. Ordinarily two of them are either oblique or horizontal, tending to ascend within the molecular layer. The third is descending; it soon divides into two very long, sometimes arched and horizontally directed branches. Moreover,

---

*This multiplicity of axons constitutes an interpretation based upon strictly morphological criteria and upon the fact that my initial research dealt exclusively with the embryonic phases of the special cells. Subsequent research in adult animals demonstrated, as we shall soon see, that these fusiform or triangular large elements possess a single axis-cylinder only. (*Note for the French edition.*)

several variations in shape, number and direction of the expansions are encountered (Fig. 160, A, B).

Those represented in Figure 160, C, D may be considered as a variety very similar to the cells just described. These elements are smaller and possess a more or less rounded body. They are especially characteristic since, besides one or more expansions arising from the protoplasmic branches, they furnish another which leaves the body, ramifying promptly and terminating by means of ascending twigs in the upper part of the molecular layer.

The large neural elements or *elongated cells with short axon* have certain special characteristics. The cell body is studded with a very limited number of protoplasmic expansions (as compared with ordinary cells). The protoplasmic prolongations are of enormous length, always becoming more or less horizontal and lacking the varicosities and spines that are characteristic of all other cortical cells (including the polygonal cells of the molecular zone). To appreciate these differences, it suffices to compare the elements of Figure 159 with those represented in Figure 160.*

---

*The lack of spines is a very characteristic trait of embryonic neurons. (*Note for the French edition.*)

Chapter 16

THE DEVELOPMENT OF THE ELONGATED OR SPECIAL CELLS OF THE MOLECULAR LAYER [172]

As WE NOTED in 1891, there are fusiform elements in the molecular layer of the rabbit. These elements possess two or three axis-cylinders, according to strictly morphological criteria, i.e., length, absence of roughness, slenderness and bifurcation at right angles. However our subsequent studies done with methylene blue,[171] the observations of Retzius on the human fetus,[205,207] those of Veratti on the rabbit,[230] and finally our later work on the brain of the newborn infant [173] all have modified our point of view. In fact, we are now certain that, of the polar or collateral prolongations of the cell, only one merits being considered as an axis-cylinder. This is a relatively thick fiber, somewhat thicker than some protoplasmic branches. Furthermore, it is horizontal and so long that it is impossible to see its extremity even in the largest sections. Finally, it is provided with collaterals which leave at a right or obtuse angle and generally ascend to terminate exclusively in the first layer.

As we had suggested in our first work on the cerebral cortex, this axis-cylinder probably is stainable by the Weigert-Pal method, for such preparations show large tangential nerve fibers in the first layer which are not in continuity with the fibers of Martinotti and which can only correspond to the axon of the horizontal or elongated cells.[162]

The dendritic character of the long polar expansions is clearly revealed by Ehrlich's method. In Figure 161, A, copied from a methylene blue preparation of the cerebrum of the adult cat, it is seen that these prolongations are smooth and without spines at the start of their journey but are covered with large varicosities at the level of their final ramifications. On the other hand the axis-cylinder never shows these varicosities. The distinction is therefore simple and reliable. (These varicosities are *postmortem* effects.)

The elongated neurons possessing the axis-cylinder that we have

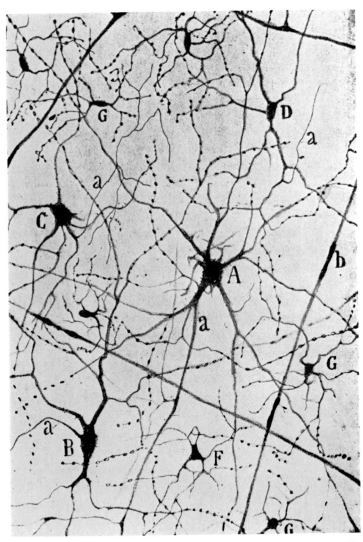

Fig. 161.   Tangential section of the plexiform layer of an adult cat. Ehrlich's
method. Note that the elongated or tangential cells appear stellate when viewed
from the surface. A) Elongated or special cell; B, C, D) large cells with short axis-
cylinder; F, G) cells whose short axis-cylinder arborizes a short distance from
its origin; a) axis-cylinder of an elongated cell; b) other, probably similar
axis-cylinders; c) bifurcation of these axis-cylinders.

just described are less numerous in small mammals (rabbit and cat). They are found at diverse heights in the plexiform layer, especially in the inferior portion near the layer of small pyramidal cells.

Golgi preparations of the elongated cells of fetuses of small mammals reveal the same peculiarities as well as certain long, tangential, and varicose dendrons. We are going to describe these in man at the same developmental stage. Unfortunately, it is very difficult and quite aleatory to observe these neurons in these small mammals where their number is very limited. The elongated cells are much more abundant and much more voluminous in man. Therefore they merit a special description. We will discuss them separately in the fetal and the adult stages.

Fetal Form. Figure 162, A, B, C shows the strange appearance of this cell, the discovery of which, in man, is credited to Retzius.[205] Note its diversity of configuration: fusiform triangular, stellate, or pyriform. However great this diversity, all possess one or more peripheral dendrons which terminate beneath the pia mater as well as two or more voluminous and very long polar branches. The latter travel horizontally describing small curves and emit innumerable, perpendicular, ascending branches which always terminate in a spherule beneath the pia mater.

Each cell ordinarily emits a great number of horizontal polar branches, which Retzius calls *tangential fibers.* Furthermore, a considerable number of them are seen in good preparations where, at diverse levels of the plexiform layer, they constitute an important system of parallel conductors. Their length is such, ordinarily, that their extremity cannot be seen (Fig. 162). The axis-cylinder travels among the polar branches; but its resemblance to them is so great that it cannot be distinguished.

Adult Form. Retzius recognized in the human fetus the special cells we described in small mammals, and he was the first to call attention to their embryonic characteristics. Although he was unable to impregnate them in the postnatal infant he claimed that the morphology of these elements does not undergo considerable change later on. Our research, executed upon newborns up to the age of 25 and 30 days, proves that this is not quite so. In fact, we have seen that: 1. Most of the ascending branches described by Retzius which emerge

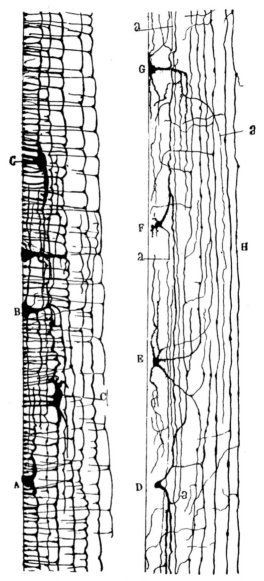

Fig. 162. Cells of the first layer or plexiform zone of an infant. Golgi method. A, B, C) Special cells of the visual cortex in the newborn infant or in the fetus near term; D, E, F, G) the same cells in the visual cortex of a 20 day old infant; H) very elongated tangential fibers; a) fine processes, apparently the axis-cylinder.

from the horizontal polar branches are embryonic arrangements destined to disappear in the one or two months following birth. Some do persist but change direction and ramify in the plexiform layer. 2. The very long horizontal branches persist indefinitely. Throughout the first layer they form a system of parallel fibers which retain their original direction and are provided with only a few fine twigs disseminated in the plexiform layer. 3. One of these horizontal branches, generally a thick one, is the axis-cylinder. It is surrounded by a myelin sheath. It travels horizontally over enormous distances and furnishes collaterals from time to time which ramify around the cells of short axis-cylinder of the first zone. It is impossible for us to say whether these characteristics are accentuated or if they are even maintained in adult man, for up to now we have not succeeded in impregnating the elongated or tangential cells in the adult.

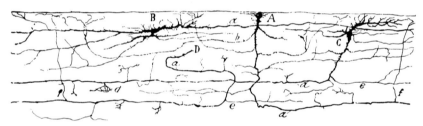

Fig. 163. Some elongated cells of the first layer of the motor area of a month old infant. Golgi method. A) Marginal or pyriform cell; B) bipolar cell; C) triangular cell; D) axis-cylinder of a nonimpregnated cell; a) axis-cylinders; b) tangential or long dendrites; c) short dendrites; d) axis-cylinder branches terminated by short and varicose arborizations; e) initial thick collaterals of the axis-cylinder.

In Figures 162, D, E, F, and 163 we have reproduced some morphological details of the elongated cells in the one or one and a half month old infant. Among the cell types are several already mentioned by Retzius. These are the *unipolar or marginal type,* even visible in Nissl preparations (Fig. 164, b), the *bipolar type,* which we have described in our first works, and the *stellate or triangular type* (Fig. 164, a, g). We will not describe them in detail, to avoid needlessly repeating what has already been stated.

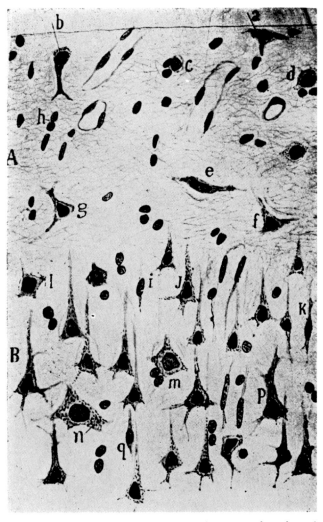

Fig. 164. Cells of the first and second layers of the ascending frontal convolution of an adult man. Nissl method. A) Plexiform layer, in which we have gathered cells that are actually spread over 3 times as great an area; B) layer of small pyramidal cells; a, b) marginal, pyriform or triangular cells; c, d) small cells with short axis-cylinder; e, f, g) horizontal cells; h) neuroglial cells; i, k) fusiform cells having a double protoplasmic tuft; l, m, n) large cells with short axis-cylinder; p) true pyramidal cells; q) fusiform cell with double dendritic tuft.

Chapter 17

NEUROFIBRILLAR DIFFERENTIATION OF THE PYRAMIDAL CELLS OF THE CEREBRAL CORTEX

B EFORE BIRTH IT is usually impossible to distinguish the Nissl bodies and the neurofibrils of Bethe, the principal elements of the nerve cell framework. On the other hand, these elements become visible after birth in the cat, the rabbit, and the dog but are small, poorly defined, and seen only in the giant pyramidal cells. As regards neurofibrils, the silver nitrate method [174] shows that the nerve cell passes through four phases in newborn mammals (Fig. 165).

Undifferentiated or Unstainable Phase. In this stage the protoplasm does not attract the specific neurofibrillar coloring agents. It is formed of a barely visible spongioplasm only, of which the granular joists are sprinkled with very fine chromatic dots. All, or almost all, the pyramidal cells are in this state before birth; the very great majority remain so for the first days of extrauterine life. The nucleus surrounds a nucleolus that has abundant spherules and some scattered granules that stain with silver nitrate.*

Phase of Superficial Neurofibrillation. The neurofibrils make their first appearance in the peripheral protoplasmic trunk and axis-cylinder of the giant pyramidal cells. They extend also to the perikaryon but are found only beneath its cell membrane, for the interior remains barely colored (Fig. 165, B). They are fine, slightly varicose, and arranged in a network with elongated meshes. This network persists in the perikaryon but seems to disappear in the protoplasmic trunk and axis-cylinder where it gives way to a fascicle of parallel filaments. In a great number of axis-cylinders the neurofibrillar framework seems to be formed by a single neurofibril only, a result of convergence and fusion of several neurofibrils within the peripheral protoplasmic trunk and the basilar dendrons. It is not rare to see nodo-

---

*We do not doubt the existence of neurofibrils in this phase, but consider them not stainable by current techniques. (*Note for the French edition.*)

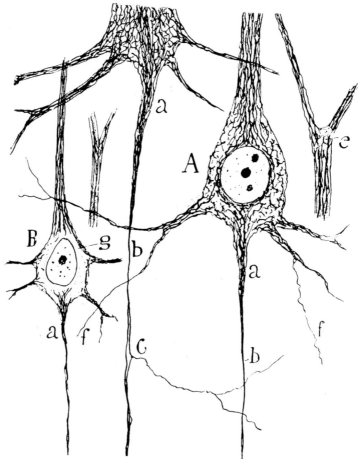

Fig. 165. Large and medium pyramidal cells of a 10 day old dog. Reduced silver nitrate method. A) Large pyramidal cell already possessing a perinuclear neurofibrillar network; B) medium pyramidal cell with a still undifferentiated cytoplasm; a) axis-cylinder; b) tip of the cone of the axis-cylinder; c) collateral buds; f) protoplasmic branches which only surround a single neurofibril.

sites on the neurofibrils, which we have named the clotted state.*

In the newborn or several day old rabbit or dog the neurofibrils

---

*Subsequent research has demonstrated that the nodosities and the incipient fusiform swellings seen in the neurofibrillar framework of the neurons of young animals (mouse, rabbit, cat) and in embryos, result from the effect of cold. (*Note for the French edition.*)

only appear in the giant pyramidal cells and in some medium sized ones; also in preparations treated by reduced silver nitrate it is very easy to follow the protoplasmic trunk and the axis-cylinder of these neurons across the cortex (Fig. 165, A).

Phase of Deep Neurofibrillation. The neurofibrillar network now extends to the center of the cell body and is arranged there in two plexuses: one dense and perinuclear, the other loose and cortical. Naturally, both are continuous with the neurofibrils of the expansions. In this stage the fibers become smoother because of the disappearance of the nodosities. The secondary neurofibrils, which are finer, seem to diminish in number but the reticulated state still persists very clearly (Fig. 165, A).

The single initial neurofibril of the axis-cylinder begins to divide by a kind of longitudinal segmentation. The neurofibrils of the collaterals seem to be formed by an offshoot or ramification at a right angle of one of the parallel filaments of the axis-cylinder (Fig. 165, C). Thus the framework of the collaterals is represented, or seems to be formed, at the start by simple branches from the division of the principal neurofibrils.

Phase of Fasciculation. There is an increase in neurofibrils in the giant pyramidal cells from the fifth to the thirtieth day after birth in the rabbit and the dog. They become very abundant and form small packets which at first pass from the trunk and from the dendritic appendages to the perikaryon, then from the latter to the axis-cylinder. The axis-cylinder no longer surrounds one or two filaments, as at the outset, but a compact fascicle of fibrils which is distributed among the collaterals. The axis-cylinder also increases its neurofibrillar contingent; only the terminal small protoplasmic and axis-cylinder branches have a single filament running through them. Finally, a great number of secondary filaments disappear or become invisible in various parts of the cell, perhaps because they are not transversely oriented. The neurofibrils also make their appearance from the fifth to the thirtieth day in the medium pyramidal cells, in the polymorphic cells, and in the large cells with short axis-cylinder.*

---

* It is necessary to bear in mind the reservations expressed in the footnote on page 347. We must not forget that the neurofibrillar technique gives very variable results depending on the formula employed. (*Note for the French edition.*)

The facts that we have just noted seem to establish that the neuro-fibrils are capable of two types of growth: by emission of true branches along their path and at their terminal extremity, and by a type of longitudinal segmentation occurring in the cell body as well as in its expansions. Future research undoubtedly will resolve this still unsettled question but its importance in the explanation of the nature and function of the neurofibrils is inescapable.

Part VI

RETINA

Chapter 18

DEVELOPMENT OF THE CONSTITUENT ELEMENTS OF THE RETINA

B EFORE DISCUSSING SOME aspects of retinal development it is fitting to review the layers of this membrane and to reproduce two schematic figures originally published quite a long while ago.[166,168] The retina is a peripheral nerve center, a sort of membranous ganglion from which arise the majority of the optic nerve fibers. These fibers terminate in free arborizations throughout the lateral geniculate body and superior colliculus. The neural elements of the retina are arranged in seven layers (not counting the limiting membranes and pigment zone): 1. the rods and cones; 2. the external granule cells or bodies of the visual cells; 3. the plexiform or external molecular layer; 4. the internal granule cells or layer of the bipolar elements; 5. the plexiform or internal molecular layer; 6. the ganglion cells; 7. the optic nerve fibers (Fig. 166).

All these elements are supported and isolated by large cells directed perpendicularly between the internal and external surfaces of the retina. These cells are called *Müller's fibers* or retinal epithelial cells. Like the sustentacular cells of the olfactory mucosa, they possess a tremendous number of facets or mortises on their surface which serve as receptacles for the cells and nerve fibers of the retina. The nuclei of Müller's fibers are at the level of the internal granular layer. The two protoplasmic extremities of the cell condense into two homogeneous limiting lamellae (limiting layers), one placed beneath the rods and cones, the other located on the vitreal surface of the retina (Fig. 167, J). The fibers of Müller are completely independent; there is only the simple relation of contact among them or between them and the nerve cells they support (Fig. 167, J, ñ).

Our first observations on retinal histogenesis were published a long time ago in a very extensive memoir [163] dealing with the structure of this membrane. We will reproduce here only the chapter of this work relating to retinal neurogenesis. We will complete the

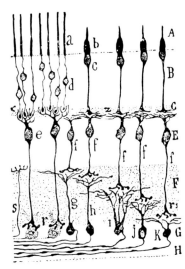

Fig. 166.   Transverse section of a mammalian retina. A) Layer of rods and cones; B) bodies of the visual cells (external granular layer); C) external plexiform layer; E) layer of bipolar cells (internal granular layer); F) internal plexiform layer; G) layer of ganglion cells; H) layer of optic nerve fibers; a) rod; b) come; c) cone cell body; d) rod cell body; e) bipolar cell contacting a rod; f) bipolar cell contacting a cone; g, h, i, l, k) ganglion cells ramified in various levels of the internal plexiform layer; r) inferior arborization of the rod bipolar cells, in connection with the cone bipolar cells; s) centrifugal nerve fiber; t) Müller or epithelial cell; x) contact between the rods and their bipolar cells; x) contact between the cones and their bipolar cells.

description of 1893 by some facts described in a later communication [169] based, like the first, on Golgi preparations. In order to avoid repetition we will summarize the first phases of retinal development; we have described the essential facts in our reviews [183,185] of this subject.

The development of the retina has been especially studied by many authors, notably Babuchin,[4] Löwe,[105] Ogneff,[133] Bellonci,[9] Koganeï,[76] and Chievitz.[26]

Our research on this subject is not yet concluded. Therefore we will restrict ourselves to summarizing the results obtained with the Golgi method concerning the metamorphoses of the fibers of Müller and some nerve cells.

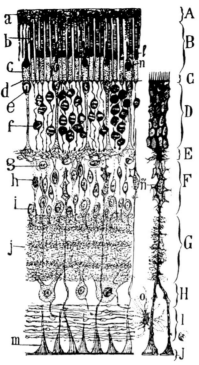

Fig. 167. Perpendicular section of the retina of a dog schematized according to the results obtained with both Golgi and hematoxylin techniques; A) layer of pigment cells; B) layer of rods and cones; C) external limiting membrane or layer; D) layer of the bodies of the visual cells; E) external plexiform layer; F) layer of bipolar cells; G) internal plexiform layer; H) layer of ganglion cells having a long axis-cylinder; I) layer of optic nerve fibers; J) internal limiting membrane; a) pigment cells; b) external segment of a rod; c) cone; d) external limiting membrane; e) nucleus of a cone cell body; f) nucleus of a rod cell body; g) horizontal cell; h) bipolar cell; i) amacrine cell or spongioblast; j) layers or granular bands of the internal plexiform zone; m) conical terminal swelling of a Müller fiber; n) ellipsoid or intercalary body of the cone; n̈) nucleus of Müller's fiber; o) neuroglial cell. At the right of this figure is an isolated epithelial cell or Müller fiber.

Our observations have been made on mouse, rabbit, calf, and chick embryos. We have been able to study the retina only subsequent to the differentiation of the internal plexiform and ganglionic layers. We have not yet succeeded in impregnating earlier stages, e.g., before the granular layers are demarcated from the ganglionic layer. Two types of retinal cells must be distinguished: the epithelial cells or *fibers of Müller* and the *nerve cells*.

EPITHELIAL CELLS

In very young retinas (Figs. 168, d and 169, a) the sustentacular cells are stained selectively and they resemble the epithelial cells of the fetal spinal cord. They are elongated, fusiform, and possess an ovoid cell body which surrounds the nucleus. Their two delicate expansions, ascending and descending, terminate at the retinal surface by means of conical swellings. The fact that the embryonic retina contains fusiform cells whose prolongations reach the two surfaces of the membrane, has been noted by Babuchin.

The cell body and nucleus of the Müller fibers is initially distributed throughout the retina, save in the layers of the ganglion cells and optic fibers (Fig. 168). But as the membrane increases in thickness and as anatomical differentiation increases, the nuclei migrate towards the central part of the retina and settle definitively in the internal granular layer (Fig. 167, ñ).

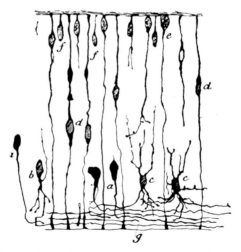

Fig. 168. Section of the retina of a 15 mm mouse embryo. a) Ganglion cell (neuroblast of His) still lacking protoplasmic prolongations; c) ganglion cell which possesses ascending and descending (g) protoplasmic prolongations; d) epithelial cell.

As the Müller fibers develop they gradually become irregular. Their anterior extremities, which were simple at first, may bifurcate and thus imitate, though in a less complicated fashion, the peripheral tufts of the radial or epithelial cells of the fetal cerebrum (Fig. 169, f).

Fig. 169. Section of the retina of a 9 cm dog embryo. a) Epithelial cells; b) bipolar cells; e) ganglion cells; f) ascending and bifurcated descending prolongations of a Müller cell; g) bodies of the visual cells; n) neuroglial cell.

Later the epithelial cells increase in thickness and lamellar expansions arise on their central and peripheral prolongations. Their external extremity becomes transformed into a flattened lamella which gives off fine filaments that penetrate among the developing visual cells. In avian embryos the lateral lamellae of Müller's fibers originate at the level of the spongioblasts. At the level of the external granular cells the lamellar structure is preceded by the formation of a rounded or oval protoplasmic mass, a type of reserve material which is destined to be transformed into lateral prolongations (Fig. 171, a).

In chick and lizard embryos we have noted an interesting fact relating to the mode of appearance of the terminal divisions of the deep prolongation of the Müller fibers. In adult animals these fibers divide at the level of the zone of amacrine cells into a bundle of descending fibers which terminate in the internal limiting membrane by means of conical thickenings. In embryos this division into fibers occurs by a kind of longitudinal splitting which begins at the ganglion cell layer and continues up to the zone of the spongioblasts or amacrine cells.

NERVE CELLS

Layer of Ganglion Cells and Optic Fibers. These layers are the first to differentiate in very young embryos, as other authors, notably Kölliker [79] and Chievitz,[26] have noted. Only subsequently does the internal plexiform zone appear. We have succeeded in staining ganglion cells at a stage prior to the development of the internal plexiform layer (Fig. 168, b, c). At the outset these elements still lie far from the layer of optic fibers and they are not arranged in an orderly layer. In the youngest elements their form is completely reminiscent of the neuroblasts of His,[69] i.e., they are pyriform and their descending pedicle is continuous with an optic nerve fiber (Fig. 168, a). The most developed ganglion cells already exhibit some rudimentary ascending and descending protoplasmic expansions. The former leave the superior aspect of the body and, after having diverged and dichotomized, terminate in the zone above by means of very thick varicosities. The latter, one, two or three in number, arise from the inferior portion of the body as well as from the base of the nervous prolongation and flow into the layer of optic fibers where they terminate freely (Fig. 168).

Later the superior expansions divide several times (Fig. 169, e) and give rise to a complicated horizontal arborization. The descending prolongations wind about the optic fibers for some time, and finally atrophy and disappear.

Thus the development of the retinal protoplasmic branches is very similar to that of the spinal cord of the chick embryo where Lenhossék [97] and we [156] have succeeded in following all the developmental phases of the neuroblasts of His. The optic nerve fibers are stained very easily in embryonic retinas and can readily be followed into this nerve. But, unfortunately, we have not yet succeeded in impregnating them in younger developmental stages when they are still growing. We cannot therefore take a definitive position in the long-standing discussion between Müller,[120] who believes that the optic fibers grow into the pedicle of the optic vesicle from the retina, and His,[65] Kölliker, and others, who recognize a growth in the contrary direction, i.e., from the brain to the optic vesicle [*sic!*].*

In such a difficult subject, if we could reason by analogy we could wholeheartedly affirm that both of these opinions can be supported. According to the new doctrines of His regarding the growth of the axis-cylinders from the neuroblasts, and the recent discoveries about

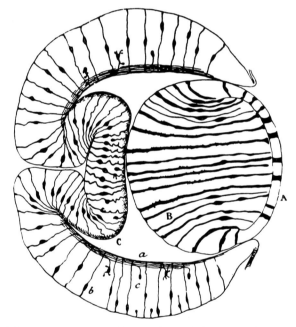

Fig. 170. Schematic anteroposterior section of the eye of a 15 mm mouse embryo. A) Anterior epithelium of the lens; B) prisms of the lens; C) retinal fold; a) layer of optic nerve fibers; b) epithelial cells; c) ganglion cell.

*Do not forget that we reproduce an 1892 text here. Our subsequent research (1906) on the development of the neuroblasts confirms the correctness of Kölliker's ideas. (See Chapter 1.)

the termination of nerve fibers, it seems quite natural to admit that the retinal fibers which arise from the ganglion cells grow in a centripetal fashion, while the fibers whose origin is found in the optic centers grow in centrifugal direction.

Figure 170 represents an antero-posterior section of the eye of a mouse embryo. A very important retinal fold (C) is observed which Kölliker has previously emphasized; in this fold the Müller fibers appear very flexuous and thick. The prisms of the lens are often colored by silver chromate and show their contours, even though they are always lacking uniting filaments. Several central prisms already lack nuclei (Fig. 170, B).

Our observations on the other layers of the retina are still very incomplete. We will say a few words about them, however.

Internal Granular Layer. The amacrine cells appear at the same time as the ganglion cells and the development of their inferior tuft marks the formation of the internal plexiform zone. The fibers of the terminal arborization are short, thick, and very varicose; they are associated with the twigs of the ascending tuft of the ganglion cells. In the 14 day chick embryo the spongioblasts are completely differ-

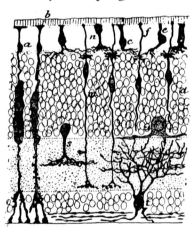

Fig. 171. Transverse section of the retina of a 14 day chick embryo. a) Epithelial cells; b) internal platform of the epithelial cells which still lacks ascending filaments; c) rod cell body; d) internal granular layer; e) oblique cone; f) mass of Landolt; m) bipolar cell; n) straight cone; s) pyriofrm amacrine cell; t) polystratified ganglion cell; u) giant amacrine cell.

entiated (Fig. 171, s, u) and the various types of amacrine cells can now be recognized.

The bipolar cells are very apparent in 13 day chick embryos (Fig. 171, m). However, their superior and inferior tufts are still very short and granular; the Landolt body is relatively thick. In the retina of younger embryos (Fig. 169), the bipolar cells cannot be distinguished from the visual cell bodies or even from imperfectly impregnated Müller fibers. However, we are inclined to believe that the bipolar cells are represented by certain fusiform cells located at various levels in the external half of the retina; they are characterized by a short descending expansion which terminates by means of a varicosity (Fig. 169, b). The external prolongation reaches the limiting membrane. But, let us hasten to say, since the external granular layer and the external plexiform layer are not yet differentiated, we cannot be completely certain about identifying these elements as bipolar cells. This is especially questionable, since they seem to possess the same properties as certain other elements which lie very near to the external limiting membrane and which could well represent rudimentary visual cells or the proliferating cells of Koganeï and Chievitz (Fig. 169, g).

Our research on the rods and cones, like that on the granule cells, is not yet very precise. The external granular layer is present in the newborn rabbit (Fig. 172). It is separated from the internal granular zone by the external plexiform zone. There are two types of external granular cells: those which offer a single ascending expansion (Fig. 172, a), and those which present an ascending and a descending one (Fig. 172, b). The descending expansion terminates in the external plexiform layer by means of a very irregular free swelling. We believe that all these granule cells belong to the rods, the cell bodies of the cones not being stained by silver chromate.

In the retina of the 13 or 14 day chick embryo the external granules are already formed and even the two varieties of cone fibers are observed: the straight fibers and the oblique fibers (Fig. 171, c, e, n). The rods and cones proper are represented, as Kölliker, Babuchin, and Chievitz have noted, by very short hyaline excrescences at the peripheral extremities of the fibers of the granule cells. These excrescences are not stained at all by silver chromate.

Fig. 172.   Nerve cells of the retina of a 2 day old rabbit. a) Cells with growth clubs; b) rods; c) internal horizontal cells possessing descending prolongations; d) horizontal cells without prolongations.

The horizontal cells are very well stained in the retina of the new-born rabbit (Fig. 172, d). They are semilunar and possess two thick horizontal expansions which ramify in the midst of the external plexiform zone. Two cellular types can be distinguished: some cells have a descending protoplasmic prolongation, others possess horizontal expansions exclusively. The latter are the more numerous and, in horizontal sections of the retina, form a close-meshed network by the intimate contacts of their protoplasmic prolongations.

While studying the development of the retina and nervous system, we often asked ourselves this question: What are the mechanical causes of nerve fiber outgrowth and the sources of the marvelous power by which nerve expansions make direct contact with far-off neural, mesodermal, or epithelial cells?

His [66,68] was concerned about this important problem. He felt that the arrangement of the epithelial cells in the central nervous system and of the obstacles (bone, cartilage, connective tissue) found in the path of growing peripheral nerves play an important part in this phenomenon. The axis-cylinders of the neuroblasts always travel, whether in spinal cord or in mesodermal tissues, in the path of least resistance.

Mechanical influences probably play an important role in the growth of the centripetal and centrifugal fibers of the optic stalk. Without denying the importance of these influences, we believe that a phenomenon analogous to Pfeffer's *chemotaxis* [138] can be accepted. The influence of chemotaxis upon leucocytes has been noted by Massart and Bordet,[117] Gabritchewsky,[46] Buchner,[22] and Metchnikoff.[119]

This last scholar even explains the exceedingly singular phenomenon of the reunion of the points of growth of embryonic blood
vessels by chemotaxis.

If one accepts chemotactic sensibility in neuroblasts, one must
suppose that these elements are capable of ameboid movements and
that they are excitable by the substances which certain nerve, epithelial,
or mesodermal cells secrete. The expansions of the neuroblasts would
be oriented in the direction of chemical gradients, and would travel
towards the secretory cells.

The first of these two properties is perfectly established by His's
elegant research and by our own on the mode of growth of spinal
ganglion cells. These elements are initially bipolar in all vertebrates
and later become unipolar in the batrachians reptiles, birds, and
mammals. This metamorphosis is accomplished by the formation of
a longer and longer pedicle from the cell body, i.e., by the migration
of the perinuclear cytoplasm towards the periphery of the ganglion
cell.

We have discovered an analogous phenomenon in the cerebellar
granule cells; at first bipolar and near to the surface of the latter, they
become unipolar by elongating and displacing their body across the
molecular zone to the zone of deep granules. Only then do the protoplasmic expansions arise.*

The chemotactic property cannot be verified by observations or
by direct experiments. If we assume it as proved, it would not always act similarly in the growth of all nerve processes. It would be
necessary to distinguish several phenomena: 1. displacement of the
cell bodies; 2. growth of axis-cylinders towards certain cells; 3. reciprocal growth of the processes of associated nerve cells; 4. growth
in different directions of the protoplasmic prolongations and axis-
cylinder of the cell, etc. †

---

*This opinion is mentioned by my brother.[143]

†We omit here the remainder of the text in which this hypothesis is developed
because we now consider it too rash. (*Note for the French edition.*)

Chapter 19

THE DEVELOPMENT OF VARIOUS RETINAL ELEMENTS [169]

RODS AND CONES

IN GENERAL, THE rods and cones are considered specialized epithelial cells and not nerve cells. In fact, a great many characteristics seem to distinguish them from the latter: the epithelial appearance of their peripheral portion; their position as marginal elements in the cavity of the primitive ocular vesicle, and even the presence of a thick layer of secretion on their external extremity (outer segments of the rods and cones). But to settle this question definitively it is necessary to ascertain whether developing rods and cones go through a neuroblastic phase. That is, does the cellulofugal or descending process, which is somewhat analogous to an axis-cylinder, appear first or do these visual elements present a unique morphology.

Excluding the portion of the rods and cones outside of the limiting membranes (inner and outer segments), which in many mammals only develop very late, the morphological development of these elements in embryonic periods has been little studied. Even the most recent authors, such as Mall [111] whose research has dealt with *Amblystoma* and *Necturus* embryos, are not concerned with this issue. Perhaps this gap in our knowledge is attributable to the great difficulty in distinguishing the cell bodies of the visual cells from those of other cells in tissue sections stained by carmine, hematoxylin, and the various aniline pigments.

By employing the double impregnation Golgi method on rolled-up specimens and by choosing the most favorable animals for impregnation, one can frequently succeed in staining the embryonic visual cells in almost all developmental phases. Up to now our best results have been on the newborn and several day old cat and dog. The first hardening bath must last 2 to 3 days, depending on the thickness of the block formed by the rolled-up retina; the second, only one day to avoid excessive friability.*

Examination of well-impregnated preparation of the retina of a new born cat (Fig. 173, d, e, f, g), reveals a great number of small cells in the external two-thirds of this membrane. These cells are poor in protoplasm and they may be unipolar or bipolar, but all are parallel to the fibers of Müller. By comparing preparations of newborn dogs and cats with those at 8 days of age, when the external granule cells are completely formed, one can unquestionably identify these uni- and bipolar cells as the cell bodies of the visual cells. This same comparison also enables us to recognize that the unipolar forms are the primordial or primitive ones, both because they are the simplest and also because, while very numerous in embryonic retinas, they become more and more rare as the animal advances in age. But among the diverse embryonic visual cells it is difficult to decide which ones correspond to the cones and which to the rods. The morphology of the portion of these elements beyond the limiting membrane does not serve as a criterion at all, for at this stage this portion is totally lacking. In our first work we left this point unsettled, as well as the question of the order of succession of the morphological phases of the visual cell.

Our recent research, however, has furnished the means of distinguishing a cone from a rod upon their first embryonic appearance. The body of the cone is slightly thicker and is colored black, undoubtedly because of the relatively voluminous protoplasmic layer which surrounds the nucleus. The body of the rod is clear, reddish, or chestnut because of the extremely slender protoplasmic cuticle

---

*To succeed, it is necessary to modify the original rolling-up procedure a bit, because of the smallness and delicacy of the retinas being handled. It is in fact impossible, without considerable crushing, to grasp these extremely tender retinas with forceps to coat them with celloidin and to separate them from the optic nerve. Thus it becomes necessary, after having opened the eye and extracted the vitreous humor, to fold the retina up to its union with the optic nerve by means of very fine forceps soaked in aqueous humor; then to coat the retina with celloidin, making use of the sclerotic coat turned backwards as a pedicle. When the celloidin is solidified the optic nerve is cut close to the sclera while holding the retina above a vessel containing the osmium-bichromate mixture into it falls without having been handled.

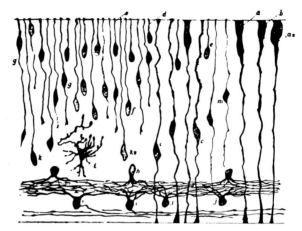

Fig. 173. Section of the retina of a newborn cat. Double impregnation Golgi method with rolling up of specimen. a) Epithelial cell with two nuclei one behind the other; a2) epithelial cell with 2 nuclei side by side; b) epithelial cell with peripheral nucleus; c) ordinary epithelial cell whose nucleus lies at about the middle of the retina; d) embryonic cone in the unipolar phase; e) rod in the same phase; f) rod whose cell body is deeply located; g) cone in bipolar phase; h) amacrine cell; i) ganglion cell; j) displaced amacrine cell; k) embryonic cone having a cell body near the external plexiform layer; k^2) rod having similar characteristics; l) embryonic horizontal cell; m) embryonic bipolar cells. In figure 173 to 185 (excepting Fig. 180) the cells are seen on edge, that is in sections perpendicular to the retina. They are also arranged so that the processes which, in the drawings, travel upwards, would penetrate the external granular zone of the same preparations.

surrounding the nucleus. This distinctive detail has been completely confirmed by studying retinas more advanced in development (4 day old cat) and those which can be considered as adult or nearly so in regard to the morphology of the external granular cells (8 to 10 day old cat). Comparison of Figures 173 and 174 clearly reveals the above-mentioned differences and at the same time allows you to judge their value for the identification of the visual cells. Furthermore, the pale tint of the silver chromate-impregnated rod cell bodies is not peculiar to embryonic retinas, it is consistently found in retinas of adult mammals and is even observed in fish and in nocturnal birds.

In view of the preceding details, the phases of development of the visual cells can readily be described. Here are the principal phases common to the rods and cones.

Germinal Phase. This corresponds to His's phase of germinal cells. Mitotic figures are found mainly, if not exclusively, in the external portion of the embryonic retina (proliferating cells of Koganeï and Chievitz), as has been described by other authors.

The shape of the visual cells during this period is irregular and spheroidal. In the newborn cat, rabbit, and dog all these cells seem to have passed the germinal phase; at least at this time it is not possible to observe mitoses with nuclear staining methods.

Unipolar Phase. The cell, relegated from the start to the vicinity of the external limiting membrane, elongates and thus gives rise to a long pedicle at the end of which the cell body is suspended. In this way the cell descends a variable distance, depending upon the position which it must occupy in the adult age. This cell body is ellipsoidal, the long axis being vertical; sometimes it is deformed by the pressure of neighboring elements. The pedicle, the sole process, is divided towards the periphery and always reaches the external limiting membrane, with which it seems to have a strict relation; it is exceedingly delicate and its path is somewhat sinuous. The cones and rods appear similar, and occupy the same positions; their only difference, as we have said, is the greater amount of protoplasm in the body of the embryonic cones.

The location of the visual cells is not restricted to the vicinity of the external limiting layer but includes the vicinity of the internal plexiform zone (Fig. 173, k). Moreover, it is impossible to distinguish the two granular layers. In reality, from the internal plexiform zone to the external limiting membrane, only an extremely dense agglomeration of granule cells is observed at this period. The bodies of the Müller fibers, the visual cells, and those of the horizontal and bipolar cells will develop from these cells.

Bipolar Phase. A very fine descending expansion emerges from the inferior extremity of the rod or cone granule. It frequently terminates in a slender granule or an irregular, transparent membranous dilatation. This prolongation does not always terminate at the same level. Sometimes it is very short and stops well before the point that it will later occupy, i.e., the external plexiform zone; other times it seems to be of enormous length, extending to the vicinity of the spongioblasts.

Adult Phase. The transition from the above forms to the almost definitive state can be readily studied in cats and dogs following the fourth day after birth and, especially, by examining the regions neighboring the optic nerve where development is most rapid and most advanced.

Those external granule cells whose soma or inferior expansion extended beyond the limit of the external plexiform zone retract and collect those portions outside of this line; at the same time an irregular, initially wavy, finely granular zone begins to be delineated, in which zone the ascending prolongations of the bipolar cells are united (Fig. 174). The descending filaments of the rods and cones still retain the same slenderness but they do not terminate similarly. That of the rod terminates in a fine granule, whereas that of the cone terminates in a conical thickening which still lacks basilar appendages. These appendages are a very late development, for we have not been able to see them in 10 to 11 day old cats.

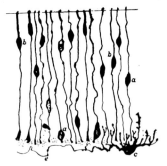

Fig. 174.   Retina of a 4 day old cat. Golgi method. a) Rod cell body; b) cone cell body; c) external horizontal cell and its fine axis-cylinder (e).

One embryonic detail is found in cones of 8 and 10 day old animals. The cell bodies of these cones, instead of bordering on the limiting membrane as in adult retinas, are disseminated throughout the external half of the granular zone. Later, the descending expansion of the cones becomes shorter and thicker (perhaps the thickening is the result of the shortening) and the nucleus gradually occupies its definitive position.

Two important conclusions can be drawn from the preceding observations:

1. The rods and cones are special cells, different from neurons and neuroglia since they exhibit a peculiar mode of development. Most assuredly they pass through a monopolar phase, as do some nerve cells; but, unlike the neuroblasts of His, the cellulopetal, not the cellulofugal, expansion develops first in the visual cells.

2. Adult rods and cones, which are so similar in morphology and connections, also undergo a similar development. As a result, from the histogenetic viewpoint one could consider the cone as a more advanced rod, one in which the morphology of the descending expansion is complicated by the addition of a tuft of basilar filaments.

In the rods and cones the first or unipolar phase (when they possess a single ascending or cellulopetal expansion) is only transitory. It differs from other neuroepithelial cells (e.g., the acoustic cristae and maculae or the hair cells of the organ of Corti) in which this stage persists definitively. Since descending or cellulofugal expansions never exist in these auditory cells, the protoplasmic body itself of these elements seems to be in rapport with the terminal nerve arborizations of a second order special sense neuron. From this point of view it would be interesting to determine the mode of development of the bipolar olfactory cells and the taste cells. These are undoubtedly morphologically homologous to the rods and cones. Like these elements, they must also pass through a unipolar phase during which they would have a centrally-placed cell body and a peripheral process.

If our inductions should be confirmed, we would possess a criterion to establish a distinction between special sense neuroepithelial cells and central nerve cells prior to the development of the cellulopetal expansion. It would follow that there are three types of cells in the nervous system capable of transmitting the nerve impulse:

1. Those which first give rise to a cellulopetal expansion (cones, rods, and gustatory cells).

2. Those which begin their development by emitting a cellulo-fugal expansion (the vast majority of multipolar cells of the central nervous system).

3. Those which seem to form the cellulopetal and cellulofugal expansions simultaneously (bipolar retinal cells, cells of the spiral ganglion, and sensory cells).

One exception would have to be made for the cerebellar granule cells which, although central multipolar cells, do not pass through the neuroblastic phase of His, but through the primitive bipolar phase of sensory cells, as Lugaro,[107] Schaper,[210] Calleja,[23] and we[166] have demonstrated. But the mode of development of the cerebellar granule cells can be reconciled with that of the second group, i.e., with that of central cells initiating their development by the produc-tion of the cellulofugal prolongation. In the cerebellar granules the cellulofugal expansion is engendered first but, instead of being simple and single, as in most central cells, it appears divided into two nervous expansions. In other words, in the cerebellar granule cells the development begins with the terminal branches instead of begin-ning with the trunk of the axis-cylinder, and only later is the axis-cylinder trunk developed, bearing at its extremity the previously formed terminal branches.

HORIZONTAL CELLS

All my efforts to detect the neuroblastic phase of these cells have been futile. Silver chromate stains these cells only in newborn mam-mals, i.e., when the axis-cylinder and the protoplasmic prolongations are quite developed although still clearly embryonic (Figs. 175, 176, 177). The study of the phases of growth of these elements is especial-ly interesting for two reasons:

1. To see whether, in these early developmental phases, it is pos-sible to reveal the anastomoses mentioned by some authors.

Fig. 175. Very embryonic horizontal cell. It does not yet show an orientation in the horizontal plane and possesses a thick, peripherally-directed prolongation.

2. To verify Dogiel's suggestion that certain horizontal cells give rise to an axis-cylinder which, after a horizontal course of variable length, descends to form part of the optic nerve fibers. Such verification could be accomplished in embryoniic retinas thanks to the shortness of the distances and to the greater affinity of silver chromate for axis-cylinders.

Our preparations reveal the presence of two types of cells in newborn animals:

1. Horizontal cells with fine axis-cylinder (these probably correspond to our external horizontal cells).

2. Horizontal cells with thick axis-cylinder (these certainly correspond to our giant or internal horizontal cells).

Fig. 176.   An embryonic external horizontal cell of a 2 day old cat.

Fig. 177.   Internal horizontal cell of a 4 day old cat. The axis-cylinder terminates in a growth cone.

Fig. 178.   An external horizontal cell possessing a fine axis-cylinder. Two day old cat.

External Horizontal Cells (Figs. 176, 178, 180). We have stained these cells mostly in the newborn cat. They appear multipolar with short, thick, and very varicose protoplasmic processes. A great number of these expansions ascend and ramify among the embryonic external granular cells, where they terminate by a thick, sometimes triangular varicosity. The more embryonic these cells, the less they are flattened, and the longer, more voluminous and more irregular are their protoplasmic expansions. As they develop the cell body flattens, the protoplasmic processes become thinner and lose their gross terminal varicosities; those processes which reach great heights are retracted, and all of them are limited in distribution to a very narrow zone of the external plexiform layer.

Among the most embryonic cells of this type (Figs. 173 and 175), it is difficult to decide whether they are external horizontal cells or giant internal horizontal cells. However, considering the volume, it seems more reasonable to consider them external ones. Whatever they are, these elements are characterized first of all by a total absence of flattening (as is seen in Figure 175, in which the axis- cylinder is more or less parallel to the fibers of Müller) and secondly by the existence of numerous short, thick processes emitted in all directions, among which one sometimes notes a thick, more or less ascending one, terminated by a large varicosity. Could this expansion represent the axis-cylinder with its growth cone? The limited number of cells of this type that we have encountered in our preparations do not permit a categorical answer to this question.

Fig. 179.   External horizontal cell with a thicker axis-cylinder. Two day old cat.

In the most developed cells (Figs. 178 and 179) the functional expansion is long, fine and flexuous. At intervals it presents varicosities at the level of which a short collateral with a terminal swelling occasionally arises. The axis-cylinder sometimes bifurcates near its termination and then the two branches describe their sinuosities in two different planes of the external plexiform zone (Fig. 178). It is possible that the exceedingly sinuous path of the nervous expansion results from the fact that the external plexiform layer is not yet fully formed; consequently, during its growth and horizontal elongation, this process is obliged to wind about the diverse elements now located in this layer.

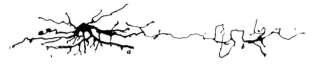

Fig. 180. Another example of a more advanced horizontal cell seen flat or
very obliquely. Four day old cat.

Internal Horizontal Cells. These are distinguished from the
preceding by their slightly greater volume and by their more
numerous, predominantly ascending, protoplasmic expansions. In
the cell reproduced in Figure 177 the axis-cylinder arises from a protoplasmic prolongation. It is very flexuous and terminated by a
thickening which might represent a vestige of the growth cone of
the neuroblastic phase. In another cell this expansion was considerably thicker (Fig. 181) and furnished several short collaterals terminated by a granule. After a short path it resolved into a number of
short, thick, exceedingly varicose twigs intermediate in appearance
between the growth cone and the embryonic nervous arborization.

Fig. 181. Large internal horizontal cell possessing a thick axis-cylinder and
ascending and descending protoplasmic prolongations. Four day old cat.

If instead of examining the newborn cat's retina we examine that
of an 8 day old cat (Fig. 183), we then see the internal horizontal
cell in nearly definitive form. The cell body is considerably thinner
and the protoplasmic prolongations are retracted and descended;
they are lined up along the external plexiform zone, and terminate
by varicosities between the feet of the rods. Finally, the axis-cylinder
has acquired such length that it is now almost impossible to follow
the cell of origin and its terminal nervous arborization. As can be
noted in Figure 182, the terminal arborization still partially retains
its embryonic appearance. The branches are considerably less ex-

tensive and branching than in the adult state and, futhermore, they present voluminous varicosities both at the level of their free extremities as well as at their bifurcations.

Fig. 182. Axis-cylinder and terminal nerve aborization of an internal horizontal cell of an 8 day old cat. The section is slightly oblique, but nearly flat to the arborization.

Some of the most delicate twigs now begin to be vertically arranged and terminate by nodosities between the feet of the rods. When the cat attains 10 days of age this terminal arborization of the axis-cylinder of the internal horizontal cell differs very little from the adult form.

Fig. 182. Axis-cylinder and terminal nerve aborization of an internal horizon-the axis-cylinder is so long that it cannot be easily followed to its termination. The ascending protoplasmic prolongations are shortened and smoothed.

We have never been able to observe the axis-cylinders of this cell type descend to the layer of optic nerve fibers, contrary to Dogiel * who has described it in the human retina. We can therefore maintain our opinion that all or at least the immense majority of the horizontal cells are cells with short axis-cylinders ramified in the external plexiform zone itself. Our recent research on birds and mammals, employing the Ehrlich method with the ammonium molybdate fixation recommended by Bethe, has confirmed the results of the Golgi method. Moreover, Kallius himself [73] who has recently worked with both methods, has entirely confirmed our descriptions.

*Perhaps Dogiel has rectified his error which, like several others committed by this scholar, resulted from the difficulty of interpreting the results of the Ehrlich-blue method; for, not only does he not mention these cells with long axis-cylinder in his latest monographs, but one even finds a passage in which he seems to admit the existence of our nerve arborizations in the external plexiform layer.[28]

Fig. 184. Cell which was located in the spongioblast or amacrine cell layer and which may be an association spongioblast. a) Its protoplasmic prolongations; b) process resembling an axis-cylinder.

BIPOLAR CELLS

We have not had any success in our attempts to impregnate these cells in the rat and rabbit fetus. It has also been impossible for us to determine the primordial phases that these cells pass through and to verify whether the two expansions, ascending and descending, are produced simltaneously (as would seem very reasonable *a priori* from what we know of the development of other sensory bipolar cells).

Mammalian bipolar cells can be impregnated only after birth. Impregnation of these elements is readily obtained in the 4 day old cat and dog, especially in the most developmentally advanced regions of the retina (i.e., in the vicinity of the optic nerve).

It is possible that these cells stain even prior to this time but their great morphological resemblance to the other elements renders their recognition arduous if not impossible. We venture to add, as a conjecture, that before the appearance of the external plexiform layer the bipolar cells are represented by cells having two poles, from each of which a fine, long process emanates. The ascending filament mounts to the limiting membrane, while the descending one reaches the internal plexiform zone, where it seems to terminate in a varicosity (Fig. 173, m). These cells are distinguished from the epithelial cells by the great delicacy of their polar prolongations and the lesser extent of the retina that they cover since, unlike Müller's fibers, they do not join the two surfaces of this membrane. If this hypothesis were confirmed, the bipolar cells of embryonic mammals would also possess a long ascending expansion—true Landolt body—which would disappear later; this transitory appearance in mammals thus would reproduce an arrangement which is permanent in lower vertebrates. The development of the bipolar cells can be better followed in birds. Here the Landolt body represents, at the outset, the entire expansion of the bipolar cell, since the tuft destined for the external plexiform layer only appears later.

Thus, as we have said, the bipolar cells impregnate well and appear quite advanced in development in the 5 to 6 day old cat and dog. Figure 185 shows that silver chromate very clearly demonstrates two types of bipolar cells (some for the cones and others for the rods). These two cell types possess extremely striking differential characteristics, perhaps even more striking in embryos than in the adult state.

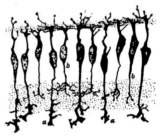

Fig. 185.   Bipolar cells of the retina of a 8 day old cat. a) Bipolar cell for rod;
b) bipolar cells for cones.

The cone bipolar cells (Fig. 185, b) are short; they extend from the external plexiform zone to the internal plexiform zone. Their cell body is oblong and exhibits a brown-colored nucleus; the ascending expansion is single and ramifies in the depths of the external plexiform layer where it forms a flattened tuft; the twigs of this tuft have no tendency to rise to the external granular zone. The descending expansion arborizes in the internal plexiform zone at a variable level. Its arborization is more or less abundant according to the degree of development attained by the cell. In certain elements, it is formed simply by two short twigs provided with a terminal granule (Fig. 185, b); in others it is more complicated and begins to show a flattening.

In general, the rod bipolar cells are a little more voluminous and appreciably long (Fig. 185, a). The ascending expansion is thick and irregular. Upon arrival at the external plexiform zone it decomposes into 2, 3, or more fibers of variable length. Some of them mount between the legs of the rods and terminate in a spherule. At the point of departure of these ascending fibrils, the trunk of the primary expansion often presents a large accumulation of protoplasm.

The descending expansion is quite characteristic. Just as in the adult, it is a little thicker than its homologue of the cone bipolar cells. It terminates, after having crossed the entire plexiform layer, by a massive, little-ramified stalk either on the body of a ganglion cell or on the origin of one of the large protoplasmic branches of these cells. In some rod bipolar cells we have seen the descending expansion furnish massive spines at the level of the inferior part of the internal plexiform layer; in others we have observed a bifurcation of the stalk.

From this description it is seen that the study of the embryonic retina completely confirms our discovery of the two varieties of bipolar cells, and it is noteworthy that absolutely no transition forms exist between these two varieties. Also observe that from the superior tuft of the bipolar cells no ascending fiber arises that one might regard as the Landolt body mentioned by Dogiel in the human retina. Furthermore, Kallius has been no more successful than we in finding this body in mammals, in spite of his use of methylene blue. To the contrary, he has been able to recognize clearly the two varieties of bipolar cells that we had described. But what seems convincing to us is the absence of these bodies in the embryonic mammalian retina; for if they existed they would stain with great constancy, as in the chick embryo, where these expansions stain better than the other parts of the bipolar cell.

GANGLION CELLS

These are the first cells to differentiate, as a great number of authors have noted. Also, the shape of the internal plexiform zone and the zone of optic nerve fibers is due, even at a relatively early time, to this developmental precocity.

This more rapid maturity also explains why these cells are the easiest elements to stain in the embryonic retina. Thus, in hundreds of sections of the retina of newborn cats and dogs, we have obtained impregnation of these elements and the Müller fibers almost exclusively. This peculiarity has been confirmed in our recent attempts to stain the retina with methylene blue. It is the ganglion cells which stain from the outset—and that holds true even in the newborn dog and cat. Of all the types of ganglion cells in retinas of newborn cats, it is the giant type which develops most rapidly and which stains most selectively (Fig. 173, i). The expansions of these giant ganglion cells, two or more in number, are thick. They are directed laterally, while diverging, and soon penetrate the internal plexiform zone, the entire thickness of which is weaved by their ramifications. Their branches, which give rise to a plexus in which the amacrine cell tufts also take part, are very long, more or less horizontal, and seem to terminate freely after repeated subdivisions. In complete impregnations of horizontal sections (which are easily obtained from retinas transformed into a large block by rolling them up), the plexus of the internal plexiform zone is so complicated and so dense that it is impossible to determine the distribution of the protoplasmic appendages of each cell.

The layers of the internal plexiform zone appear late. In the cat they appear from the eighth to the tenth day after birth, at which moment one begins to observe small ganglion cells and sizable amacrine cells in various phases. The ganglion cells direct their functional expansion to the layer of optic nerve fibers. Some other elements are now seen quite near the ganglion cells. No trace of a functional expansion can be found in these elements; we consider them *displaced or inferior amacrine cells* because of their properties and location (Fig. 173, j).

EPITHELIAL CELLS

We can add nothing essential to our previous study of these elements. Our recent research confirms that the lamellar or filiform lateral expansions emitted by the epithelial cells of Müller during their journey across the various layers of the retina, are formed subsequent, not prior, to the morphologic differentiation of the nerve cells. Thus, for example, in the retina of the newborn cat (Fig. 173), a great number of ganglion cells, spongioblasts, and rods are differentiated and arranged in special zones, whereas the epithelial cells are not yet differentiated (as regards the appearance of epithelial appendages interposed among the nerve elements). That makes us believe that the epithelium does not necessarily direct the development of the nerve cells, as His believed. On the contrary, the development of the epithelium is subordinate to the latter and only later does the epithelium emit expansions which fill the empty spaces.

Let us add one detail of some importance. On examining epithelial cells of a sufficiently embryonic retina, e. g., a newborn cat, one observes two types of epithelial cells: 1. The most numerous ones possess a single nucleus, lodged in different planes throughout the retina but especially in the middle regions. 2. The remaining less abundant ones are usually voluminous and have a large nucleus which hugs the external limiting membrane. The nucleus of this second type of epithelial cell is frequently double (Fig. 173, a) and the two nuclei appear oriented like a string of beads, one behind the other along the Müller fiber (a) or slightly behind and lateral to the other (a^2). These arrangements increase the thickness of the external extremity of the Müller fiber. These fibers with double nuclei must be considered proliferating embryonic cells. The increase in number of epithelial cells during retinal development must be attributed to these proliferating cells.

Chapter 20

DEVELOPMENT OF THE HORIZONTAL
NEURONS IN THE MOUSE RETINA AND
THEIR ACCIDENTAL ALTERATIONS OF
LOCATION AND DIRECTION*

W E KNOW VERY little about the ontogeny of the short-axon retinal cells or of similar ones of other nerve centers. Because of the inadequacy of the methods employed, the histogenetic studies of Babuchin, Müller, Löwe, Ognef, Bellonci, Koganeï, Chiewitz, Falchi, Martin, Mall, Fürst, Leboucq, Weyesse, and Burgos do not touch on this point, or do so only in passing. In a previous work we furnished some very incomplete data which we seek to develop in the present memoir.

The incompleteness of our knowledge relative to the initial arrangement of the short-axon cells therefore justifies our recent attempts to impregnate the mammalian retina. For two major reasons we have chosen to study the white mouse, examining newborn and several day old specimens. 1. Relatively early phases of the horizontal retinal cells of the mouse can be revealed by the reduced silver nitrate procedure. These cells stand out perfectly clearly against a nonimpregnated yellow background. 2. The very embryonic state of the retina of the newborn mouse renders neurogenetic analysis singularly easy. Our descriptions and drawings relate therefore to this subject.

For this investigation we have preferentially employed the reduced silver nitrate formula with fixation in pyridine (immersion of the specimens in 8 parts water to 20 parts pyridine for 36 hours; wash for 12 hours; subsequent hardening in alcohol; finally, silver nitrate, etc.).

For further verification we have used routine staining methods and the Bielschowsky procedure. The latter is very difficult to apply to such small specimens.

---

*This article was originally published in 1919 under a different title.[191] We have changed the title in order to convey a more exact idea of the contents of the text. (*Note for the French edition.*)

DEVELOPMENT OF THE HORIZONTAL CELLS

Since we have not been successful, in the mouse fetus or in any mammalian fetus, in differentiating the most precocious phases of these cells, i.e., those which appear immediately after His's germinal cell state, our description will deal again with relatively late states.

To simplify our description we will divide the developmental periods into four phases: 1. initial phase or phase of vertical bipolarity; 2. phase of the stellate cell with divergent dendrons and wandering axon; 3. phase of horizontal orientation of the dendrons and axon; 4. phase of definitive modeling of the cell.

Initial Phase. During the last two days of fetal life in the mouse the internal retinal zones appear relatively differentiated and the external ones excessively retarded. As can be noted in Figure 186, the following are present although rudimentary: zone of spongioblasts or amacrine cells (C); the internal plexiform layer (D); the layer of the optic fibers (F); two limiting membranes. But external to the layer of amacrine cells one only perceives a very compact wall of nucleated elements that are exceedingly poor in protoplasm. The primitive forms of the cell bodies of the cones and rods, the bipolar and horizontal cells appear to be intermixed without order in this more external region. Sections stained with hematoxylin or Unna's polychromic blue only reveals the nuclei of the afore-mentioned elements. In the interior of these nuclei several intensely stained chromatic clumps stand out.

However, even in this precocious phase of retinal development some elements are seen which because of their small number their position, and their large size, can be identified as horizontal cells (c). They are found at the junction of the external one fourth and the internal three fourths of the visual membrane and are irregularly disseminated. It is impossible to decide if all these cells correspond to the large types (our *horizontal internal neurons*). However, in view of the relation between embryonic size and adult size, it seems probable to us that these cells are those gigantic ones which send ascending branches into the zone of rods in adult mammals. However that may be, the large neurons to which we refer possess a voluminous nucleus larger than that of all the neighboring elements, a sturdy

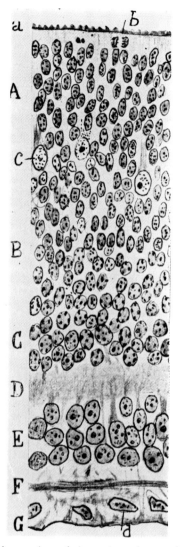

Fig. 186.   Perpendicular section of the retina of a newborn white mouse. A) region of the cell bodies of the rods and cones; B) region of the bipolar cells; C) region of the amacrine cells; D) the already-differentiated internal plexiform layer; E) ganglion cells; F) optic nerve fibers; G) internal limiting membrane; a) external limiting membrane; b) arising mounds of the rods; c) embryonic horizontal cells; d) neuroglial cells.

nucleolus and, towards the external pole of the perikaryon a protoplasmic mass which is drawn out into a thick, more or less clearly visible radial dendron. Internal expansions are not observed in hematoxylin preparations. It follows that the general form of these neurons is that of a monopolar cell with the trunk directed externally. Note, furthermore, that not all the neurons with which we are concerned lie in the same plane but that they are irregularly disseminated throughout quite an extensive area of the large external nuclear formation. This dispersion decreases in the days following birth. It would seem that, because of their ameboid movements and attractive influences of unknown origin, these cells have a tendency to concentrate more and more in their future locality.

The true morphology of the horizontal elements at this developmental phase (fetus near term and newborn mouse) is not well revealed in sections stained by reduced silver nitrate. As is seen in Figure 187, the youngest cells (a) are clearly bipolar, while others, perhaps more developed, appear monopolar (b). In any case, even

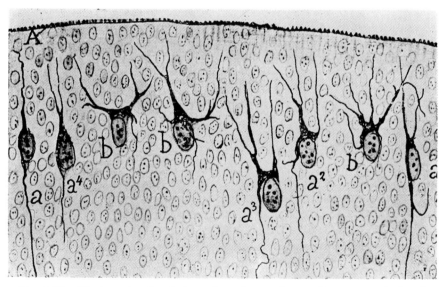

Fig. 187. Horizontal cells of the retina of a newborn white mouse. Reduced silver nitrate technique after fixation in 70% pyridine and subsequent hardening in 96% alcohol. a, a^2, a^3, a^4) Bipolar types; b) cell types having a large, ramified, ascending dendritic trunk.

though the internal expansion may be lacking, the external one is never missing. It is thick at its origin, emerging from a region rich in protoplasm and, dividing prematurely, it gives rise to two or more ascending branches which are often arciform and which become progressively thinner. Many of these branches approach the external limiting membrane and some, albeit few, succeed in touching it. Careful examination of the protoplasmic pole from which the external expansion arises reveals a neurofibrillar network or woof of relatively robust strands, from which the skeleton of the afore-mentioned branches or appendages leave. This region where neurofibrillar genesis seems to be initiated is in all respects similar to the neurofibrillogenetic zone observed by Held [58] and ourselves [183] in the early spinal neuroblasts of the chick embryo. The bipolar and monopolar types occur throughout the retina but they are more abundant anteriorly than in the vicinity of the optic nerve. They are also more abundant in fetal than in newborn mice. This is why we consider them antecedent to the multipolar type with which they are already intermixed in the newborn mouse, as can be noted in Figures 187 and 192.

Although no protoplasm is perceived on the internal side of the horizontal neurons, we do not doubt that a small quantity is present. Naturally, differentiating neurofibrils are not seen in this region. It

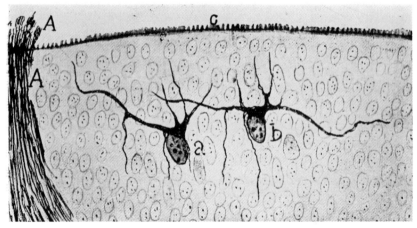

Fig. 188.   Section of the retina of a 1 day old mouse. A) Region of the optic nerve; a, b) horizontal cells with long tangential prolongations; c) rudiment of the rod layer.

is surprising that the internal expansion, nearly always very slender, arises from the afore-mentioned fibrillogenetic zone, i.e., from the external protoplasmic pole. In its descending course it extends along one side of the nucleus, becoming successively thinner until it terminates in a point at a variable distance from the spongioblast layer. These facts suggest the hypothesis that during their multiplication the *neurobiones* (ultramicroscopic units of the neurofibrils) are propagated from the external pole to the internal pole of the cell body and to its developing expansions by a kind of infection. Consequently, they migrate from the center of the afore-mentioned formation as microbial colonies grow and disseminate in the solid parts of a culture. It is superfluous to add that each cell is independent of congeneral ones during this stage of development.

Phase of the Stellate Cell with Divergent Expansions. Almost at the same time as the previous phase, some horizontal cells appear in the retina. These resemble the preceding ones as regards size, position of the soma, and shape and direction of the internal expansion. But from their fibrillogenetic region, a region very rich in protoplasm, two or more divergent dendrons leave, some ascending and others oblique and horizontal. Their ascending appendages are usually oriented in a very ample arc (Figs. 187, b, and 188). These elements seem more numerous in the region of emergence of the optic nerve. They are very numerous in the newborn mouse.

Let us now note the existence of neurons which have, instead of one descending appendage, two very delicate descending ones which skirt the nuclear contour; some of them also travel for quite considerable distances.

In certain regions of the retina, especially peripherally where development seems relatively retarded, the horizontal stellate cells occupy diverse, very scattered levels. In Figure 194, f, ñ, we show some of these cells which could be termed dislocated. These elements are distinguished from the true spongioblasts or amacrine cells by the fact that the latter possess descending branches distributed throughout the internal plexiform zone. The neuron designated "f" (Fig. 194), has two fine descending expansions, the longer of which, upon arriving at the internal plexiform layer, turns backwards forming an arc. We shall see that such arciform arrangements later increase.

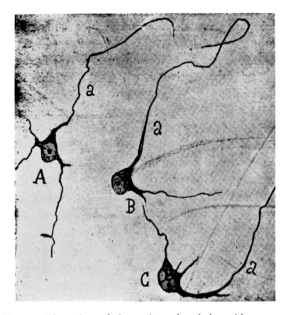

Fig. 189.   Tangential section of the retina of a 4 day old mouse. Cells copied from 2 sections. A, B, C) Horizontal neurons which have a long prolongation (a).

The axon cannot be distinguished clearly during the first two developmental phases of the horizontal cells. The axon probably does exist but neurofibrillar methods fail to demonstrate it. We would be certain that the axon is present if we could consider the commonly observed, longest prolongation (Fig. 189, a) as being axonal. This appendage, generally more delicate than the others, is frequently ascending; its position and orientation coincide with the appendage which, in perpendicular sections, often is arciform and of remarkable delicacy (Fig. 192, n). But this characterization (fineness, more or less descending direction, remarkable length) can be misleading sometimes. It occurs frequently in cells which possess two long, tenuous, unramified appendages which travel in a horizontal or descending direction. On the other hand, the growth cone which is characteristic of the axon of long-axon embryonic neurons of the brain, spinal cord and retina itself (ganglion cells), is always lacking in the most embryonic horizontal elements. In summary, it appears probable, but not certain, that in the fetal and newborn mouse, the longest out-growth, usually descending, represents the axon.

From 2 to 6 days after birth, the dendritic ramifications of the horizontal cells become complicated; the external branches multiply, scatter, and often become frankly tangential. As we have said, the arrangement of the external prolongations begins to take shape in the newborn mouse; it is most apparent initially in the vicinity of the optic nerve, a region always more advanced in development (Fig. 194).

Finally, 8 days after birth, the external branches are remarkably robust. They emit numerous secondary branches which invade relatively extensive areas; some secondary rami succeed in touching the external limiting membrane. The internal prolongation grows but little. On the other hand, when it is quite developed it frequently traces an arc and returns backwards after a variable distance, as if aware of its wandering (Fig. 192). There are some sections in which these arcs, axonal in appearance, are exceedingly numerous. We will discuss their significance later.

Phase of Horizontal Orientation of the Dendrons and Axon. Up to now we have seen that both the internal and the external outgrowths travel preferentially in a radial direction, i.e., crossing zones with which they are unrelated in the adult state. It seems they follow the path offering least resistance to their progress. But from the twelfth to the eighteenth day, an important phenomenon arises which completely changes matters. The zone of rods and cones begins to form (Fig. 190, B) and, at the level of the future external plexiform zone the descending outgrowths of the rods stop in an abrupt and regular manner. The rods are enormously more numerous than the cones in the mouse—it must not be forgotten that this animal belongs to the nocturnal category. In actuality, this zone is present in a more or less perfect form from the twelfth to the fifteenth day. The above-mentioned change in the architecture of the external retinal layers rapidly affects the horizontal cells, which lose and retract the ascending and descending outgrowths. They regularize the position of the principal dendrons. The latter take their definitive tangential orientation and give rise to an increasingly greater number of secondary appendages which are in part ascending. From this it follows that

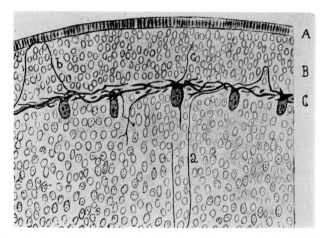

Fig. 190.   Section of the retina of a 12 day old mouse. Reduced silver nitrate technique. A) Layer of rods and cones; B) zone of the cell bodies of the visual cells; C) zone of horizontal neurons; a) arciform axon; b, c) aberrant ascending prolongations.

the immense majority of these appendages (either pre-existent or newly-formed) are arranged in a horizontal plexus beneath the rudimentary feet of the rods and cones. We are therefore in the presence of two concomitant activities: one, of topographical rectification of the old outgrowths, and the other, of formation of new correctly oriented prolongations. It is impossible to decide in what proportion the two processes occur. They continue during succeeding days, up to the twenty-fourth or thirtieth day after birth.

In this phase the axon is readily distinguishable. It appears with unquestionable clarity in some neurons (Fig. 191, m, n). Needless to say, only in tangential sections can one observe and follow the origin, course, and terminal arborization of the axon. This expansion ordinarily arises from the fibrillogenetic zone or superior pole of the neuron by a fine cone of origin. It then thins considerably and becomes quite pale; afterwards it often describes a great detour and progressively thickens to terminate finally by two or more relatively thick divergent branches. Such a rudimentary terminal arborization (Fig. 191, a, b, c, d) as well as the very long path of the outgrowth constitute clear cut evidence of the axonal nature of this appendage.

As regards the anastomoses described a long time ago by Dogiel, Embden, Renaut and others, they are never seen in either the dendrons or axons. But if they did exist, they would easily be recognized during this phase because of the simplicity of the fibrillar plexus of the plexiform layer.

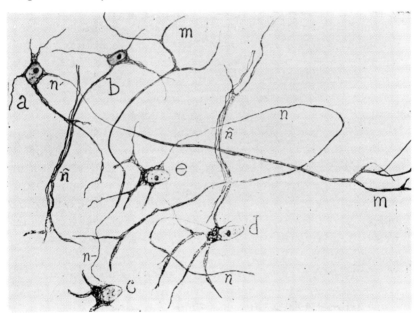

Fig. 191. Tangential section of the retina of 13 day old mouse illustrating various types of horizontal cells. Cells copied from 2 successive sections. n) Axon or neurite, m) terminal arborization of the latter; n) fascicles of young dendrites.

Some recent impregnations that we made by the formol-uranium method confirm previous ones,[188] and have convinced us that the fibrillogenetic zone located, as we have said, on the external side of the horizontal cells, contains the Golgi apparatus and the centrosome as well. The same fact is observed in spinal neuroblasts, as we have noted,[188] and in the retinal ganglionic and bipolar elements. It is interesting that the afore-mentioned reticular apparatus always is found in the region of maximal protoplasmic growth capacity and, consequently, in the region most capable of generating outgrowths. This corroborates, for the retina, the law we established [189] regarding the initial orientation of the Golgi network, viz.: The Golgi apparatus always chooses, at its outset, the "worldly" pole of the cell, i.e., the somatic side directed towards the external world. Since the retinal vesicle is a simple ectodermal fold, this pole can only be at the side oriented towards the cavity or intercalated space between the visual membrane and the pigment layer. For the same reason, the ganglion cells, bipolar cells, and epithelial cells also show this apparatus in their posterior segment. Only the spongioblasts are exceptions; but there are reasons to believe, in these cells, that after the external radial outgrowth is resorbed the apparatus migrates towards the internal appendage, the new territory of maximal growth.

We have already alluded to the frequent arciform arrangement of the internal outgrowth and to the probability of the axonal nature of this appendage. We now add that these axonal arcs are more frequent during the 4 to 8 days following birth and that quite a good number of them, after a long detour, succeed in channeling back and rejoining the external plexiform zone from where they began. Because of this peculiarity, and for brevity, we designate them *arcs of rectification.*

In Figure 192, b, c, we reproduced 2 great arcs of rectification. In one, the strayed appendage (probably axonal in nature) runs against the internal plexiform layer, from which it retraces its steps to very near the level of the cell origin. The other arc is shorter; the axon turns about above the spongioblast zone. It is important to note that arcs of rectification are lacking or are rare in the late fetal and newborn mouse. They therefore represent a phenomenon associated with the differentiation and growth of the functional prolongation. Finally, Figure 190, a, reproduces a retinal section from a 12 day old mouse in which a very long arc of rectification still exists, in addition to an external arc which borders the external limiting membrane (b). There are however some cases in which the strayed arciform appendage has seemed to show dendritic characteristics.

Phase of Definitive Formation of the Horizontal Cells. From 12 to 24 days after birth, when the mouse has opened his eyes, all the expansions of the horizontal cells lie aligned in their normal plane, i.e., in the external plexiform zone or a little beneath the latter. Large

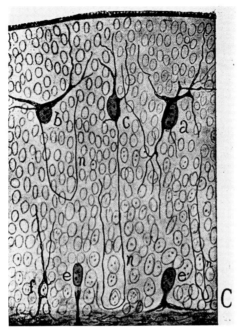

Fig. 192. Section of the retina of a 6 day old mouse. Cells copied from several sections. C) External plexiform zone; a, b, c) embryonic horizontal cells; e) amacrine cells; f) amacrine cell with ascending prolongations; n) axons showing arcs of rectification.

arcs of rectification cannot be found. However, one does perceive an occasional arciform fibrillar interlacing, extending beneath the level of the horizontal elements (Fig. 193, d), and one or more superfluous ascending appendages undergoing resorption (Fig. 193, c).

As we have said, the dendritic plexus appears at its natural level. Since the chain is very complicated it is impossible to differentiate the primordial dendrons. The neurofibrils of both elements appear robust and even more vigorously impregnated than those of all other retinal elements. Neurofibrils as well as descending filiform appendages are lacking beneath some nuclei. It is often difficult to make out the position of the perikaryon because of its extreme pallor. In summary, when the animal has opened his eyes one can say that the zone of horizontal cells is substantially formed. In view of the complexity of the horizontal plexus and the proximity of the dendrons

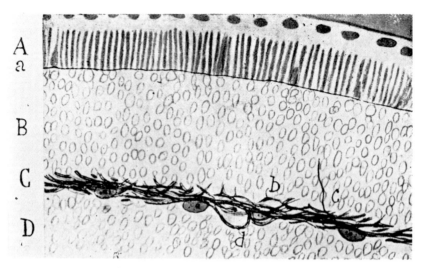

Fig. 193. Section of the retina of an 18 day old mouse. A) Layer of rods; B) cell bodies of the visual cells; C) zone of horizontal neurons; a) external limiting membrane; c) ascending appendage undergoing atrophy; d) descending arc destined to disappear.

(which are often gathered into fascicles), it is impossible to decide whether intercellular anastomoses exist. However, we find no reason to accept them since they are not manifest in the earlier phases of development.

FUSIFORM SPONGIOBLASTS

The initial fusiform morphology of the retinal neurons can be noted in the amacrine cells. As a general rule, in the newborn mouse these elements are considerably more advanced in development than the horizontal cells. In neurofibrillar preparations almost all show the typical pyriform configuration without ascending or external appendage. They are provided with a robust, perfectly demarcated internal outgrowth distributed in the internal plexiform zone. The reticulum, almost invisible at the level of the cell body, ordinarily stands out well in the afore-mentioned prolongation (Fig. 192, e, and 194, j).

But, in spite of the appearance of the majority of cells, much younger bipolar amacrine cells do exist in the region of the ora serrata, a region late in differentiation. Figure 194, g, h, i, reproduces some cells of this type collected from several sections. One of them is frankly fusiform with two fine outgrowths, one ascending and the other descending (i). The other amacrine cells represented possess a more complex neurofibrillar apparatus with one or two ascending

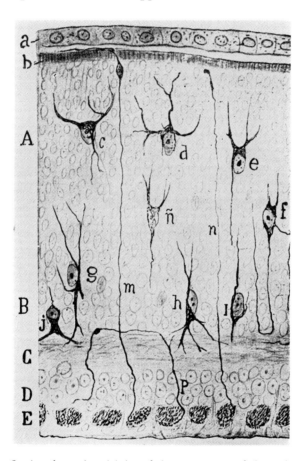

Fig. 194.   Section from the vicinity of the ora serrata of the retina of a new-born mouse. Cells copied from 3 successive sections. a) Pigment cells; B) amacrine cells; C) internal plexiformlayer; D) ganglion cells; E) optic nerve fibers; A) level in which horizontal cells abound; f, n) dislocated or migrating horizontal neurons; g, h, i) bipolar amacrine cells; m, n) strayed axons from the layer of optic nerve fibers; p) an axon which seems to have reached its destination.

outgrowths and one, two or more descending prolongations distributed in the internal plexiform layer.

Is it not possible that such cells represent displaced horizontal neurons? There are some cases, in fact, where doubt seems justified in view of the presence of some very deeply located horizontal cells in the same sections. I consider it probable, nevertheless, that every cell located near the internal plexiform layer, whose principal ramification is distributed in this layer and which possesses very fine ascending branches, represents a true amacrine cell. And, on the other hand, every cell, even through very deeply located, whose descending prolongation is fine and retraces its steps after having described an arc, and does not emit branches to the afore-mentioned internal plexiform layer, would be a dislocated horizontal element.

In summary: Because of accommodation to the terrain (direction of the interstices of the epithelial cells), the spongioblast, in its earliest growth phases is often fusiform with two or more ascending outgrowths and a variable number of descending ones.

STRAYED AXONS OF GANGLION CELLS

In various neurogenetic works,[183,184] we have called attention to the curious wandering of sensory and motor axons of embryonic nerve cells. Instead of following the route of their fellows, these strayed neurites become lost in long, generally arciform detours, and ultimately become incorporated in the principal nervous contingent. This phenomenon, whose theoretical significance seems important to us, is one of the most common occurrences in the sprouts or offshoots of regenerated nerves. Finally, experiments on regeneration of the transected optic nerve (Tello,[221] Ortin and Arcaute [135]) also show that when necrotic processes of cut axons are found in the optic fiber layer of the retina it is not rare to perceive robust misplaced axis-cylinders which, instead of traveling towards the visual nerve, bend abruptly almost at a right angle, traverse the retinal layers and finally stop there. In their blind advance they occasionally reach the zone of pigment cells where they terminate in a ball of arrest.

We asked ourselves whether such a curious phenomenon of axonal straying, resulting from obstacles and mishaps of growth, could not sometimes occur in the normal retinal neurogenesis as well. On examining retinal sections of the 1 to 6 day old mouse we noted many perforating axis-cylinders. The presence of these can only signify the accidental anticipation of optic nerve emergence. Perhaps the perforating axis-cylinders have mistaken an opening along their path for the pore or foramen of emergence of the optic nerve.

In Figure 194, m, n, we have grouped some typical cases of strayed fibers which have been followed throughout all or a great part of their aberrant journey. Note how they emerge from the fascicles of the optic nerve, then, becoming thicker, cross the internal plexiform zone and afterwards become considerably thinner while crossing all the subsequent retinal layers. They finally terminate in a very fine pointed filament, either beside the zone of rods (n) or immediately beneath the pigment layer (m). In places where the axon struck obstacles and was obliged to stop, a ball undergoing vacuolar degeneration frequently appears. The longest perforating fiber, m, shows two tumefactions of arrest, one in front of the external limiting membrane and the other a little behind it. Finally, other fibers, very likely of the same type, are detained considerably before the layer of rods and cones. The one represented in Figure 194, p, has been detained at the external limit of the internal plexiform layer. It retraces its steps to the zone of optic fibers after having given rise to a ball of detention. In its journey it emits a fine initial exploratory branch. One could also say that the afore-mentioned wandered axis-cylinders might represent centrifugal fibers. But since these fibers can never be stained by neurofibrillar methods in young or adult mammals, we are inclined to favor the opinion described above.

Some fibers of this category show such delicacy and pallor in the terminal portion of their path that they cannot be followed in their entirety. They are most likely wandered axons undergoing reabsorption—which leads us to discuss the later fate of these wandered axons as well as of all such exploratory cellular appendages, be they axonal or dendritic.

One highly significant fact attracts our attention from the very first. Strayed axons are never found in the adult state (we allude especially to the motor and sensory axons whose normal pathway is well known). They therefore represent accidental phenomena produced during neurogenesis. They are completely absent in the medulla, the spinal cord and, it goes without saying, in the retina of adult mammals, organs which we have studied a great deal. The last wandered axis-cylinders found in the retina of the mouse do not persist beyond the eighth day after birth.

It is therefore beyond doubt that such strayed fibers ultimately disappear. The same is true of supernumary strayed dendrites. In the retina of the 15 day old mouse we have observed the last projections of this type, already very much reduced in length. These very rare appendages always terminate in a pale point, comparable to the *corrosion point* that we have described in degenerating cerebral axons.[187]

There is no question that every strayed axon or dendrite (one which fails to establish a functional connection because it inhabits a foreign cellular territory or because it follows a route which completely prevents it from attaining its proper destination) is progressively resorbed starting from the peripheral or terminal end. This resorption is indicated by the increasing pallor of the neurofibrils and the progressive thinning of the process. The globules or balls of arrest are more persistent but ultimately they also degenerate and disappear, as do the large terminal buttons of regenerated nerve sprouts.[178]

Nevertheless, there are less serious cases of straying. We have cited several examples of these in previous pages. In these cases it is possible that the strayed outgrowth may be utilized. We allude to the axons and dendrons which describe arcs not very far from the cell of origin and whose terminal tip ultimately succeeds in establishing physiological connections. The numerous instances of abnormally descending and arciform axons of the horizontal cells incline us to believe that the eccentric path of the axis-cylinder diminishes progressively until it dissappears completely.

In summary, concerning the fate of the strayed fibers, we consider extremely probable: 1. that all the long dislocated fibers that fail to re-establish their normal connection are irrevocably destroyed by absorption. After this the cell of origin is obliged either to form a new neurite (we have not seen the slightest indication of such a phenomenon) or to degenerate and die from disuse; 2. that the fibers which do not deviate far from the cell of origin and which succeed in finding their destination persist. They gradually reduce and rectify their aberrant curves, ultimately taking part in the normal architecture of the neural zones to which they belong.

DISCUSSION

From the preceding analysis of the morphology and development of the retinal neurons the following conclusions emerge. These conclusions are in perfect harmony with the results of our previous studies.

1. The neurons with short axon and even those lacking a neurite (amacrine cells) pass, as do long-axon nerve cells, through a fusiform phase of radial orientation, during which the soma emits two outgrowths (sometimes more), one internal and the other external. This peculiar morphology first noted by us many years ago in the spinal cord of the embryonic chick,[156] and confirmed by Held, undoubtedly results from the combination of two conditions: the generative impulse of the outgrowths (*continuous growth* of His, *vis á tergo* of Held) and the transverse pressure of the neighboring cells, especially the epithelial cells or embryonic Müller fibers whose orientation perpendicular to the retinal plane makes only radially-oriented pathways readily available to the new appendages. The *stereotropism* of Loeb, confirmed by Harrison[53] and Marinesco[114] in their ganglion culture experiments and by us[198] in our observations on nerve regeneration, could also play a role in such a growth phenomen.

2. During this initial phase, the neurons do not seem to obey any neurotropic influence. In the struggle with mechanical obstacles, they merely project the growing expansions in the direction of least resistance as if to explore the terrain while awaiting the appearance of sources of attractive substances or orienting enzymes. Some of the appendages which emerge during this time are temporary and are destined to disappear, as we demonstrated a long time ago in the embryonic Purkinje elements of the cerebellum.[172] It is superfluous to say that the principles of the *shortest route,* of the *morphologic predetermination of the neuron,* and of *axonal growth according to a pre-established direction,* suggested by Harrison and other scholars, are not applicable to this phase of development any more than are

His's principle of *regulatory barriers* and Held's *predetermined intracellular pathways*. Quite to the contrary, the immense variety of cellular forms, the topographical dislocations of cell bodies, and the diversity in number and direction of the primitive appendages, produces the impression that the neuron enjoys a complete freedom of movement, being transformed like a leukocyte which ventures across a complicated web that is laden with obstacles.

3. Since the horizontal cells initially occupy various retinal planes and are later concentrated in a regular, concentric plane or stratum, it is necessary to accept not only the validity of neuroblastic ameboidism (suggested a long time ago by Lenhossék and us) but also the migratory property of the soma and processes.

4. Since we have not succeeded in impregnating (or locating) the horizontal cells prior to their bipolar phase, i.e., during the stage immediately after the germinal cell phase, we do not know whether the two polar appendages arise simultaneously or whether one appears before the other. However, we are inclined to believe that the external appendage, always the more robust, appears first. And in fact, it is unique in some elements. In any case, the question is not important since both the internal as well as the external derive, in reality, from the external region or worldly pole of the neuronal protoplasm. This induces us to formulate a principle which we have already stated elsewhere, although in a different context, viz.: that the formation of the first outgrowths is related not to the initial orientation of the nerve cell, as Harrison and others believed,[53] but to the location of the Golgi apparatus in the primitive protoplasm. The location of the afore-mentioned apparatus always constitutes the nidus from which emerge both the primordial axonal outgrowth as well as the first dendrons. Only later, when the afore-mentioned intraprotoplasmic reticulum is transformed from the concentrated state to the diffuse perinuclear one, are the protoplasmic outgrowths able to emerge from the neuronal cell body.

5. The aberrant deviations of the axons and dendrons result from the absence of chemotactic influences during the first developmental phases. These wanderings decisively demonstrate that it is wrong to apply the principle of *growth in a straight line* (Harrison) to the development of nerve cells unless it be considered as an ideal

tendency, attainable only when the axon can grow freely and without obstacles (as in Harrison's experiments with nerve cultures *in vitro*). On the other hand, we have confirmed one fact which this American scholar has stressed, viz.: the appearance of exploratory fibers, to which are added many other subsequently differentiated fibers. In the embryonic retina, especially with regard to dendrons, we have frequently seen fascicles of horizontal appendages (Fig. 191, ñ), an arrangement explainable by our mechanism of reciprocal chemotaxis.[198]

6. Neurotropic sources* are created relatively late in the retina. Their presence must be invoked to explain the transformation from the phase of disorientation of the perikaryon and its outgrowths to that of their alignment and concentric organization. The appearance of these orienting influences always coincides with the formation of the visual cell bodies and with the alignment of the feet or deep ends of the latter at the level of the future external plexiform zone. It does not seem too speculative therefore to imagine that the required substances may be liberated by the inferior ends of the cones and rods. We do not completely exclude the possibility that the external tufts of the bipolar rod cells may function in the elaboration of nutritive and orienting enzymes. Quite convincing proof of the effectiveness of this process of neuronal attraction and regularization, as we have said above, is seen in the arcs of rectification of the strayed axons and the unusual detours of the wandered dendrons.

7. All those excessively dislocated processes which, during the 15 days after birth, do not succeed in traveling towards the region of their normal termination are probably condemned to destruction. Supernumary outgrowths would share the same fate. This annihilation would take place by the progressive atrophy of useless appendages, which become paler and thinner, especially at the corrosion

---

*Although we have already said it elsewhere, we repeat again that the neurotropic concept merely represents a working hypothesis. The action of orienting chemical substances could be replaced by a physical explanation, e.g., by invoking neuronal movements caused by differences in electrical potential or by other mechanisms impossible to foresee now. What is essential to note is that at the end of the phase of initial disorientation a new condition appears which, by its diffuse *activity, renders possible the rectification of some developmental errors. (Note for the French edition.)*

points of the terminal end. We do not reject the possibility of phenomena of *autotomy,* similar to that found in the terminal balls and
rings of regenerated nerve sprouts [198] and in wounds of the central
nervous system.[187] When an axon of an almost mature cell (axis-
cylinder of ganglion cells) strays and becomes lost in the posterior
zones (perforating fibers of Tello), it is very likely that not only the
axon, but also the cell of origin as well, undergoes irreversible degeneration. From which it follows (as we have suggested many times
in our previous works) that during development the initial contingent
of nerve cells undergoes losses of some importance as a consequence
of unavoidable mechanical incidents and the unforeseen straying of
some neurons and axons.

To anticipate insurmountable mechanical obstacles and adverse
contingencies of all kinds, an overproduction of nerve branches (not
of axons) and of dendrons would have to occur during development.
For the same purpose there may be a superabundance of germinal
cells and even of typical neuroblasts. However we lack sufficient objective data relative to this point.

We must therefore acknowledge that during neurogenesis there
is a kind of competitive struggle among the outgrowths (and perhaps
even among the nerve cells) for space and nutrition. The victorious
neurons, dendrons and nerve branches would be those most advan-
tageously established *ab initio,* with regard to nutritive and neurotropic sources, as well as in relation to the neurons with which they
must establish dynamic relations. They would have the privilege of
attaining the adult phase and of developing stable dynamic connections. However, it is important not to exaggerate, as do certain embryologists, the extent and the importance of the cellular competition
to the point of likening it to the Darwinian struggle which has been
rigorously proved for certain organisms.

Therefore, even though it may be very rash to speak categorically
and impossible to quantify this delicate point, we consider it extremely likely, thanks to the prudent coordination of the other tissues, that
the immense majority of the neuroblasts survive to term and succeed
in collaborating with the normal structures of the adult central nervous system. We obviously omit those cases studied by the neuro-
pathologist and the psychiatrist in which mechanical or pathological

agents intervene during development and disturb or partially delay the developmental processes of the nervous system.

The action of light probably plays a very important role in the differentiation of the horizontal cells and of the external retinal layers in general. This point merits special study.

Chapter 21

DEVELOPMENT OF THE RETICULAR APPARATUS OF THE RETINA [189,190]

To CONCLUDE THIS exposition on retinal ontogenesis we will reproduce some data on the orientation and location of the Golgi apparatus in the retina of early embryos as well as newborn and young animals. The following figures are reproduced from preparations obtained by means of our uranium-formol formula.

Internal Reticular Apparatus in Very Early Chick Embryos. In sections of the optic vesicle of a 44 or 50 hour embryo, one can dis-

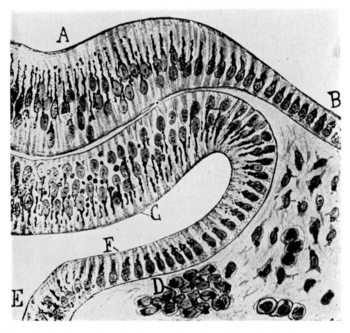

Fig. 195. Sagittal section of the ectodermal region destined to differentiate into the lens. Fifty hour chick embryo. Uranium-formol method. A) epithelial rudiment of the lens; C) anterior rudiment of the ocular vesicle (rudiment of the retina); posterior membrane which is destined to form the pigment layer of the retina.

tinctly see the rudiment of the retina as well as the cutaneous epithelial thickening from which the crystalline lens will develop (Fig. 195). If one observes the lenticular rudiment, he will be struck by the notable elongation of its epithelial cells, by the deep position of its nuclei, and especially by the superficial location of the Golgi apparatus, which is usually arranged in nearly parallel varicose bundles or trabeculae. These bundles, stained intensely by silver, begin beside the nucleus and are prolonged frontally without reaching the external epithelial pole. Towards the back and along the sides, the lenticular thickening is composed of successively shorter cells, provided with Golgi apparatuses that become progressively shorter and more compact up to the cutaneous margin (which does not take part at all in the production of the crystalline lens) (Fig. 195, B).

As is known, the embryonic retina, an anterior prolongation or diverticulum of the forebrain vesicle, is composed of two leaves, *the anterior leaf* (C) which gives rise to the neural layers of the visual membrane and the *posterior leaf* (F) which later forms the retinal pigment layer. Between these leaves there is a crevice which gradually disappears.

Let us now note an interesting fact: the anterior wall of the retinal vesicle now possesses elongated elements, among which certain radial cells predominate (the future epithelial cells?). These cells have a funicular Golgi apparatus located at their deep pole. Since this pole corresponds ontogenetically to the cellular portion which looked out upon the external world, before the fusion of the margins of the neural canal, i.e., the superficial portion of the embryo, it follows that, during the earliest phases of the ontogenetic development of the retina and of the nervous system in general the reticular apparatus of Golgi always occupies the cellular pole or segment which looks out upon the external world (our "worldly" pole). Obviously, as the neuronal elements are transformed and migrate from the initial layer the position of the pole which supports the reticular apparatus will change orientation gradually while simultaneously undergoing important structural additions and complications. Thanks to these alterations, this network succeeds in surrounding the entire contour of the nucleus and, as is well-known, invades a great part of the protoplasmic mass, excepting the axon or neurite and the secondary dendritic prolongations.

Retina of Young Mammals. The afore-mentioned primordial orientation of the Golgi apparatus is still maintained in great part in the retina of newborn or young animals, e.g., in the 15 to 20 day old cat (Fig. 196). But, disregarding this orientation, let us note the arrangement of the afore-mentioned intraprotoplasmic network in the various young retinal cells.

As we demonstrated in 1908 by a special impregnation formula with a formol-acetone base, the *ganglion cells* possess a robust Golgi apparatus preferentially located above the nucleus. Its trabeculae sometimes penetrate into the site of origin of the dendrons (12 day old dog).*

This apparatus is always clearly seen in the spongioblasts, the bipolar cells, and the horizontal neurons, in all of which it is located beside the worldly pole. In the spongioblasts it is occasionally beneath the nucleus at the origin of the trunk (Fig. 196, B). In general, in the elongated cells (bipolar cells, spongioblasts, epithelial cells) this reticular apparatus appears considerably simplified, being reduced to strings which extend the length of the external or cellulopetal process. In the horizontal cells the Golgi network widens and becomes complex; it lies above the nucleus (Fig. 196, E). Finally, in the cones and rods it is broken up into unconnected filaments, parallel to the processes, and resides preferentially in the supranuclear prolongation [188] (Fig. 196, F). Note that in the still undifferentiated elements located beneath the external limiting membrane (external half of the external granular zone) the said apparatus is absent or else it appears represented by fine disseminated granules. Certain monopolar cells, probably embryonic visual cones (Fig. 196, G), located beneath the basal membrane exhibit a dense clump in the external outgrowth which undoubtedly represents an undifferentiated endocellular apparatus.

In general, the undifferentiated elements not far beyond the germinal phase do not possess any Golgi apparatus but show some dis-

---

The reader will find an illustration of the Golgi apparatus of the ganglion cells of the 12 day old dog in Volume II, page 321, of our "Histologie du Système Nerveux." [185]

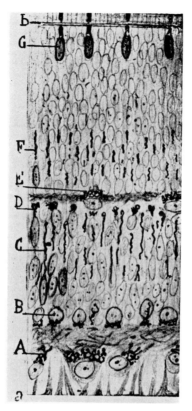

Fig. 196.   Golgi apparatus of the retinal neurons of a 20 day old cat. Note that the layer of rods and cones is not yet differentiated A) Ganglion cells; B, D) amacrine cells; C) bipolar cells; E) horizontal cells; F) cell bodies of the visual cells; G) cones; a, b) limiting membranes.

seminated granules from which this apparatus is probably construct-ed. This point requires more thorough observations, however.

We do not yet have precise observations relative to the adult retina. We presume that the Golgi reticulum of adult retinal cells will appear more or less fragmented as in other fully-developed nerve centers.

REFERENCES

EXPLANATORY NOTE FOR REFERENCES

The translator has checked and corrected every bibliographical reference at the National Library of Medicine in Washington, D. C. The corrected references, including full title, author's name, and inclusive pagination, are listed alphabetically by author, as prescribed by modern scientific usage. References marked with an asterisk (*) were not found in the National Medical Library, either because the volume is not in the library or because the original reference is too inaccurate to permit the article to be located. Some references not obtainable in the library were found in the bibliography of the following two books:

1. Polyak, S. The Vertebrate Visual System. Edited by H. Klüver. Chicago, University of Chicago Press, 1957.
2. Kappers, C. U. Ariëns, G. C. Huber, and E. C. Crosby. The Evolution of the Nervous System in Invertebrates, Vertebrates and Man. 2 volumes. New York, The Macmillan Co., 1936.

Those references found in Polyak's bibliography are marked with a dagger (†) and those in Kappers, Huber and Crosby are marked with a double dagger (‡).

I have placed in brackets the text page on which the reference is mentioned.

REFERENCES

1. Andriezen, W. L. The neuroglia elements in the human brain. Brit. M. J., 227-230, July 29, 1893. [330]
2. Aoyagi, T. Zur Histologie des N. phrenicus, des Zwerchfells und der motorischen Nervenendigung in demselben. Mitth. a. d. med. Fac. d. k.-jap. Univ., Tokio, 10:233, 1912. [213]
3. Athias, M. Recherches sur l'histogénèse du carvelet. J. de l'anat. et physiol., Par., 33:372-404, 1897. [295, 297]
4. Babuchin, A. Beiträge zur Entwicklung des Auges, besonders der Retina. Würzb naturwiss. Ztschr., 4:71, 1863-64† [354]

5. Balfour, F. M. A treatise on comparative embryology. London, Macmillan & Co., 2 volumes, 1880-81. [5]

6. Beard, J. The development of the peripherical nervous system in vertebrates. Part I.-Elasmobranchii and Aves. *Quart. J. micr. Sc., Lond.*, 29:153-234, 1888. [5]

7. Beard, J. The histogenesis of nerve. *Anat. Anz.*, 7:290-302, 1892. [5]

8. Bechterew, W. Ueber die hinteren Nervenwurzeln, ihre Endigung in der grauen Substanz des Rückenmarks und ihre centrale Fortsetzung im letzteren. *Arch. f. Anat. u. Physiol., Leipz. Anat. Abth.*, 126-136, 1887. [238]

9. Bellonci, G. Contribution à l'histogenèse de la couche moléculaire interne de la rétine. *Arch. ital. de biol., Turin*, 3:196-197, 1883. [354]

10. Bergmann. *Ztschr. f. rat. Med.*, Vol. 8.* [264]

11. Besser, L. Zur Histogenese der nervösen Elementartheile in den Cerebralorganen des neugeborenen Menschen. *Arch. f. path. Anat. u. Physiol.*, 36:305-334, 1866. [325]

12. Besta, C. Ricerche intorno alla genesi ed al modo di formazione della cellula nervosa nel midollo spinale e nella protuberanza del pollo. *Riv. sper. di freniat., Reggio-Emilia*, 30:96-119, 1904. [76]

13. Besta, C. Ricerche intorno al modo con cui si stabiliscono i rapporti mutui tra gli elementi nervosi embrionali e sulla formazioni della reticulo interno della cellula nervosa. *Riv. sper. di freniat., Reggio-Emilia*, 30:633-647, 1904. [76]

14. Bethe, A. Allgemeine Anatomie und Physiologie des Nervensystems. Leipzig, C. Thieme, 1903. [6]

15. Boeke, J. Ueber eine aus marklosen Fasern hervorgehende zweite Art von hypolemmalen Nervendplatten bei den quergestreiften Muskelfasern der Vertebraten. *Anat. Anz.*, 35:481-484, 1910. [213]

16. Boeke, J. Beiträge zur Kenntnis der motorischen Nervenendigungen. *Internat. Monatschr. f. Anat. u. Physiol., Leipz.*, 28:377-443, 1911. [213]

17. Boeke, J. Über die Regenerationserscheinungen bei der Verheilung von motorischen mit sensiblen Nervenfasern. *Anat. Anz.*, 43:366-378, 1913. [118]

18. Boeke, J. and J. G. Dusser de Barenne. The sympathetic innervation of the cross-striated muscle fibers of vertebrates. *Kon.*

Akad. v. Wetensch. te Amsterdam, Proc. sect. sc., 21:1227, 1919. [213]

19. Boll, F. Die Histiologie und Histiogenese der nervösen Central-organe. *Arch. f. Psychiatr., Berl.*, 4:1-138, 1873-74. [325]

20. Bourckhardt, K. R. Histologische Untersuchugen am Rücken-mark der Tritonen. *Arch. f. mikr. Anat., Bonn*, 34:131-156, 1889. [329]

21. Brock, G. Untersuchungen über die Entwicklung der Neuro-fibrillen des Schweinefötus. *Monatschr. f. Psychiat. u. Neu-rol.*, 18:467-480, 1905. [77]

22. Buchner. Die chemische Reizbarkeit der Leukocyten und deren Beziehung zur Entzündung und Eiterung. *Berl. klin. Wchnschr.*, 27:1084-1089, 1890. [362]

23. Calleja, C. Histogénesis de los centros nerviosos. *Doctoral thesis*, 1896* [370]

24. Cameron, J. The histogenesis of nerve fibers: a cytologic study of the embryonic cell-nucleus. *J. Anat. & Physiol., Lond.*, 41:8-29, 1906-07. [81]

25. De Castro, F. Nota sobre algunas terminaciones aberrantes de fibras trepadoras estudiadas en el cerebelo del perro joven. *Trab. Lab. Invest. biol., Univ., Madr.*, 18:199-206, 1920. [315]

26. Chievitz, J. H. Die Area und Fovea centralis retinae beim menschlichen Foetus. *Internat. Monatschr. f. Anat. u. Phy-siol., Leipz.*, 4:201-226, 1887. [354, 358]

27. Denissenko, G. Zur Frage über den Bau der Kleinhirnrinde bei verschiedenen Klassen von Wirbeltieren. *Arch. f. mikr. Anat., Bonn*, 14:203-242, 1877. [260]

28. Dogiel, A. S. Die Retina der Vögel. *Arch. f. mikr. Anat., Bonn*, 44:622-648, 1895. [374]

29. Dogiel, A. S. Ueber die Nervenendigungen in den Geschmacks-Endknospen der Ganoideen. *Arch. f. mikr. Anat., Bonn*, 49:769-790, 1897. [185]

30. Dohrn, A. Studien zur Urgeschichte des Wirbelthierkörpers Ganglienzellen und Nervenfasern. *Mitth. a. d. zool. Station zu Neapel, Leipz.*, 1891.* [5]

31. Dohrn, A. Studien zur Urgeschichte des Wirbeltierkörpers 25. Der Trochlearis. *Mitth. a. d. zool. Station zu Neapel, Leipz.*, Vol. 18, 1907.* [114]

32. Dustin, A. P. Le rôle des tropismes et de l'odogenèse dans la

régénération du système nerveux. *Arch. de biol., Par.,* 25: 269-388, 1910. [121]

33. Duval, M. Recherches sur le sinus rhomboïdal des oiseaux: sur son développement et sur la névroglie périépendymaire. *J. de l'anat. et physiol., Par.,* 13:1-38, 1877. [329]

34. Duval, M. Sur le sinus rhomboïdal des oiseaux. *Gaz. méd. de Par., n.°* 34.* [329]

35. Edinger, L. Vergleichend-entwicklungsgeschichtliche und anatomische Studien im Bereiche des Centralnervensystems. 2) Über die Fortsetzung der hinteren Rückenmarkswurzeln zum Gehirn. *Anat. Anz.,* 4:121-128, 1889. [238]

36. Edinger, L. Zwölf Vorlesungen über den Bau der nervösen Centralorgane. Second edition. Leipzig, Vogel, 1889. [272, 336]

37. Eichorst, H. Ueber die Entwickelung des menschlichen Rückenmarkes und seiner Formelmente. *Arch. f. path. Anat., Berl.,* 64:425-475, 1875. [249, 325]

38. Estable, C. Notes sur la structure comparative de l'écorce cérébelleuse, et dérivées physiologiques possibles. *Trab. Lab. Invest. biol., Univ. Madr.,* 21:169-256, 1923. [318]

39. Exner, S. Zur Kenntniss vom feineren Baue der Grosshirnrinde. *Sitzungsb. d. k. Akad. d. Wissensch., Wien,* 83:151-167, 1881. [336]

40. Falzacapa. Genesi della cellula specifica nervosa e intima struttura del sistema centrale nervoso degli uccelli. *Boll. d. Soc. di nat. in Napoli, ser. 1, Vol. 2,* 1888.* [246, 329]

41. Forel, A. Einige hirnanatomische Betrachtungen und Ergebnisse. *Arch. F. Psychiat., Berl.,* 18:162-198, 1887. [286]

42. Fragnito, O. Su la genesi delle fibre nervose centrali e il loro rapporto con le cellule ganglionari. *Ann. di nevrol.,* 23:1-11, 1905. [77]

43. Fragnito, O. La prima apparizione delle neurofibrille nelle cellule spinali dei vertebrati. Comunicazione al V Congresso intern. di Psicologia in Roma. *Ann. di Nevrol.,* 23:436-442, 1905. [45, 77]

44. Fragnito, O. Le fibrille et la sostanza fibrillogena nelle cellule ganglionari dei vertebrati. *Ann. di nevrol.,* 25:209-224, 1907. [77]

45. Froriep, A. Über die Einstülpung der Augenblase, *Arch. f. mikr. Anat., Bonn,* 66:1-11, 1905. [56]

46. Gabritchewsky, G. Sur les propriétés chimiotactiques des leucocytes. *Ann. de l'Inst. Pasteur, Par.*, 4:346-362, 1890. [362]

47. Gierke, H. Die Stutzsubstanz des Centralnervensystems. *Arch. f. mikr. Anat., Bonn, I Theil*, 25:441-553, 1885; *II Theil*, 26:129-228, 1885. [329]

48. Golgi, C. Sulla fina anatomia degli organi centrali del sistema nervoso. Milano, U. Hoepli. 1886. [246, 249, 329]

49. Gurwitsch, A. Die Histogenese der Schwann'schen Scheide. *Arch. F. Anat u. Physiol., Leipz., Anat. Abth.*, 85-94, 1900. [11]

50. Hadlich, H. Ueber varicöse Hypertrophie des Hauptnervenfortsatzes der grossen ganglienzellen der Kleinhirnrinde. *Arch. f. path. Anat., Berl.*, 46:218-222, 1869. [261]

51. Harrison, R. G. Über die Histogenese des periphären Nervensystems bei Salmo salar. *Arch. f. mikr. Anat., Bonn*, 57:354-445, 1901. [13]

52. Harrison, R. G. Neue Versuche über die Entwicklung der periphärischen Nerven der Wirebelthiere. *Sitzungsb. d. medenhein. Gesellsch. nat u. Heilk. zu Bonn.* 1904.* [11]

53. Harrison, R. G. The outgrowth of the nerve fiber as a mode of protoplasmic movement. *J. Exp. Zool.*, 9:787-848, 1910. [397, 398]

54. Heidenhain, M. Plasma und Zelle. In: Bardeleben, Handb. d. Anat., Jena, G. Fischer, 1911.† [198]

55. Heidenhain, M. Über die Sinnesfelder und die Geschmacksknospen der Papilla foliata des Kaninchens. Beiträge zur Teilkörpertheorie III. *Archiv. f. mikr. Anat., Bonn*, 85:365-479, 1914. [185]

56. Heidenhain, M. Ueber die Geschmacksknospen als Objekt einer allgemeine Theorie der Organisation. *München. med. Wchnschr.*, 65:579-581, 1918. [185]

57. Held, H. Die Entstehung der Neurofibrillen. *Neurol. Centralbl., Leipz.*, 24:706-710, 1905. [74, 77]

58. Held, H. Zur Histogenese der Nervenleitung. X^{te} Versamml. d. Anat. Gesellsch. zu Rostock. *Anat. Anz., Jena*, 28: 560, 1906. [77, 384]

59. Held, H. Zur Histogenese der Nervenleitung. *Anat. Anz.*, 29: 185-205, 1906. [74]

60. Held, H. Kritische Bemerkungen zu der Verteidigung der Neu-

roblasten und der Neuronentheorie durch R. Cajal. *Anat. Anz.*, 30:369-391, 1907. [71]

61. Held, H. Untersuchungen über den feineren Bau des Ohrlabyrinthes der Wirbelthiere. II. Zur Entwicklungsgeschichte des Cortischen Organs und der Macula acustica bei Säugethieren und Vögeln. *Abhandl. d. math.-phys. Cl. d. K. sächs. Gesellsch. d. Wissensch.*, 14:339, 1909.‡ [173]

62. Held, H. Die Entwicklung des Nervengewebes bei den Wirbelthieren. Leipzig, A. Barth, 1909.‡ [178]

63. Henle, J. Handbuch der Nervenlehre des Menschen. Vol. 3 of Handbuch der systematischen Anatomie des Menschen. Braunschweig, Vieweg, 1867-79, p. 267. [260, 264]

64. Hensen. Die Entwickelungsmechanik der Nervenbahnen, etcétera. Kiel u. Leipzig, 1903.* [76]

65. His, W. Untersuchungen über die erste Anlarge des Wirbelthierleibes. Leipzig, 1868.* [359]

66. His W. Zur Geschichte des menschlichen Rückenmarkes und der Nervenwurzeln. *Abhandl. dd. math.-phys. Cl. d. K. sächs. Gesellsch. d. Wissensch.*, 13:477, 1887. [286, 362]

67. His, W. Die Entwickelung der ersten Nervenbahnen beim menschlichen Embryo. *Arch. f. Anai. u. Physiol., Leipz., Anat. Abth.*, 368-378, 1887. [286]

68. His, W. Zur Geschichte des Gehirns sowie der centralen und peripherischen Nervenbahnen beim menschlichen Embryo. *Abhandl. d. math.-phys. Cl. d. K. sächs. Gesellsch. d. Wissensch.*, 14:339, 1888.† [362]

69. His, W. Die Neuroblasten und deren Entstehung im embryonalen Mark. *Arch. f. Anat. u. physiol., Leipz., Anat. Abth.*, 249-300, 1889. [217, 358]

70. His, W. Die Neuroblasten und deren Entstehung im embryonalen Mark. *Abhandl. d. math.-phys Cl d. k. sächs. Gesellsch. d. Wissensch.*, 15:311, 1890. [11, 217, 325]

71. His, W. Histogenese und Zusammenhang der Nervenelemente. *Arch. f. Anat. u. Physiol., Leipz., Anat. Abth, supp.*, 95-119, 1890. [84]

72. Kahler. Lehrbuch der Gewebelehre, 1888.* [238]

73. Kallius, E. Untersuchungen über die Netzhaut der Saügetiere. *Anat. Hefte, Wiesb.*, 3:527-582, 1894. [374]

74. Kappers. Der Geschmack, perifer und central. Zugleich eine

Skizze der phylogenetischen Veränderungen in den sensiblen VII, IX und X Wurzeln. *Fol. Psychiat. en neurolog., Balden,* 18:82-138, 1914. [185]

75. Kerr, G. On some points in the early development of motor nerve trunks and myotomes in Lepidosiren paradoxa (Fitz.). *Tr. Roy. Soc. Edin.,* 41:119-128, 1904. [12]

76. Koganeī, J. Untersuchungen uber die Histiogenese der Retina. *Arch. f. mikr. Anat., Bonn,* 23:335-357, 1884. [354]

77. Kohn, A. Über die Entwicklung des sympathischen Nervensystems der Säugetiere. *Arch. f. mikr. Anat., Bonn,* 70:266-317, 1907. [107]

78. Kölliker, A. v. Handbuch der Gewebelehre des Menschen fur Aerzte und Studirende. First edition. Leipzig, Engelmann, 1852. [336]

79. Kölliker, A. v. Embryologie; ou, Traité complet du développement de l'homme et des animaux supérieurs. Tr. by A. Schneider. Paris, Reinwald, 1882. [325, 358]

80. Kölliker, A. v. Histologische Mitteilungen. *Sitzungsb. d. Wurzb. phys-med. Gesellsch.,* 166-169, 1889. [286, 288, 329]

81. Kölliker, A. v. Uber den feineren Bau des Rückenmarkes. *Sitzungsb. d. Würzb. phys.-med. Gesellsch.,* 44-56, 1890. [288]

82. Kölliker, A. v. Das Kleinhirn. *Ztschr. f. wissensch. Zool.,* Vol. 49, 1890. [288]

83. Kölliker, A. v. Zur feineren Anatomie des centralen Nervensystems. Das Rückenmark. *Ztschr. f. wissensch Zool.,* Vol 51. [330]

84. Kölliker, A. v. Die Entwicklung der Elemente des Nervensystems. *Ztschr. f. wissensch. Zool.,* 82:1-38, 1905. [10, 12, 329]

85. Kolmer, W. Beiträge zur Kenntnis des feineren Baues des Gehörorgans mit besonderer Berücksichtigung der Haussäugetiere. *Arch. f. mikr. Anat., Bonn,* 70:695-767, 1907. [181]

86. Kolmer, W. Die Entwickelung der anatomischen Kenntnisse über das Labyrinth von Corti bis zur neuester Zeit. *Ztschr. f. Sonderabhandl. a. Pollitzer Geschichte der Ohrenheilkunde, Vol. 2,* 1910.* [173]

87. Koschewnikoff, A. Axencylinderfortsatz der Nervenzellen im

kleinen Hirn des Kalbes. *Arch. f. mikr. Anat.*, Bonn, 5:332-333, 1869. [261]

88. Lachi, P. Contributo alla istogenesi della nevroglia nel midollo spinale del pollo. *Atti. d. Soc. tosc. di sc. nat. Mem.*, Pisa, 11:267-310, 1891. [217, 329]

89. Lahousse, E. La cellule nerveuse et la névroglie. *Anat. Anz.*, 1: 114-116, 1886. [329]

90. Langley, J. N. The Autonomic Nervous System. Cambridge, W. Heffer & Sons, Ltd., 1921. [211]

91. La Pegna, E. Su la genesi ed i rapporti reciproci degli elementi nervosi nel midollo spinale di pollo. *Ann. di. nevrol.*, 22: 543-556, 1904. [77]

92. Lenhossék, M. v. Untersuchungen über Entwicklung der Markscheiden und den Faserverlauf in Rückenmark der Maus. *Arch. f. mikr. Anat.*, Bonn, 33:71-124, 1889. [240]

93. Lenhossék, M. v. Ueber den Verlauf der Hinterwurzeln im Rückenmark. *Arch f. mikr. Anat.*, Bonn, 34:157-196, 1889. [238]

94. Lenhossék, M. v. Über Nervenfasern in den hinteren Wurzeln, welche aus dem Vorderhorn entspringen. *Anat. Anz.*, 5: 360-362, 1890. [221]

95. Lenhossék, M. v. Zur ersten Entstehung der Nervenzellen und Nervenfasern beim Vogelembryo. *Mitth. a. d. anat. Inst. im Vasalianum in Basel*, 1890.* [325]

96. Lenhossék, M. v. Die Entwickelung der Ganglienanlagen bei dem menschlichen Embryo. *Arch. f. Anat. u. Physiol., Leipz., Anat. Abth.*, 1-25, 1891. [325]

97. Lenhossék, M. v. Zur Kenntniss der ersten Entstehung der Nervenzellen und Nervenfasern beim Vogelembryo. *Verhandl. d. X. internat. med Cong., Berl. Abth.*, 2:115-124, 1891. [13, 329, 358]

98. Lenhossék, M. v. Der feinere Bau und die Nervenendigungen der Geschmacksknospen. *Anat. Anz.*, 8:121-127, 1893. [185]

99. Lenhossék, M. v. Die Nervenendigungen im Gehörorgan. *Verhandl. d. anat. Gessellsch., Jena*, 7:199-200, 1893. [181]

100. Lenhossék, M. v. Zur Frage nach der Entwickelung der peripherischen Nervenfasern. *Anat. Anz.*, 28:287-297, 1906. [13]

101. Levi, G. Connessioni e struttura degli elementi nervosi svilup-

pati fuori dell'organismo. *Atti. d. r. Accad. d. Lincei, sér.* 5, *12*:142, 1917. [121]

102. Lissauer, H. Beitrag zum Faserverlauf im Hinterhorn des menschlichen Rückenmarks und zum Verhalten desselben bei Tabes dorsalis. *Arch. f. Psychiat., Berl., 17*:377-438, 1886. [238]

103. Lorente de Nó, R. La regeneración de la medula espinal in las larvas de batracio. *Trab. Lab. Invest. biol., Univ. Madr., 19*: 147-183, 1921. [141]

104. Lorente de Nó, R. Études sur le cerveau postérieur. III. Sur les connexions extracérébelleuses des fascicules afférents au cerveau, et sur la fonction de cet organe. *Trab. Lab Invest. biol., Univ. Madr., 22*:51-65, 1924. [297]

105. Löwe, L. Die Histogenese der Retina nebst vergleichenden Bemerkungen über die Histogenese des Central-Nervensystems. *Arch. f. mikr. Anat., Bonn, 15*:596-629, 1878. [354]

106. Löwe, L. Beitraege zur Anatomie und zur Entwickelungsgeschichte des Nervensystems der saeugethiere und des menschen. Bd. I Die Morphogenesis des centralen Nervensystems. Berlin, Denicke, 1880. [325, 329]

107. Lugaro, E. Ueber die Histogenese der Körner der Kleinhirnrinde. *Anat. Anz., 9*:710-713, 1894. [370]

108. Lugaro, E. Sulla istogenesi dei granuli della corteccia cerebellare. *Monitore zool. ital., 5*:152-158, 1894. [292]

109. Lugaro, E. Sui metodi di dimostrazione della neurofibrille. *Riv. di patol. nerv. e mentale, 9*:549-550, 1904. [12]

110. Magini, J. Nouvelles recherches histologiques sur le cerveau du foetus. *Arch. ital. de biol., Turin, 10*:384-387, 1888. [246, 325, 329]

111. Mall, F. Histogenesis of the retina in Amblystoma and Necturus. *J. Morphol., 8*:415-432, 1893. [364]

112. Marinesco, G. Essai de biocytoneurologie au moyen de l'ultramicroscope. *Nouv. Iconogr. de la Salpêtrière, 25*:193-222, 1912. [121]

113. Marinesco, G. Recherches anatomo-cliniques sur les névromes d'amputations douloureux. Nouvelles contributions à l'étude de la régéneration nerveuse et du neurotropisme. *Phil. Tr., Lond., ser. B, 209*:224-304, 1920. [121, 149]

114. Marinesco, G. and J. Minea. Essai de culture des ganglions spinaux de mammifères in vitro. *Anat. Anz.,* *42*:161-176, 1912. [397]

115. Martinotti, C. Su alcuni miglioramenti della tecnica della reazione al nitrato d'argento nel centri nervosi per ottenerla su pezzi di grandi dimensioni. *Ann. di freniat., Torino,* *1*:26-36, 1889. [271]

116. Martinotti, C. Beitrag zum Studium der Hirnrinde und dem Centralursprung der Nerven. *Internat. Monatschr. f. Anat. u. Physiol., Leipz.,* *7*:69-89, 1890. [336]

117. Massart, J. and C. Bordet. Le chimiotaxisme des leucocytes et l'infection microbienne. *Ann. de l'Inst. Pasteur, Par.,* *5*: 417-444, 1891. [362]

118. Merk. Die Mitosen im Centralnervensysteme. *Denkschr. d. k. Akad. d. Wissensch., Wien, Vol.* *53*, 1887. [329]

119. Metchnikoff, E. Lectures on the comparative pathology of inflammation. Tr. by F. A. Starling and E. H. Starling. London, Paul, Trench, Trübner, 1893. [362]

120. Müller, W. Über die Stammesentwicklung des Sehorgans der Wirbelthiere. *Beitr. z. Anat. u. Physiol. als Festgabe C. Ludwig, Leipz.,* p. 76, 1874. [359]

121. Nageotte, J. Étude sur la greffe des ganglions rachidiens: variations et tropismes du neurone sensitif. *Anat. Anz.,* *31*:225-245, 1907. [115]

122. Nageotte, J. Action des métaux et de divers autres facteurs sur la dégénération des nerfs en survie. *Compt. rend Soc. de biol., Par.,* *69*:556-559, 1910. [140]

123. Nageotte, J. Le processus de la cicatrisation des nerfs. Généralités, faits particuliers. *Rev. neurol., Par.,* *27*:505-521, 1915. [119]

124. Nageotte, J. Substance collagène et névroglie dans la cicatrisation des nerfs. *Comp. rend. Soc. de biol., Par.,* *79*:322-327, 1916. [119]

125. Nageotte, J. Sur la greffe des tissus morts, etc. *Compt. rend. Soc. de biol., Par.,* *79*:883, 940, 1031, 1121.* [119]

126. Nageotte, J. Étude expérimentale de la cicatrisation des nerfs. *Lyon Chir.,* *15*:245-292, 1918. [119]

127. Nageotte, J. Rapport des neurites avec les tissus dans la cornée. *Compt. rend. Soc. de biol., Par.,* *172*:94-96, 1921. [119, 120]

128. Nageotte, J. and Guyon. Aptitudes néoplastiques de la névroglie périphérique greffée et non réinnervée, etc.* [119]

129. Neal, H. V. The development of the ventral nerves of Selachii. I. Spinal ventral nerves in Mark. Anniversary Vol. Art. 15, 1903.* [11]

130. Obersteiner, H. Eine partielle Kleinhirnatrophie; nebst Bemerkungen über den normalen Bau des Kleinhirnes *Allg. Ztschr. f. Psychiat., Berl.,* 27:74-85, 1870. [264]

131. Obersteiner, H. Der feinere Bau der Kleinhirnrinde bei Menschen und Tieren. *Biol. Centralbl.,* Vol. 3, No. 5, 1880.* [263]

132. Obersteiner, H. Anleitung beim Studium des Baues der nervösen Zentralorgane im gesunden und kranken Zustande. First edition. Leipzig, Deuticke, 1888. [135, 265, 272, 336]

133. Ogneff, J. Histiogenese der Retina. *Centralbl. f. d. med. Wissensch., Berl.,* 19:641-645, 1881. [354]

134. Oppenheim, H. Lehrbuch der Nervenkrankheiten für Arzte und Studierende. Sixth edition. Berlin, Karger, 1913. [185]

135. Ortin, L. and L. R. Arcaute. Procesos regenerativos del nervio óptico y retina con ocasión de injertos nerviosos. *Trab. Lab. Invest. biol. Univ. Madr.,* 11:239-254, 1913. [136, 394]

136. Paladino, G. De la continuation de la névroglie dans le squelette myélinique des fibres nerveuses et de la constitution pluricellulaire du cylinderaxe. *Arch. ital. de biol., Turin,* 19:26-32, 1893. [5]

137. Paton, S. The reactions of the vertebrate embryo to stimulation and the associated changes in the nervous system. *Mitth. a. d. zool. Station zu Neapel, Leipz.,* Vol. 18, 1907, H. ⅔.* [74]

138. Pfeffer, *Untersuch. a. d. bot. Inst. in Tübingen.* Vol. 1, p. 363.* [362]

139. Pighini. *Bibliogr. anat.,* 14:1904.* [77]

140. Popoff, S. Zur Frage über Histogenese der Kleinhirnrinde. *Biol. Centralbl.,* 15:745-752, 1895. [295, 297]

141. Popoff, S. Weiterer Beitrag zur Frage über Histogenese der Kleinhirnrinde. *Biol. Centralbl.,* 16:462-466, 1896. [295, 297]

142. Prenant, A. Traité d'histologie. Paris Schleicher Frères & Cie, 2 vols., 1904-11. [173]

143. Ramón y Cajal, P. El encéfalo de los reptiles. *Trab. Lab. histol. Zaragoza,* p. 30, 1891.† [292]

144. Ramón y Cajal, S. Estructura del cerebelo de las aves. *Rev. trim. Histol.*, May, 1888.* [253]

145. Ramón y Cajal, S. *Rev. trim. Histol.*, No. 2.* [256]

146. Ramón y Cajal, S. Sur la morphologie et les connexions des éléments de la rétine des oiseaux. *Anat. Anz.*, 4:111-121, 1889. [249]

147. Ramón y Cajal, S. Sur l'origine et la direction des prolonga-tions nerveuses de la couche moléculaire du cervelet. *Internat. Monatschr. f. Anat. u. Physiol., Leipz.*, 6:158-174, 1889. [256, 288]

148. Raymón y Cajal, S. Sobre las conexiones generales de los ele-mentos nerviosos. *Med. práct., Madrid*, No. 88, 1889.* [236]

149. Ramón y Cajal, S. Contribución al estudio de la médula espinal. *Rev. trim. Histol.*, March, 1889.* [255, 270, 288]

150. Ramón y Cajal, S. Sobre las fibras nerviosas de la capa granulos del cerebelo y evolución de los elementos cerebelosos. *Rev. trim. Histol.*, March, 1889.* [266]

151. Ramón y Cajal, S. *Revista trim. Histol. normal y patológica*, nums. 3 y 4, March, 1889.* [231]

152. Ramón y Cajal, S. Nuevas aplicaciones del método de Golgi. October, 1889.* [232, 249, 287]

153. Ramón y Cajal, S. Manual de Histología normal y técnica micrográfica. Valencia, Aguilar, 1889. [246]

154. Ramón y Cajal, S. Sur l'origine et les ramifications des fibres nerveuses de la moelle embryonnaire. *Anat. Anz.*, 5:85-95 and 111-119, 1890. [222, 231, 288]

155. Ramón y Cajal, S. Réponse à M. Golgi à propos des fibrilles collatérales de la moelle épinière, et de la structure générale de la substance grise. *Anat. Anz.*, 5:579-587, 1890. [243]

156. Ramón y Cajal, S. À quelle époque apparaissent les expansions des cellules nerveuses de la moelle épinière du poulet? *Anat. Anz.*, 5:631-639, 1890. [76, 217, 325, 358, 397]

157. Ramón y Cajal, S. Sur les fibres nerveuses de la couche gran-uleuse du cervelet et sur l'évolution des éléments cérébelleux. *Internat. Monatschr. f. Anat. u. Physiol., Leipz.*, 7:12-31, 1890. [253, 271, 275, 282, 297]

158. Ramón y Cajal, S. À propos de certains éléments bipolares du cervelet avec quelques détails nouveaux sur l'évolution des fibres cérébelleuses. *Internat. Monatschr. f. Anat. u. Physiol., Leipz.*, 7:447-468, 1890. [271]

159. Ramón y Cajal, S. Sobre la estructura de la médula espinal de los mamíferos. April 1890.* [288]

160. Ramón y Cajal, S. Sobre la terminación de los nervios y trá-queas en los músculos de las alas de los insectos. April 1890.* [287]

161. Ramón y Cajal, S. Sur la fine structure du lobe optique des oiseaux et sur l'origine reélle des nerfs optiques. *J. internat. d'anat. et physiol.*, 8:337, 1891.† [249, 255]

162. Ramón y Cajal, S. Sur la structure de l'écorce cérébrale de quelques mammifères. *La Cellule*, 7:125-178, 1891. [325, 341]

163. Ramón y Cajal, S. La rétine des vertébrés. *La Cellule*, 9:119-258, 1893. [51, 57, 84, 353]

164. Ramón y Cajal, S. Estructura de la corteza occipital inferior de los pequeños mamíferos, etc. 1893.* [325]

165. Ramón y Cajal, S. The Croonian Lecture. La fine structure des centres nerveux. *Proc. Roy. Soc. Lond.*, 444-468, 1894. [254]

166. Ramón y Cajal, S. Les nouvelles idées sur la structure du sys-tème nerveux chez l'homme et chez les vertébrés. Tr. by L. Azoulay. Paris, Reinwald, 1894. [292, 353, 370]

167. Ramón y Cajal, S. Apuntes para el estudio del bulbo requideo, cerebelo y origen de los nervios encefalicos. XVI. Nucleo del facial. *An. de Historia Natural.* Sesión del 6 de Febrero de 1895. p. 25.‡ [319]

168. Ramón y Cajal, S. Elementos de histología normal y de técnica micrográfica; para uso de estudiantes. Madrid, Moya, 1895. [353]

169. Ramón y Cajal, S. Nouvelles contributions à l'étude histologi-que de la rétine et à la question des anastomoses et des pro-longements protoplasmiques. *J. de l'anat. et physiol.*, Par., 32:481-543, 1896. [51, 57, 354, 364]

170. Ramón y Cajal, S. *Anat. Anz.*, 1897.* [13]

171. Ramón y Cajal, S. Las células de cilindro-eje corto de la capa molecular del cerebro. *Rev. trim. microgr.*, 2:105-127, 1897. [341]

172. Ramón y Cajal, S. Textura del sistema nervioso del hombre y vertebrados. Madrid, Moya, 2 vols., 1899-1904. [13, 292, 295, 297, 325, 341, 397]

173. Ramón y Cajal, S. Estudios sobre la corteza cerebral humana. *Rev. trim. microgr.*, *Vols. 4, 5 and 6*, 1899, 1900 and 1901. [341]

174. Ramón y Cajal S. Une méthode simple pour la coloration élective du réticulum protoplasmique et ses résultats dans les divers centres nerveux. Tr. by L. Azoulay. *Bibliogr. anat. 14*:1-93, 1904. [76, 201, 302, 304, 306, 316, 347]

175. Ramón y Cajal, S. Association de la méthode au nitrate d'argent réduit avec celle embryonnaire pour l'étude des foyers sensitifs et moteurs. *Trab. Lab. Invest. biol., Univ. Madr., 3*: 69-103, 1904. [37, 76, 181]

176. Ramón y Cajal, S. Contribution à l'étude de la structure des plaques motrices. *Trab. Lab. Invest. biol., Univ. Madr., 3*: 105-109, 1904. [201, 206]

177. Ramón y Cajal, S. Le réticule neurofibrillaire dans la rétine. Trab. *Lab. Invest. biol. Univ. Madr., 3*:201-229, 1904. [57]

178. Ramón y Cajal, S. Mécanisme de la régénérescence des nerfs. *Trab Lab. Invest. biol., Univ. Madr., 4*:123-218, 1905. [13, 64]

179. Ramón y Cajal, S. Genèse des fibres nerveuses de l'embryon et observations contraires à la théorie catenaire. *Trab. Lab. Invest. biol., Univ. Madr., 4*:219-284, 1905. [5, 82, 130, 143, 178]

180. Ramón y Cajal, S. Communication à la section anatomique du XV Congrès intern. de Médecine de Lisbonne. April 1906.* [77]

181. Ramón y Cajal, S. Die histogenetischen Beweise der Neuronentheorie von His und Forel. *Anat. Anz., 30*:113-144, 1907. [71]

182. Ramón y Cajal, S. Les métamorphoses précoces des neurofibrilles dans la dégénération et la régénération des nerfs. *Trab. Lab. Invest. biol., Univ. Madr., Vol. 5*, 1907.* [113]

183. Ramón y Cajal, S. Nouvelles observations sur l'évolution des neuroblasts, avec quelques remarques sur l'hypothése neurogénétique de Hensen-Held. *Anat. Anz., 32*:1-25 and 65-87, 1908. [71, 130, 354, 384, 394]

184. Ramón y Cajal, S. Terminación periférica del nervio acústico de las aves. *Trab. Lab. Invest. biol., Univ. Madr., 6*:161-176, 1908. [181, 394]

185. Ramón y Cajal, S. Histologie du système nerveux de l'homme et des vertébrés. Tr. by L. Azoulay. Paris, Maloine, 2 vols., 1909-11. [254, 257, 288, 318, 354, 404]

186. Ramón y Cajal, S. Algunas observaciones favorables a la hipóthesis neurotrópica. *Tram. Lab. Invest. biol., Univ. Madr.,* 8:63-134, 1910. [138, 150]

187. Ramón y Cajal, S. Los fenómenos precoces de la degeneración traumática de los cilindros-ejes del cerebro. *Trab. Lab. Invest. biol., Univ. Madr.,* 9:39-95, 1911. [400]

188. Ramón y Cajal, S. Fórmula de fijación para la demostración fácil del aparato de Golgi y apuntes sobre la disposición de dicho aparato en la retina, en las nervios y algunos estados patológicos. *Trab. Lab. Invest. biol., Univ. Madr.,* 10:209-220, 1912. [389, 404]

189. Ramón y Cajal, S. Algunas variaciones fisiológicas y patológicas del aparato reticular de Golgi. *Trab. Lab. Invest. biol., Univ. Madr.,* 12:127-227, 1914. [390, 402]

190. Ramón y Cajal, S. Consideraciones generales sobre la polarización ontogénica del aparato de Golgi. (Considérations générales sur la polarisation ontogénique de l'appareil de Golgi) *Boletín de la Soc. española de Biol.,* March 1915.* [402]

191. Ramón y Cajal, S. La desorientación inicial de las neuronas retinianas de axon corto. (Algunos hechos favorables a la concepción neurotrópica.) *Trab. Lab. Invest. biol., Univ. Madr.,* 17:65-86, 1919. [149, 380]

192. Ramón y Cajal, S. Acción neurotrópica de los epitelios (algunos detalles sobre el mecanismo genético de las ramificaciones nerviosas intraepiteliales, sensitivas y sensoriales). *Trab. Lab. Invest. biol., Univ. Madr.,* 17:181-228, 1919. [131, 144, 149]

193. Ramón y Cajal, S. Algunas observaciones contrarias a la hipótesis *syncytial* de la regeneración nerviosa y neurogénesis normal. *Trab. Lab. Invest. biol., Univ. Madr.,* 18:275-302, 1920. [117]

194. Ramón y Cajal, S. Une formule pour colorer dans les coupes les fibres amédullées et les terminaisons centrales et périphériques. *Trab. Lab. Invest. biol., Univ. Madr.,* 23:237-240, 1925. [206]

195. Ramón y Cajal, S. Quelques remarques sur les plaques motrices de la langue des mammifères. *Trab. Lab. Invest. biol., Univ. Madr.*, 23:245-254, 1925. [206]

196. Ramón y Cajal, S. Démonstration photographique de quelques phénomènes de la régénération des nerfs. *Trab. Lab. Invest. biol., Univ. Madr.*, 24:191-213, 1926. [126]

197. Ramón y Cajal, S. Sur les fibres mousseuses et quelques points douteux de la texture de l'écorce cérébelleuse. *Trab. Lab. Invest. biol., Univ. Madr.*, 24:215-251, 1926. [302, 304]

198. Ramon y Cajal, S. Degeneration and regeneration of the nervous system. Tr. and ed. by R. M. May. London, Oxford Univ. Press, 2 vols., 1928. [116, 117, 127, 136, 140, 149, 214, 397, 399, 400]

199. Ranvier, L. De la névroglie. *Arch. de physiol. norm. et path., Par., ser. 3*, 1:177-185, 1883. [249, 329]

200. Rauber, A. Die Kerntheilungsfiguren im Medullarrohr der Wirbelthiere. *Arch. f. mikr. Anat., Bonn*, 26:622-644, 1886. [329]

201. Renaut, J. Recherches sur les centres nerveux amyéliniques. *Arch. de physiol. norm. et path., Par., ser. 2.*, 9:593-638, 1882. [249]

202. Retzius, G. Das Gehörorgan der Wirbelthiere; morphologisch-histologische Studien. Stockholm, Sanson and Willin, 2 vols., 1881-84. [181]

203. Retzius, G. Kleinere Mittheilunge von dem Gebiete der Nervenhistologie. *Biol. Untersuch., Stockholm*, 4:57-66, 1892.

204. Retzius, G. *Biol. Untersuch., Stockholm. Vol. 4*, 1892. [185]

205. Retzius, G. Die Cajal'schen Zellen der Grosshirnrinde beim Menschen und bei Säugethieren. *Biol. Untersuch., Stockholm*, 5:1-8, 1893. [341, 343]

206. Retzius, G. *Biol. Untersuch., Stockholm, Vol. 5*, 1893. [185]

207. Retzius, G. Weitere Beiträge zur Kentniss der Cajal'schen Zellen der Grosshirnrinde des Menschen. *Biol. Untersuch., Stockholm*, 6:29-36, 1894. [341]

208. Retzius, G. Zur Kenntniss der Entwicklung der Elemente des Rückenmarks von Anguis fragilis. *Biol. Untersuch., Stockholm*, 8:109-113, 1898. [13]

209. Rossbach and Sehrwald. Ueber d. Lymphwege des Gehirns. *Centralbl. f. d. med. Wissensch.*, No. 47, 1888.* [232, 272]

210. Schaper, A. Einige kritische Bemerkungen zu Lugaro's Aufsatz: "Ueber die Histogeneses der Körner der Kleinhirnrinde." *Anat. Anz.*, 10:422-426, 1895. [297, 370]

211. Schültze, O. Beiträge zur Histogenese des Nervensystems. I. Über die multizelluläre Entstehung der peripheren sensiblen Nervenfaser und das Vorhandensein eines allgemeinen End-netzes sensibler Neuroblasten bei Amphibien larven. *Arch. f. mikr. Anat., Bonn*, 66:41-115, 1905. [8]

212. Schültze, O. Weiteres zur Entwickelung der peripheren Nerven mit Berücksichtigung der Regenerationsfrage nach Nerven-verletzungen. *Verhandl. d. phys.-med. Gesellsch. in Würzb.*, 37:267-296, 1905. [8]

213. Schwalbe, G. A. Lehrbuch der Neurologie. Vol. 6 of Hoff-mann's Lehrbuch der Anatomie des Menschen. Erlangen, E. Besold, 1881. [263, 265, 272]

214. Sedgwick, A. On the inadequacy of the cellular theory of de-velopment, and on the early development of nerves, partic-ularly of the third nerve and of the sympathetic in Elasmo-branchii. *Quart. J. Micr. Sc., Lond.*, 37:87-101, 1894. [6]

215. Sheldon, R. E. The phylogeny of the facial nerve and chorda tympani. *Anat. Rec.*, 3:593-617, 1909. [185]

216. Smirnow, A. E. Einige Bemerkungen über myelinhaltige Nerv-enfasern in der Molecularschicht des Kleinhirns beim er-wachsenen Hunde. *Arch. f. mikr. Anat., Bonn*, 52:195-201, 1898. [321]

217. Tello, J. F. Les neurofibrilles chez les vertébrés inférieurs. *Trab. Lab. Invest. biol., Univ. Madr.*, 3:124-166, 1904. [303, 306]

218. Tello, J. F. Terminaisons sensitives dans les poils et autres or-ganes. *Trab. Lab. Invest. biol., Univ Madr.*, 4:45-75, 1905. [166]

219. Tello, J. F. Terminaisons dans les muscles striés. *Trab. Lab. In-vest. biol., Univ. Madr.*, 4:107-117, 1905. [206]

220. Tello, J. F. Dégénération et régénération des plaques motrices après la section des nerfs. *Trab. Lab. Invest. biol., Univ. Madr.*, 5:117-149, 1907. [115, 206, 208]

221. Tello, J. F. La régénération dans les voies optiques. Note pré-liminaire. *Trab. Lab. Invest. biol., Univ. Madr.*, 5:236-248, 1907. [136, 394]

222. Tello, J. F. Algunas experiencias de ingertos nerviosos conservados "in vitro." *Trab. Lab. Invest. biol., Univ. Madr., 12:* 273-284, 1914. [140]

223. Tello, J. F. Génesis de las terminaciones nerviosas motrices y sensitivas. I. En el sistema locomotor de los vertebrados superiores. Histogénesis muscular. *Trab. Lab. Invest. biol., Univ. Madr., 15:*101-199, 1917. [131, 149, 208]

224. Tello, J. F. Genèse des terminaisons motrices et sensitives. II. Terminaisons dans les poils de la souris blanche. *Trab. Lab. Invest. biol., Univ. Madr., 21:*257-384, 1923. [166]

225. Terni, T. 1922.* [25]

226. Terrazas, R. Notas sobre la neuroglia del cerebelo y el crecimiento de los elementos nerviosos. *Rev. trim. microgr., 2:* 49-65, 1897. [292, 297]

227. Unger, L. Untersuchungen über die Entwicklung der centralen Nervengewebe. *Sitzungsb. d. k. Akad. d. Wissensch., Wien, 80:*282-315, 1879. [329]

228. Vadillo, J. G. Sur l'existence et l'évolution de certains éléments ganglionaires hétérotopiques et d'autres anomalies du développement médullaire des mammifères. *Trab. Lab. Invest. biol., Univ. Madr., 22:*235-259, 1924. [212]

229. Van der Stricht, N. L'histogenèse des parties constituantes du neuroépithélium acoustique, des taches et des crêtes acoustiques et de l'organe de Corti. *Arch. de biol., Par., 23:*541-693, 1908. [173]

230. Veratti, E. Ueber einige Struktureigentümlichkeiten der Hirnrinde bei den Säugetieren. *Anat. Anz., Jena, 13:*377-389, 1897. [341]

231. Vignal, W. Développement des éléments de la moelle épinière chez les mammifères. *Arch. de physiol. norm. et path., Par.,* 1884. [249]

232. Vignal, W. Sur le développement des éléments de la moelle des mammifères. *Arch. de physiol. norm. et path., Par.,* No. 7, 1885. [325]

233. Vignal, W. Recherches sur le développment des éléments des couches corticales du cerveau et du cervelet chez l'homme et les mammifères. *Arch. de physiol. norm. et path., Par., 2:* 228-254, 1888. [263, 264, 272, 325, 329]

AUTHOR INDEX

SUBJECT INDEX

A

Aberrant sensory neurons, 41-44 (*See also* Developmental errors)

Adventitial cells (*See also* Lemmoblasts)
    relation to peripheral nerves, 40-41, 56, 60-61, 101
    time of appearance, 11, 12, 13, 20, 30-31, 51

Apolar cell, 77-81 (*See also* Neuroblast, phases of development of)

Apotrophic cells, 121 (*See also* Lemmoblasts)

B

Basket cells of cerebellum, 297-301

C

Catenary theory, 5-7, 37

Cellules migratrices of Vignal, 263

Cerebellar nests, 255-256, 282-284

Cerebellum, 253-321
    ansiform fibers of Cajal-Smirnow, 310, 319-321
    basket cells, 297-301
    cerebellar nests, 255-256, 282, 284
    climbing fibers, 256, 257, 258, 282-286
    external granule cells, 370
    internal granular layer, 253-263, 268, 280-281, 305
    internal granule cells, 258, 260, 263, 267, 268, 275-276, 290-292, 305
    large stellate cells of granular layer, 258-259, 263, 268, 270, 280-281, 292-295
    molecular layer, 256-258, 263, 267, 268, 275-277
    mossy fibers, 253-255, 263, 281, 295-297, 313
    parallel fibers, 292, 316, 318-319

    Purkinje cells, 254, 259-263, 267-268, 277-280, 281-282, 302-317
    small stellate cells of the molecular layer, 266, 267, 297-301
    superficial granular zone, 263-267, 272-274, 276, 290-292, 305, 311, 313

Cerebral cortex, 325-350

Chemotaxis, 38, 54-55, 95, 97, 105, 115, 362-363 (*See also* Neurotropism)

Choleocyte, 123 (*See also* Lemmoblast)

Climbing fibers of cerebellum, 256, 257, 258, 282-286

Cochlea
    development of nerve terminations in, 173-178
    hair cells of, 177
    organ of Corti, 173, 178
    spiral ganglion, 174, 176

Cold temperature—effect on neurofibrils, 57-58, 76, 110, 315-316, 348

Collateral fibers of the spinal cord, 233-236, 238
    functional significance of, 236
    time of appearance, 223, 225, 226, 228

Cones, *see* Retina.

Cornea, 151-155

Corpus callosum, 325, 326, 328

Cutaneous nerve terminations, 155-165

D

Developmental errors
    aberrant sensory neurons, 41-44
    gigantic growth cones and misplaced axons, 88-89
    intraventricular neuroblasts, 92-94
    inverted neuroblasts, 89-92
    mass of arrest, 66
    of CNS and PNS, 211-212